Lecture Notes in Computer Science   10837

Commenced Publication in 1973
Founding and Former Series Editors:
Gerhard Goos, Juris Hartmanis, and Jan van Leeuwen

Junhu Wang · Gao Cong
Jinjun Chen · Jianzhong Qi (Eds.)

Databases Theory
and Applications

29th Australasian Database Conference, ADC 2018
Gold Coast, QLD, Australia, May 24–27, 2018
Proceedings

 Springer

Editors
Junhu Wang
ICT
Griffith University
Southport, QLD
Australia

Gao Cong (iD)
Nanyang Technological University
Singapore
Singapore

Jinjun Chen
Faculty of Information and Communication
  Technologies
Swinburne University of Technology
Hawthorn, VIC
Australia

Jianzhong Qi
The University of Melbourne
Melbourne, VIC
Australia

ISSN 0302-9743 ISSN 1611-3349 (electronic)
Lecture Notes in Computer Science
ISBN 978-3-319-92012-2 ISBN 978-3-319-92013-9 (eBook)
https://doi.org/10.1007/978-3-319-92013-9

Library of Congress Control Number: 2018944378

LNCS Sublibrary: SL3 – Information Systems and Applications, incl. Internet/Web, and HCI

Printed on acid-free paper

This Springer imprint is published by the registered company Springer International Publishing AG
part of Springer Nature
The registered company address is: Gewerbestrasse 11, 6330 Cham, Switzerland

Preface

It is our great pleasure to present the proceedings of the 29th Australasian Database Conference (ADC 2018). The Australasian Database Conference is an annual international forum for sharing the latest research advancements and novel applications of database systems, data-driven applications, and data analytics between researchers and practitioners from around the globe, particularly Australia and New Zealand. The mission of ADC is to share novel research solutions to problems of today's information society that fulfil the needs of heterogeneous applications and environments and to identify new issues and directions for future research. ADC seeks papers from academia and industry presenting research on all practical and theoretical aspects of advanced database theory and applications, as well as case studies and implementation experiences.

ADC 2018 was held during May 23–25, 2018, on the Gold Coast, Australia. As in previous years, ADC 2018 accepted all the papers that the Program Committee considered as being of ADC quality without setting any predefined quota. The conference received 53 submissions, each of which was carefully peer reviewed by at least three independent reviewers, and in some cases four or five reviewers. Based on the reviewer comments, we accepted 23 full research papers, six short papers, and three demo papers. The Program Committee that selected the papers comprised 52 members from around the world including Australia, China, USA, Finland, Denmark, Switzerland, Japan, New Zealand, and Singapore. The conference programme also includes keynote talks and invited tutorials for ADC's PhD school.

We are grateful to Professor Xiaofang Zhou (University of Queensland, ADC Steering Committee member) for his helpful advice, Professor Rui Zhang (University of Melbourne, ADC 2018 General Chair), and Dr. Sen Wang (Griffith University, ADC 2018 Local Organization Chair) for their tireless work in coordinating the conference activities. We would like to thank all members of the Organizing Committee, and the many volunteers, for their support in the conference organization. Special thanks go to the Program Committee members and the external reviewers who contributed their time and expertise in the paper review process. We would also like to thank the invited speakers, all authors who submitted their papers, and all conference attendees.

May 2018

Junhu Wang
Gao Cong
Jinjun Chen
Jianzhong Qi

General Chair's Welcome Message

Welcome to the proceedings of the 29th Australasian Database Conference (ADC 2018)! ADC is a leading Australia- and New Zealand-based international conference on research and applications of database systems, data-driven applications, and data analytics. In the past 10 years, ADC has been held in Brisbane (2017), Sydney (2016), Melbourne (2015), Brisbane (2014), Adelaide (2013), Melbourne (2012), Perth (2011), Brisbane (2010), Wellington (2009), and Wollongong (2008). This year, the ADC conference came to the Gold Coast.

In the past, the ADC conference series was held as part of the Australasian Computer Science Week (ACSW). Starting from 2014, the ADC conferences departed from ACSW as the database research community in Australasia has grown significantly larger. Now the new ADC conference has an expanded research program and focuses on community-building through a PhD School. ADC 2018 was the fifth of this new ADC conference series.

In addition to 23 full research papers, six short research papers, and three demo papers carefully selected by the Program Committee, we were also very fortunate to have five invited talks presented by world-leading researchers: Kyuseok Shim from Seoul National University, South Korea, Reynold Cheng from The University of Hong Kong, Hong Kong SAR, Shuai Ma from Beihang University, China, Lina Yao from The University of New South Wales, Australia, and Hongzhi Yin and Weiqing Wang from The University of Queensland, Australia. We had a two-day PhD School program as part of this year's ADC.

We wish to take this opportunity to thank all speakers, authors, and organizers. I would also especially like to thank our Organizing Committee members: Program Committee Chairs Junhu Wang, Gao Cong, and Jinjun Chen, for their dedication in ensuring a high-quality program, Proceedings Chair Jianzhong Qi, for his effort in delivering the conference proceedings timely, Local Organization Chairs Sen Wang and Sibo Wang, for their consideration in covering every detail of the conference logistics, and Publicity Chair Lijun Chang, for his efforts in disseminating our call for papers and attracting submissions. Without them, this year's ADC would not have been a success.

The Gold Coast is a coastal city and ADC 2018 was held at the Mantra On View Hotel in the heart of Surfers Paradise. We hope all ADC 2018 participants had a wonderful experience with the conference and the city.

Rui Zhang

Organization

General Chair

Rui Zhang   University of Melbourne, Australia

Program Chairs

Junhu Wang	Griffith University, Australia
Gao Cong	Nanyang Technical University, Singapore
Jinjun Chen	Swinburne University of Technology, Australia

Proceedings Chair

Jianzhong Qi   University of Melbourne, Australia

Publicity Chair

Lijun Chang   University of Sydney, Australia

Local Organization Chairs

Sen Wang	Griffith University, Australia
Sibo Wang	University of Queensland, Australia

Steering Committee

Rao Kotagiri	University of Melbourne, Australia
Timos Sellis	RMIT University, Australia
Gill Dobbie	University of Auckland, New Zealand
Alan Fekete	University of Sydney, Australia
Xuemin Lin	University of New South Wales, Australia
Yanchun Zhang	Victoria University, Australia
Xiaofang Zhou	University of Queensland, Australia

Program Committee

Tarique Anwar	Swinburne University of Technology, Australia
Zhifeng Bao	RMIT University, Australia
Huiping Cao	New Mexico State University, USA
Xin Cao	University of New South Wales, Australia
Lijun Chang	University of Sydney, Australia
Muhammad Aamir Cheema	Monash University, Australia

Lisi Chen   Hong Kong Baptist University, SAR China
Farhana Murtaza   RMIT University, Australia
  Choudhury
Shumo Chu   University of Washington, USA
Kaiyu Feng   Nanyang Technological University, Singapore
Janusz Getta   University of Wollongong, Australia
Yusuke Gotoh   Okayama University, Japan
Tao Guo   Nanyang Technological University, Singapore
Michael E. Houle   National Institute of Informatics, Japan
Wen Hua   University of Queensland, Australia
Guangyan Huang   Deakin University, Australia
Zi Huang   University of Queensland, Australia
Md. Saiful Islam   Griffith University, Australia
Guoliang Li   Tsinghua University, China
Jianxin Li   University of Western Australia
Xiang Lian   Kent State University, USA
Jixue Liu   University of South Australia
Jiaheng Lu   University of Helsinki, Finland
Parth Nagarkar   Arizona State University, USA
Quoc Viet Hung Nguyen   Griffith University, Australia
Makoto Onizuka   Osaka University, Japan
Miao Qiao   Massey University, New Zealand
Lu Qin   University of Technology, Sydney, Australia
Goce Ristanoski   Data61, Australia
Shazia Sadiq   University of Queensland, Australia
Timos Sellis   Swinburne University of Technology, Australia
Michael Sheng   Macquarie University, Australia
Jingkuan Song   University of Queensland, Australia
Bela Stantic   Griffith University, Australia
Farhan Tauheed   Oracle Labs Zurich, Switzerland
Anwaar Ulhaq   Victoria University, Australia
Hua Wang   Victoria University, Australia
Hongzhi Wang   Harbin Institute of Technology, China
Chuan Xiao   Nagoya University, Japan
Yajun Yang   Tianjin University, China
Weiren Yu   University of New South Wales, Australia
Wenjie Zhang   University of New South Wales, Australia
Ying Zhang   University of Technology, Sydney, Australia
Kai Zheng   University of Electronic Science and Technology
                               of China, China
Yongluan Zhou   University of Copenhagen, Denmark
Rui Zhou   Swinburne University of Technology, Australia
Yi Zhou   University of Technology, Sydney, Australia
Yuanyuan Zhu   Wuhan University, China
Can Wang   Griffith University, Australia

External Reviewers

Taotao Cai	University of Western Australia
Xuefeng Chen	University of New South Wales, Australia
Qixu Gong	New Mexico State University, USA
Yifan Hao	New Mexico State University, USA
Nguyen Quoc Viet Hung	Griffith University, Australia
Md Zahidul Islam	University of South Australia
Saiful Islam	Griffith University, Australia
Selasi Kwasie	University of South Australia
Yadan Luo	University of Queensland, Australia
Yue Qian	Dalian University of Technology, China
Nguyen Khoi Tran	University of Adelaide, Australia
Edgar Ceh Varela	New Mexico State University, USA
Can Wang	Griffith University, Australia
Fan Wang	Aston University, UK
Lujing Yang	University of South Australia

Invited Talks

MapReduce Algorithms for Big Data Analysis

Kyuseok Shim

Seoul National University

Abstract. There is a growing trend of applications that should handle big data. However, analyzing big data is very challenging today. For such applications, the MapReduce framework has recently attracted a lot of attention. MapReduce is a programming model that allows easy development of scalable parallel applications to process big data on large clusters of commodity machines. Google's MapReduce or its open-source equivalent Hadoop is a powerful tool for building such applications. In this tutorial, I will first introduce the MapReduce framework based on Hadoop system available to everyone to run distributed computing algorithms using MapReduce. I will next discuss how to design efficient MapReduce algorithms and present the state-of-the-art in MapReduce algorithms for big data analysis. Since Spark is recently developed to overcome the shortcomings of MapReduce which is not optimized for of iterative algorithms and interactive data analysis, I will also present an outline of Spark as well as the differences between MapReduce and Spark. The intended audience of this tutorial is professionals who plan to develop efficient MapReduce algorithms and researchers who should be aware of the state-of-the-art in MapReduce algorithms available today for big data analysis.

Short Biography. Kyuseok Shim is currently a professor at electrical and computer engineering department in Seoul National University, Korea. Before that, he was an assistant professor at computer science department in KAIST and a member of technical staff for the Serendip Data Mining Project at Bell Laboratories. He was also a member of the Quest Data Mining Project at the IBM Almaden Research Center and visited Microsoft Research at Redmond several times as a visiting scientist. Kyuseok was named an ACM Fellow for his contributions to scalable data mining and query processing research in 2013. Kyuseok has been working in the area of databases focusing on data mining, search engines, recommendation systems, MapReduce algorithms, privacy preservation, query processing and query optimization. His writings have appeared in a number of professional conferences and journals including ACM, VLDB and IEEE publications. He served as a Program Committee member for SIGKDD, SIGMOD, ICDE, ICDM, ICDT, EDBT, PAKDD, VLDB and WWW conferences. He also served as a Program Committee Co-Chair for PAKDD 2003, WWW 2014, ICDE 2015 and APWeb 2016. Kyuseok was previously on the editorial board of VLDB as well as IEEE TKDE Journals and is currently a member of the VLDB Endowment Board of Trustees. He received the BS degree in electrical engineering from Seoul National University in 1986, and the MS and PhD degrees in computer science from the University of Maryland, College Park, in 1988 and 1993, respectively.

Meta Paths and Meta Structures: Analysing Large Heterogeneous Information Networks

Reynold Cheng

University of Hong Kong

Abstract. A heterogeneous information network (HIN) is a graph model in which objects and edges are annotated with types. Large and complex databases, such as YAGO and DBLP, can be modeled as HINs. A fundamental problem in HINs is the computation of closeness, or relevance, between two HIN objects. Relevance measures, such as PCRW, PathSim, and HeteSim, can be used in various applications, including information retrieval, entity resolution, and product recommendation. These metrics are based on the use of meta paths, essentially a sequence of node classes and edge types between two nodes in a HIN. In this tutorial, we will give a detailed review of meta paths, as well as how they are used to define relevance. In a large and complex HIN, retrieving meta paths manually can be complex, expensive, and error-prone. Hence, we will explore systematic methods for finding meta paths. In particular, we will study a solution based on the Query-by-Example (QBE) paradigm, which allows us to discovery meta paths in an effective and efficient manner.

We further generalise the notion of a meta path to "meta structure", which is a directed acyclic graph of object types with edge types connecting them. Meta structure, which is more expressive than the meta path, can describe complex relationship between two HIN objects (e.g., two papers in DBLP share the same authors and topics). We develop three relevance measures based on meta structure. Due to the computational complexity of these measures, we also study an algorithm with data structures proposed to support their evaluation. Finally, we will examine solutions for performing query recommendation based on meta paths. We will also discuss future research directions in HINs.

Short Biography. Dr. Reynold Cheng is an Associate Professor of the Department of Computer Science in the University of Hong Kong. He was an Assistant Professor in HKU in 2008–2011. He received his BEng (Computer Engineering) in 1998, and MPhil (Computer Science and Information Systems) in 2000, from the Department of Computer Science in the University of Hong Kong. He then obtained his MSc and PhD from Department of Computer Science of Purdue University in 2003 and 2005 respectively. Dr. Cheng was an Assistant Professor in the Department of Computing of the Hong Kong Polytechnic University during 2005-08. He was a visiting scientist in the Institute of Parallel and Distributed Systems in the University of Stuttgart during the summer of 2006.

Dr. Cheng was granted an Outstanding Young Researcher Award 2011–2012 by HKU. He was the recipient of the 2010 Research Output Prize in the Department of Computer Science of HKU. He also received the U21 Fellowship in 2011. He received the Performance Reward in years 2006 and 2007 awarded by the Hong Kong Polytechnic University. He is the Chair of the Department Research Postgraduate Committee, and was the Vice Chairperson of the ACM (Hong Kong Chapter) in 2013. He is a member of the IEEE, the ACM, the Special Interest Group on Management of Data (ACM SIGMOD), and the UPE (Upsilon Pi Epsilon Honor Society). He is an editorial board member of TKDE, DAPD and IS, and was a guest editor for TKDE, DAPD, and Geoinformatica. He is an area chair of ICDE 2017, a senior PC member for DASFAA 2015, PC co-chair of APWeb 2015, area chair for CIKM 2014, area chair for Encyclopedia of Database Systems, program co-chair of SSTD 2013, and a workshop co-chair of ICDE 2014. He received an Outstanding Service Award in the CIKM 2009 conference. He has served as PC members and reviewer for top conferences (e.g., SIGMOD, VLDB, ICDE, EDBT, KDD, ICDM, and CIKM) and journals (e.g., TODS, TKDE, VLDBJ, IS, and TMC).

Approximate Computation for Big Data Analytics

Shuai Ma

Beihang University

Abstract. Over the past a few years, research and development has made significant progresses on big data analytics with the supports from both governments and industries all over the world, such as Spark, IBM Watson and Google AlphaGo. A fundamental issue for big data analytics is the efficiency, and various advances towards attacking these issues have been achieved recently, from theory to algorithms to systems. In this talk, we shall present the idea of approximate computation for efficient and effective big data analytics: query approximation and data approximation, based on our recent research experiences. Different from existing approximation techniques, the approximation computation that we are going to introduce does not necessarily ask for theoretically guaranteed approximation solutions, but asks for sufficiently efficient and effective solutions in practice.

Short Biography. Shuai Ma is a full professor in the School of Computer Science and Engineering, Beihang University, China. He obtained two PhD degrees: University of Edinburgh in 2010 and Peking University in 2004, respectively. His research interests include database theory and systems, and big data. He is a recipient of the best paper award of VLDB 2010, the best challenge paper award of WISE 2013, the National Science Fund of China for Excellent Young Scholars in 2013, and the special award of Chinese Institute of Electronics for progress in science and technology in 2017 (8/15). He is an Associate Editor of VLDB Journal since 2017.

Understanding Human Behaviors via Learning Internet of Things Interactions

Lina Yao

The University of New South Wales

Abstract. Internet of Things (IoT) enables the connection and integration of physical world and virtual world. A vast amount of interactive data between human and the real world being created by diverse sensing sources can be readily collected. Such growing interconnections powered with intelligent approaches open up a new world of broader possibilities and innovations with a deeper understanding of human behaviors. In this tutorial, I will introduce the methodologies to learn actionable knowledge from the monitored environment, in order to take actions on the situations and improve decision-making process, present real-world application examples and discuss the future research directions.

Short Biography. Lina Yao is currently a lecturer in the School of Computer Science and Engineering, University of New South Wales. Her research interests lie in data mining and machine learning applications with the focuses on Internet of Things, recommender systems, human activity recognition and Brain-Computer Interface.

Mining Geo-social Networks – Spatial Item Recommendation

Hongzhi Yin and Weiqing Wang

The University of Queensland

Abstract. The rapid development of Web 2.0, location acquisition and wireless communication technologies has fostered a profusion of geo-social networks (e.g., Foursquare, Yelp and Google Place). They provide users an online platform to check-in at points of interests (e.g., cinemas, galleries and hotels) and share their life experiences in the physical world via mobile devices. The new dimension of location implies extensive knowledge about an individual's behaviors and interests by bridging the gap between online social networks and the physical world. It is crucial to develop spatio-temporal recommendation services for mobile users to explore the new places, attend new events and find their potentially preferred spatial items from billions of candidate ones. Compared with traditional recommendation tasks, the spatio-temporal recommendation faces the following new challenges: Travel Locality, Spatial Dynamics of User Interests, Temporal Dynamics of User Interests, Sequential Influence of user mobility behaviors and Real-time Requirement. In this talk, I will present our recent advancement of spatio-temporal recommendation techniques and how to address these unique challenges.

Short Biography. Dr. Hongzhi Yin is now working as a lecturer in data science and an ARC DECRA Fellow (Australia Discovery Early Career Researcher Award) with The University of Queensland, Australia. He received his doctoral degree from Peking University in July 2014. After graduation, he joined the school of ITEE, the University of Queensland. He successfully won the ARC DECRA award in 2015 and obtained an ARC Discovery Project grant as a chief investigator in 2016. His current main research interests include social media analytic, user profiling, recommender system, especially spatial-temporal recommendation, topic discovery and event detection, deep learning, user linkage across social networks, knowledge graph mining and construction. He has published over 70 peer-reviewed papers in prestigious journals and top international conferences including ACM TOIS, VLDBJ, IEEE TKDE, ACM TKDD, ACM TIST, ACM SIGMOD, ACM SIGKDD, VLDB, IEEE ICDE, AAAI, SIGIR, WWW, ACM Multimedia, ICDM, WSDM and CIKM. He has been actively engaged in professional services by serving as conference organizers, conference PC members for PVLDB, SIGIR, ICDE, IJCAI, ICDM, CIKM, DASFAA, ASONAM, MDM, WISE, PAKDD and reviewer of more than 10 reputed journals such as VLDB Journal, TKDE, TOIS, TKDD, TWeb, IEEE Transactions on Cybernetics, WWW Journal, Knowledge-based system and etc.

Dr. Weiqing Wang is now working as a Research Fellow in the school of ITEE, the University of Queensland, where she also obtained her PhD in July on 2017. She will join Monash University as a lecturer in data science in this July. Her major research interests include user modelling and recommender systems, especially spatial-temporal recommender systems. She has published over ten peer-reviewed papers in prestigious journals and top conferences including IEEE TKDE, ACM TOIS, ACM TIST, ACM SIGKDD, ACM SIGIR, IEEE ICDE, ACM Multimedia, and CIKM.

Contents

Full Research Papers: Theories and Methodologies

Short Research Papers

Demo Papers

Full Research Papers: Database and Applications

Adaptive Access Path Selection
for Hardware-Accelerated DRAM Loads

Markus Dreseler[⊠], Timo Gasda, Jan Kossmann, Matthias Uflacker,
and Hasso Plattner

Hasso Plattner Institute, Potsdam, Germany
markus.dreseler@hpi.de

Abstract. For modern main memory database systems, the memory
bus is the main bottleneck. Specialized hardware components of large
NUMA systems, such as HPE's GRU, make it possible to offload memory transfers. In some cases, this improves the throughput by 30%, but
other scenarios suffer from reduced performance. We show which factors
influence this tradeoff. Based on our experiments, we present an adaptive
prediction model that supports the DBMS in deciding whether to utilize
these components. In addition, we evaluate non-coherent memory access
as an additional access method and discuss its benefits and shortcomings.

1 Introduction

Current in-memory databases are significantly limited by the main memory's
latency and bandwidth [2]. In the time spent for transferring a cache line from
DRAM to the CPU (roughly 100 ns), a modern CPU can execute 300 instructions
or more. When the compute part of database operators executes in fewer cycles,
the CPU stalls and waits for more data to arrive. This gets exacerbated in NUMA
setups where remote DRAM accesses take roughly 200 ns with a single NUMA
hop. Scale-up systems, as used for big SAP HANA or Oracle databases, can
include multiple NUMA hops and up to 48 TB of memory. These connect up to
eight blades with four processors each to a single, cache-coherent network using
a proprietary interconnect. In such setups, memory latency from one end to the
other can reach hundreds of nanoseconds, making the influence even bigger.

Closely related to memory latency is memory bandwidth. On our test system (cf. Sect. 3), we measured a NUMA node-local bandwidth of slightly over
50 GB/s, while remote accesses on the same blade had a reduced bandwidth of
12.5 GB/s and remote blades of 11.5 GB/s. As such, making good use of the
available physical bandwidth is vital. Doing so includes reducing the amount of
data transferred by using compression for a higher logical bandwidth (i.e., more
information transferred per byte) or organizing the data in a cache line-friendly
way. This could be a columnar table layout where each cache line only holds
values from the column that is accessed and *cache line bycatch*, i.e., data that is
loaded into the CPU but never used, is avoided for column store-friendly queries.

Making the DBMS more aware of NUMA can significantly improve the performance [7]. By ensuring that data is moved across the NUMA network only

J. Wang et al. (Eds.): ADC 2018, LNCS 10837, pp. 3–14, 2018.
https://doi.org/10.1007/978-3-319-92013-9_1

when it is unavoidable, the memory access costs can be reduced. Still, there remain cases in which a load from a distant node cannot be avoided. This happens when joins access data from a remote table or when the data (and thus the load) is imbalanced and an operator cannot be executed on the optimal node.

In addition to NUMA optimization and better data layouts, developers use dedicated hardware to increase the effective bandwidth [1,6,9]. There are several approaches, but no one-size-fits-all technique. In this paper, we look at one specific method that is used to improve the physical bandwidth available to database operators, namely the Global Reference Unit (GRU) built into systems like SGI's UV series or HPE's Superdome Flex. The GRU provides an API that can be used to offload certain memory operations, allowing the CPU to work on other data in the meantime. Previous work [3] has shown that this can result in a performance benefit of up to 30% for table scans. We extend on this by evaluating which factors lead to an advantage of the GRU over the CPU in some cases and what causes it to be slower in others. This knowledge can be used by the DBMS to automatically choose between the CPU and GRU access paths. Furthermore, we present relaxed cache coherence as another access method.

This paper is organized as follows: Sect. 2 gives background information on the hardware discussed in this paper. To gather data on the memory bus utilization and better profile the physical properties of database operations, we use performance counters as described in Sect. 3. These are then used in Sect. 4 to discuss the factors that influence if one method or another gives the higher effective bandwidth. Section 5 explains how a DBMS can use these results in order to choose an access method. In Sect. 6, we show how relaxing cache coherency could further improve the physical bandwidth of a table scan. Related work is discussed in Sect. 7 and a summary is given in Sect. 8.

2   Hardware Used for Accelerating DRAM Reads

In the previously mentioned scale-up systems, four NUMA nodes (i.e., processors) are grouped into blades as shown in Fig. 1. Each node is connected via QPI links to other processors on the same blade, however the two diagonal QPI connections are omitted. The free QPI port on each processor is then connected to one of the two so-called HARPs that are part of each blade.

HARPs connect the entire scale-up system, as each HARP is directly connected with every other using a special interconnect called NUMAlink. This creates an all-to-all topology that allows the addition of more CPUs and more memory by attaching additional blades to the machine. In order to make the memory of one blade accessible to another blade, the HARPs participate in the QPI ring of their blades and mimic a NUMA node with a large amount of main memory, i.e., the memory of every other blade [8].

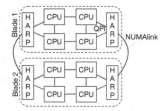

Fig. 1. General architecture of the discussed system

The component in the HARP that is responsible for transparently extending the memory space and translating memory addresses is the Global Reference Unit (GRU). In addition to this transparent access, the GRU also provides a user-level API that enables developers to instruct the GRU directly.

Previous work has shown that using the GRU API for database operations improves throughput by up to 30% when scanning remote data [3]. For a more in-depth discussion of the GRU hardware and the actual implementation of the GRU scan, we refer to that paper. This performance advantage is achieved by using the gru_bcopy function, a block copy instruction that is executed by the GRU, and a double-buffered scan. We divide the data vector into equally sized chunks, and allocate two temporary buffers of that chunk size. The asynchronous bcopy operation is used to copy chunks from the data vector into one of the local buffers, which is processed while bcopy is filling the other buffer. The buffers are switched and the process is repeated until the entire vector is scanned.

There are three reasons why this can achieve better performance compared to a regular CPU scan: Firstly, bcopy executes asynchronously and allows the CPU to run other computations while the GRU handles the memory transfer. As a result, the CPU can process one local chunk while the GRU is loading the other chunk in the background. Secondly, the HARP can access remote memory more efficiently than the CPU. This is because a CPU's memory access performance is limited by the number of outstanding read requests that it can handle before it stalls and waits for loads to complete. Stalls are especially noticeable in large NUMA systems with high memory access latencies, because it takes longer for a read request to return and allow the next request to be issued. This means that for the systems discussed here, an increase in latency results in a decrease in bandwidth. The HARPs can handle more outstanding read requests than a CPU and can therefore achieve higher throughput. Thirdly, because the cache coherency directories (used to maintain a consistent view of data across processors) are located on the HARP, we expect the HARPs to handle cache coherency more efficiently. While this does not improve single operations, the decreased cache coherency overhead can improve memory performance over time.

3 Quantifying the Memory Bandwidth Utilization

To better utilize the available memory bandwidth, it is vital to understand how much of it is actually used and where the bottleneck is. This information is both needed by developers of database operators and by the DBMS itself when it decides which scan will be used. We use the Intel Processor Counter Monitor (PCM) to monitor the QPI traffic on relevant nodes.

For every QPI link, PCM can measure the amount of both incoming data and outgoing traffic. Incoming data (*dataIn*) only includes the transferred payload. Outgoing traffic (*trafficOut*) includes both the payload as well as any overhead such as cache coherency traffic. The incoming traffic or the outgoing data cannot be retrieved from PCM, but can be computed in most cases. Also, the information from where and to where data flows is not available.

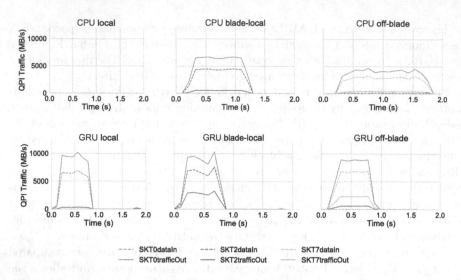

Fig. 2. QPI traffic when scanning a 4 GB vector of integers

Figure 2 displays the QPI traffic as measured[1] by PCM for a scan on a 4 GB vector of integers, i.e., approximately one billion integers. In the benchmark, the same scan is executed three times, each time with a different memory placement relative to the executing thread. After each run, the CPU caches are flushed using `CLFLUSH`. The data is always located on NUMA node 0 ("storage node"), while the executing thread is pinned to nodes 0, 2, and 7 ("execution node") for the node-local, blade-local, and off-blade cases respectively. For the local scan using the CPU, no QPI traffic is seen because the traffic is node-local. The GRU implementation, on the other hand, copies data from the storage node to the execution node even when these are identical. This explains why a GRU scan is detrimental for local data. Continuing to blade-local CPU scans (top center), we see two significant lines, one for outgoing traffic of the storage node, and one for incoming data of the executing node. The difference between the two can be attributed to the cache coherency overhead. When using the GRU, the overall bandwidth is higher, resulting in a lower execution time. A similar image can be seen for off-blade scans. Here, the bandwidth difference between CPU and GRU is even more pronounced. The fact that Socket 2 appears in the graph is surprising at first. We attribute it to additional caches that we have no control over and take this as a reason to look into non-cache coherent loads in Sect. 6.

The same library can be used to get numbers on the current load on the memory bus. We gather information about the QPI utilization of all relevant nodes and feed it into the adaptive model described in Sect. 5.

---

[1] All benchmarks were executed on an SGI UV 300H with 6 TB RAM and eight Intel E7-8890 v2 processors. Our code was compiled with gcc 7.2 at `-O3`.

4   Factors that Influence the CPU/GRU Tradeoff

In this section, we describe how the throughput of the GRU scan is affected by different factors and how deciding between GRU and CPU scans is only possible by looking at a combination of these factors. We classify these factors into two groups: Internal and external factors. The former are parameters that come from the scan itself, such as the size of the table. The latter are unrelated to the particular scan operator, for example the utilization of the system.

We use the table scan as an example for an operator with sequential access patterns. Compared to operators such as the join, it is strictly memory-bound, so the influences of improved memory bandwidth utilization are better to see. Latency-bound operators cannot be improved by the bcopy approach.

4.1   Internal Influences

Data Size. One of the most important factors is the size of the scanned table. Figure 3 shows how the throughput of different access methods is influenced by the size of the table when accessing an off-blade table. Both approaches reach their maximum throughput only when the table has a certain size. For GRU scans, this happens when the data size reaches at least 60 MB. CPU scans deliver the maximum throughput for smaller table sizes, approximately 1 MB.

This can be explained with fixed setup costs for the table scan as well as having to wait for the first cache lines to arrive from a remote location. For the GRU scan, the additional system calls required to obtain the execution contexts and to execute the bcopy method mean that bigger tables are needed to reach the break-even point.

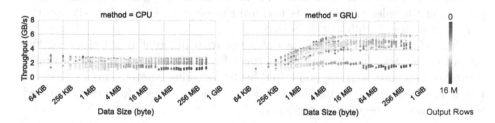

Fig. 3. Influence of the input data size for off-blade CPU and GRU scans - each dot is one measured data point

Data Locality. Depending on where the input data is located relative to the executing CPU, it needs to be transferred through zero to multiple NUMA hops. Figure 4 shows that the throughput for the regular CPU scan changes depending on NUMA distance. The highest throughput of 8 GB/s is achieved on the same node. With increasing NUMA distance, the throughput rates decrease. For a blade-local scan, the throughput rates reach up to 5 GB/s, and scanning an off-blade vector only nets approximately 3 GB/s. The GRU scan performance stays

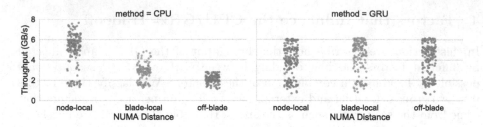

Fig. 4. Influence of the NUMA distance for CPU and GRU scans

stable for all NUMA distances at around 6 GB/s. For both CPU and GRU, a high variance is measured. This is dependent on the other execution parameters as described in this section. It shows that there are parameters other than the data locality, especially for small tables, that play an important role in deciding if the CPU or the GRU is faster.

For the model described in Sect. 5, we take the latency (instead of the number of hops) between source and destination node as it describes a linear variable, not a discrete one. This makes it easier to adapt the model to other systems where the latency between hops is different.

Result Size. When scanning the input data vector, i.e., the column in an in-memory database, the operation also needs to save the results. In this implementation, the scan returns a vector of indexes of the input vector where a certain search value was found. This means that both the value distribution and the given search value have an impact on how large the result gets. We have chosen to take both the data size and the result size as parameters instead of just using the selectivity. This is because the impact of the selectivity on the scan cost varies for different data sizes.

Figure 5 shows the performance of scans with different result sizes. As the output size grows, the amount of time spent for writing the output vector slowly grows as well, and at some point, surpasses the value comparisons in terms of runtime. Consequently, after that point, the benefits gained from our improved scanning method become insignificant.

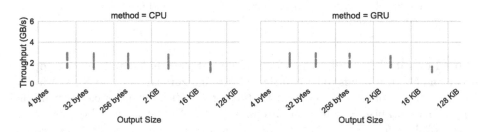

Fig. 5. Influence of the output size when scanning an off-blade vector of 512 KiB

4.2 External Influences

Background QPI Traffic. In a production environment, the executed operator is not the only memory-intensive operation on the system. Therefore, it makes sense to also take a look at the influence of memory traffic caused by other processes. To identify how this affects performance, we use PCM (as described in Sect. 3) to measure QPI traffic right before executing our scan operations.

For the benchmark, we generate background traffic by using two types of background workers. One copies data between the worker and the data node and then scans the remote data with a SIMD scan on 32 bit integers. The second worker uses bcopy to asynchronously copy data back and forth between the worker and data node. This generates both QPI and Numalink traffic.

By doing so, we can vary the background traffic and measure the performance for varying QPI loads. Our measurements show that the impact of high QPI utilization is higher on CPU scans. If no parallel workers are consuming QPI bandwidth, the throughput is unaffected. In the worst case, a busy QPI interface decreases the throughput by 2 GB/s. For the GRU, scans on a high-load system only have a throughput that is 1 GB/s lower.

Background HARP Traffic. Because the GRU is responsible for referencing memory of other blades, it is involved in memory accesses even when the GRU API is not used. Consequently, the load of the GRUs has an effect on other memory operations in the system as shown in Fig. 6. Different from previous figures, all combinations of data sizes and data locality are combined in the graph. For GRU scans, the scan throughput stays in a small window just below 7 GB/s when the GRU is not busy. When other explicit GRU operations are run simultaneously, the throughput is reduced significantly. For the CPU scans, background GRU traffic does not affect the maximum throughput as much.

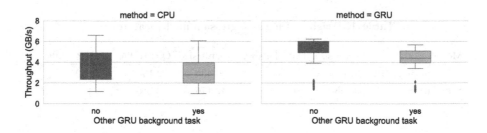

Fig. 6. Influence of a GRU background traffic for vectors bigger than 32 MB

5 Self-tuning Access Path Selection

The measurements presented in Sect. 4 have shown that directly utilizing the GRU has performance benefits in some situations. In others, such as with local data, small tables, or a high number of output results, the CPU is preferred. We have identified the most important parameters that impact GRU performance with microbenchmarks. This chapter introduces a cost model for table scans. Such a model can be used by the query optimizer or scheduler of a database system to decide whether to use a GRU or regular table scan. The features of the model are the above presented influence factors. Because different database servers have different characteristics, the model can be trained for other systems easily. This allows the DBMS to adapt to varying factors, such as NUMA topologies and latencies.

5.1 Scan Decision Model

The model is part of the query optimizer where estimated execution costs are calculated before every scan execution. A vital requirement for the model is a low prediction time. In addition, models vary for different hardware characteristics. Therefore, a new model is trained for each machine individually which demands for low training times and robustness. Thus, we decided to use linear regression. For these models, inference is achieved by multiplying the observation values with their respective feature coefficients. The overhead of such calculations is negligible compared to query execution times.

We measure the execution times for a large number of randomized feature combinations. By repeating the experiments for each combination at least 50 times with and without GRU, we collect more than 200 000 observations and minimize variability effects. The resulting data is used to create models that predict the runtime of normal and GRU scans. Table 1 shows the models' weights as calculated on our system.

When generating the query plan, the optimizer collects the necessary parameters for inference from the database's statistics component and the PCM API. The retrieved parameters are applied to both models which return predicted execution times. Based on these, the faster scan is scheduled/planned.

Table 1. Weights of linear regression model features

Model	Data size	Data locality	Result size	QPI traffic	HARP traffic
Scan runtime CPU	174.091	33.335	96.436	−2.135	−4.049
Scan runtime GRU	345.849	−6.756	332.176	3.215	5.942

5.2 Evaluation

To validate the models used for decision-making, we evaluate their accuracy in this section. The R^2 score is our metric to determine how well the model explains the observed runtime. We also consider the model's precision, recall, and the F1 score to judge the decision between normal and GRU scan. These metrics were evaluated with a training and testing set split of 80% and 20%.

Table 2 shows that both models can explain over 93% of the occurring variance with the above presented features. For the GRU, the model is slightly more accurate with a higher R^2 coefficient. This is mostly due to the stability of GRU operations with different NUMA distances or latencies as seen in Fig. 4. Precision, recall and F1 score are used for classification models and only the combination of both models, as described above, can be used for classification.

We also compared our linear regression model to another lightweight model, a *decision tree*. Some of the presented scores outperform linear regression slightly, but our linear regression model offers more flexibility since it returns run times and not only a decision on which of the scan types is more efficient. In addition, predictions can be made faster. Since variance is not an appropriate metric for classification models, R^2 is not reported for the decision tree.

As an additional quality metric, we looked at how close to optimal the performance of such a self-adapting DBMS is. For this, we chose between CPU and GRU using the two models described above. Over all table scans in the test set, the performance was within 2% of the best possible solution.

Table 2. Cost model accuracy

Model	R^2	Precision	Recall	F1 score
Scan runtime CPU	0.9347	0.9	0.77	0.83
Scan Runtime GRU	0.9671			
Decision Tree	–	0.87	0.95	0.91

5.3 Model Adaptivity

We have discussed the overhead of predicting the runtime for new observations above. Another important factor for the viability of using the model is the overhead caused by training and observation gathering. The training for linear regression models of such size is negligible, but generating large numbers of observations is time-consuming. Since the results highly depend on the specific hardware configuration, it is necessary to calibrate the model on each particular system upfront. To speed up this process, the database system can run the measurements for only a subset of features with a reduced number of parameters at system start and train models based on this small amount of observations. Later, during normal system operation, further observations can be collected. With these new observations, we improve the model by adapting it to the specific hardware configuration. This adaptive approach also ensures that the model is accurate when the data held in the database itself changes since data characteristics are one of the considered features. Unfortunately, because we only have access to HARP-based systems with the same hardware layout, we cannot evaluate this for varying hardware configurations.

6 Non-cache Coherent GRU Scan

So far, we have looked at cache-coherent memory accesses where the CPUs coordinate to make sure that all cores access the same version of the data. This greatly simplifies multithreading and many DBMS programmers (us included) would not want to work without it. In certain cases, however, cache coherency is not needed. If a part of the data reaches a state in which it will not be modified anymore, cache coherency increases the communication overhead and uses up bandwidth that could be used for actual data.

An example for this can be found in databases that use insert-only Multi-version Concurrency Control (MVCC) [5]. Instead of physically updating rows, the database invalidates them by setting a flag for that row and inserts the new version at the end of the table. This means that the data part of the row will not be modified until it is removed as part of some clean up job.

For cases like this, where the life time of an area of memory is well-defined, cache coherency could be seen as unnecessary overhead. Especially when data is stored in a large read-only main partition and a small differential buffer (delta partition), it is easy to see how most of the data does not require any cache synchronization. By using the GRU's `IAA_NCRAM` instead of the `IAA_RAM` access method, we can copy data without checking its cache coherency state. It is both undocumented and unsupported, likely because of the issues discussed next.

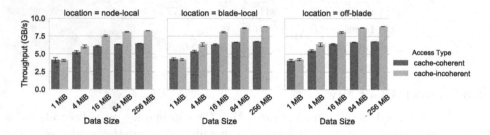

Fig. 7. Throughput of a cache-coherent and non-cache coherent GRU table scan

Figure 7 shows the performance of the previously discussed GRU bcopy scan compared to that of a non-coherent implementation. For this benchmark, the output size has been set to one element and no further background QPI traffic is present. The input data sizes and NUMA distances vary.

With an effective throughput of almost 9 GB/s for off-blade scans, the non-cache coherent scan is approximately 3.5 GB/s faster than the regular scan in the best case. Unfortunately, even though we have carefully flushed all buffers that we are aware of using `CLFLUSH`, `gru_vflush`, and `gru_flush_tlb`, the scan results are not completely correct. Most likely, there are still some buffers or directory caches that have not yet been flushed. Also, this instruction is not officially supported. As such, we did not include this access method in the previous sections and are not using it for actual table scans. Instead, we are presenting it here to show the potential of relaxed cache coherency.

7 Related Work

Copying or moving blocks of data is a very common operation, especially in applications that make use of buffering. Examples include the TCP/IP stack and applications in data centers [4]. Traditionally, copies use CPU instructions like memcpy, which blocks the CPU from doing other work. That is why some applications offload memory accesses to other components.

In the database world, an example are the database accelerators (DAX) built into Oracle's Sparc M7 processors [6]. These can be used to decompress, scan, filter, or translate the data in a table. Located on the memory controller, the DAX has direct access to the DRAM and, according to the documentation, access to additional bandwidth that is not used by the cores. In addition to a higher bandwidth, it can be used to free the processor to do other work and reduce cache pollution by only forwarding data that is actually needed [6]. Compared to the hardware-accelerated table scan discussed in this paper, the DAX has a bigger feature set and can be used to execute some database operators (mostly) without support from the CPU. This is different from our approach, where only the data transfer is offloaded to the GRU and the CPU still has to do the scanning.

Ungethüm et al. discuss adaptions to the Tomahawk platform, a multiprocessor system-on-a-chip [9] that add database-related primitives like hashing and sorted set operations to the instruction set of the processor. They optimize memory access by pushing down filters to a custom memory controller. It contains an intelligent DMA controller (iDMA) that is able to filter and search data before giving it to the processor. Instead of retrieving a large vector from the memory controller and have the CPU search for a specific value, this can be pushed down to the iDMA, which will then return the results to the application.

8 Summary

By directly instructing the memory hardware using the GRU API, the effective throughput of an in-memory table scan can be improved by up to 30%. In this paper, we have shown how this best-case result is influenced by a number of factors, both internal factors regarding the scan and external factors of the system. These include the size of the scanned table, the output size, but also the amount of parallel QPI traffic. For a DBMS to make effective use of this new access method, it has to take these factors into account and estimate the runtimes for normal and GRU supported scans. We have shown how a self-adapting model can be trained and how runtimes can be inferred using linear regression. This model can be used by a self-tuning database that automatically decides between regular and GRU scans. Compared to an omniscient model that always chooses the most efficient scan type, our model performs within 2% of the optimum as an evaluation on our test set demonstrates.

Furthermore, we have discussed non-cache coherent bcopy as a hardware method that could be considered for improving the effective memory throughput This delivers significantly higher bandwidth in cases where the DBMS can ensure that the data will not change during the execution of an operator. However, even though we have flushed all caches that we are aware of, the results were still slightly incorrect. Because of that, we do not use non-cache coherent bcopy at this point but suggest that this is an area worth exploring.

Future work shall be directed into exploring more hardware-supported memory access methods. We see great potential in allowing the DBMS developer to selectively relax cache coherency.

Acknowledgments. We thank Martin Boissier and Rainer Schlosser for their helpful input on the estimation model.

References

1. Abadi, D.J., Madden, S., Ferreira, M.: Integrating compression and execution in column-oriented database systems. In: ACM SIGMOD International Conference on Management of Data (2006)
2. Boncz, P.A., Manegold, S., Kersten, M.L.: Database architecture optimized for the new bottleneck: memory access. In: 25th International Conference on Very Large Data Bases (1999)
3. Dreseler, M., et al.: Hardware-accelerated memory operations on large-scale NUMA systems. In: Eighth International Workshop on Accelerating Analytics and Data Management Systems Using Modern Processor and Storage Architectures (ADMS) (2017)
4. Foong, A.P., et al.: TCP performance re-visited. In: IEEE International Symposium on Performance Analysis of Systems and Software (ISPASS) (2003)
5. Neumann, T., Mühlbauer, T., Kemper, A.: Fast serializable multi-version concurrency control for main-memory database systems. In: ACM SIGMOD International Conference on Management of Data (2015)
6. Oracle. Oracle's SPARC T7 and SPARC M7 Server Architecture. Technical report. https://www.oracle.com/assets/sparc-t7-m7-serverarchitecture-2702877.pdf. Accessed 12 June 2017
7. Psaroudakis, I., et al.: Adaptive NUMA-aware data placement and task scheduling for analytical workloads in main-memory column-stores. In: Proceedings of the VLDB (2016)
8. Thorson, G., Woodacre, M.: SGI UV2: a fused computation and data analysis machine. In: International Conference on High Performance Computing, Networking, Storage and Analysis (2012)
9. Ungethüm, A., et al.: Overview on hardware optimizations for database engines. In: Datenbanksysteme für Business, Technologie und Web (BTW) (2017)

Privacy Preservation for Trajectory Data Publishing by Look-Up Table Generalization

Nattapon Harnsamut, Juggapong Natwichai$^{(\boxtimes)}$, and Surapon Riyana

Data Engineering and Network Technology Laboratory,
Department of Computer Engineering, Faculty of Engineering,
Chiang Mai University, Chiang Mai, Thailand
nattapon.ha@up.ac.th, juggapong@eng.cmu.ac.th, surapon.riyana@gmail.com

Abstract. With the increasing of location-aware devices, it is easy to collect the trajectory of a person which can be represented as a sequence of visited locations with regard to timestamps. For some applications such as traffic management and location-based advertising, the trajectory data may need to be published with other private information. However, revealing the private trajectory and sensitive information of user poses privacy concerns especially when an adversary has the background knowledge of target user, i.e., partial trajectory information. In general, data transformation is needed to ensure privacy preservation before data releasing. Not only the privacy has to be preserved, but also the data quality issue must be addressed, i.e., the impact on data quality after the transformation should be minimized. *LKC*-privacy model is a well-known model to anonymize the trajectory data that are published with the sensitive information. However, computing the optimal *LKC*-privacy solution on trajectory data by the brute-force (BF) algorithm with full-domain generalization technique is highly time-consuming. In this paper, we propose a look-up table brute-force (LT-BF) algorithm to preserve privacy and maintain the data quality based on *LKC*-privacy model in the scenarios which the generalization technique is applied to anonymize the trajectory data efficiently. Subsequently, our proposed algorithm is evaluated with experiments. The results demonstrate that our proposed algorithm is not only returns the optimal solution as the BF algorithm, but also it is highly efficient.

Keywords: Privacy · Trajectory data publishing · *LKC*-privacy

1 Introduction

Location-aware devices such as mobile phones, GPS devices, POS terminals, RFID tag readers are now part of everyday life. With the increasing of the number of location-aware devices [1,2], it is easy to collect the location data of the users, along with time stamps to form spatio-temporal data. The collected

© Springer International Publishing AG, part of Springer Nature 2018
J. Wang et al. (Eds.): ADC 2018, LNCS 10837, pp. 15–27, 2018.
https://doi.org/10.1007/978-3-319-92013-9_2

data, so called trajectory data or moving object data, contains the sequences of spatio-temporal doublets denoted as (loc_i, t_i).

The trajectory data are usually high-dimensional [3–5] and also often contains detailed information about the individuals, their favorites, and other sensitive personal information. For many applications, the trajectory data need to be published with sensitive attributes, such as disease, income, and job for analysis purposes. For example, trajectory data from users with sensitive information such as job category, and their driving-behavior can be collected by some vehicle-insurance company [6]. Or, Octopus card, a smart card payment system in Hong Kong, collects transportation data and the payment data at various sites such as service stations and convenience stores for users. The other example is an RFID patient tagging system of hospital stores patients data, trajectory data, and medical data in a centralized database [7–9].

Although the effective data analytics and data mining tasks require the high-quality trajectory data publishing, revealing the private trajectory and sensitive information can pose privacy concerns [2].

For instance, consider the dataset in Table 1. Suppose that an RFID patient tagging system of a hospital releases data for further data analysis [4,10,11]. Each record contains a path or a trajectory and sensitive information such as diagnosis. A trajectory of patient forms a sequence of spatio-temporal doublets (loc_i, t_i). The location loc of each doublet can be represented by the location name such as reception, emergency room, or operating room. The timestamp t_i can be discretized from the real-world clocks, however, only the sequence can be considered here for simplicity. From the data, record#5 shows that the tagged patient visited locations d, b, and e with timestamps t_1, t_2, and t_3, respectively and has the Fever disease.

Table 1. Raw trajectory database T.

Rec. #	Path	Diagnosis
1	$(a, t_2) \rightarrow (f, t_3)$	Flu
2	$(a, t_2) \rightarrow (f, t_3)$	Flu
3	$(a, t_1) \rightarrow (d, t_2)$	HIV
4	$(b, t_2) \rightarrow (e, t_3)$	Fever
5	$(d, t_1) \rightarrow (b, t_2) \rightarrow (e, t_3)$	Fever
6	$(b, t_1) \rightarrow (c, t_2)$	Flu
7	$(d, t_1) \rightarrow (b, t_2) \rightarrow (e, t_3)$	Fever

Most privacy protection techniques blind the sensitive information before the release by removing identifying attributes, such as name and social security number. By considering the trajectory dataset in Table 1 alone, one could misjudge that the privacy of the individuals contained in the dataset is preserved by removal of identifiers. Although removing the identifier attributes technique can protect the data privacy, it is not effective against privacy attacks. Especially when an adversary has background knowledge of the target user with regard to the spatial trajectory information. An adversary can still perform two kinds of privacy attack with sufficient background knowledge [4, 10, 12]:

Identity Linkage Attack: If a trajectory in the database is so specific that not many trajectories can match it, the adversary can use some background knowledge to identify all trajectory data and the sensitive information of such target patient. For example, suppose that the adversary has background knowledge of a target patient, Alice. The adversary knows that the data of Alice is in Table 1 and also knows that she visited locations b and c at timestamps t_1 and t_2, respectively. Thus, the adversary can identify that Alice has Flu because record#6 is the only record containing both (b, t_1) and (c, t_2). Moreover, all trajectory data of Alice can be disclosed.

Attribute Linkage Attack: If a sensitive value occurs frequently with some sequences of doublets, it is possible to infer the sensitive value from these sequences even though the record of the victim cannot be uniquely identified. For example, suppose that the adversary knows Bill visited (a, t_1) and (d, t_2). The adversary can infer that Bill has HIV with $1/1 = 100\%$ confidence because only the Records#3 which contains (a, t_1) and (d, t_2) has the HIV value.

In order to protect both identity linkage attack and attribute linkage attack, Mohammed et al. [1] proposed a well-known privacy technique called *LKC*-privacy model to protect these attacks on a relational data. This privacy model is based on a number background knowledge of adversary which limits to L knowledge with regard to a target victim, i.e., the maximum background knowledge of adversary with regard to the previously visited spatio-temporal doublets of the target victim is limit to L. This model ensures that for each record of every possible combination projection of values in attributes $QID_j \subseteq QID$ with a maximum length of background knowledge of adversary L in the data table, there are at least $K - 1$ other indistinguishable records in the data, with respect to the selected attributes. The confidence of inferring any sensitive values in S is not greater than C threshold. The L, K, C thresholds and S are specified by the data holders. Computing the optimal *LKC*-privacy solution is NP-Hard [1].

The *LKC*-privacy model have been adopted widely to other trajectory data anonymization problems [4, 5, 10–12]. Typically, the suppression techniques are proposed to anonymize the trajectory data to achieve the privacy constraints. However, the drawback of suppression techniques is that the data utility can be lost, i.e., a lot of data are to be suppressed at high volume, thus only a few remained data are left for data analytics and data mining task.

Based on the practical assumption that an adversary has only limited background knowledge on a target victim, we also adopt *LKC*-privacy model for trajectory data anonymization with the "generalization technique", which takes into consideration not only identity linkage attacks on the trajectory data, but also attribute linkage attacks via trajectory data. An anonymized data of the original dataset in Table 1 which satisfies the *LKC* privacy constraints ($L = 2$, $K = 2$, and $C = 0.5$) is shown in Table 2 by generalization technique which

Table 2. The anonymized trajectory database which satisfies $L = 2$, $K = 2$, and $C = 0.6$ by generalization technique.

Rec. #	Path	Diagnosis
1	$(ab, t_2) \rightarrow (f, t_3)$	Flu
2	$(ab, t_2) \rightarrow (f, t_3)$	Flu
3	$(ab, t_1) \rightarrow (cd, t_2)$	HIV
4	$(ab, t_2) \rightarrow (e, t_3)$	Fever
5	$(cd, t_1) \rightarrow (ab, t_2) \rightarrow (e, t_3)$	Fever
6	$(ab, t_1) \rightarrow (cd, t_2)$	Flu
7	$(cd, t_1) \rightarrow (ab, t_2) \rightarrow (e, t_3)$	Fever

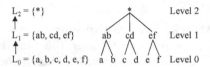

Fig. 1. An example of domain and value generalization hierarchies of location.

replacing some selected data with a generalized version of them to preserve the privacy based on a domain generalization hierarchy (DGH) and a corresponding value generalization hierarchy (VGH) in Fig. 1. It can be seen that all data after generalization could either remain intact, otherwise they are a more general value.

However, computing the optimal LKC-privacy solution on trajectory data by the BF algorithm with generalization technique can be time-consuming as illustrated in [13]. This is because dataset projection and dataset generalization determining by counting for achieving optimal data quality can be redundancy tasks for every possible combination projection of values in attributes or timestamps with a maximum length of background knowledge of adversary L.

In this paper, we propose a look-up table brute-force (LT-BF) algorithm to preserve the privacy and maintain the data quality in the scenarios which the generalization technique is to be applied to anonymization the trajectory data that published with sensitive attributes. The look-up table replaces the redundancy tasks of the brute-force (BF) algorithm by comparing the label of lattice vectors from the pre-constructed look-up table, hence it can help improving the efficiency. In order to evaluate our work, thorough experiment results are presented including the effectiveness and the efficiency of the algorithm.

The organization of this paper is as follows. Section 2 presents the problem definitions addressed in this paper. Subsequently, the proposed algorithm for such the problem is present in Sect. 3. Our work is evaluated by experiments in Sect. 4. Finally, we present the conclusion and future work in Sect. 5.

2   Problem Definition

In this section, the basic notations, the full-domain generalization technique, and the problem definition are presented.

2.1   Basic Definitions

Definition 1 *(Trajectory Dataset).* Let a trajectory dataset $D = \{d^1, d^2, \ldots, d^n\}$ be a collection of moving object tuples. Tuples in a table are not necessary to be unique. Let $T = \{t_1, t_2, \ldots, t_m\}$ be a set of all timestamps of the trajectory dataset. Let $LOC = \{loc_1, loc_2, \ldots, loc_u\}$ be a set of all locations of the trajectory dataset. Let $G = \{g_1, g_2, \ldots, g_v\}$ be a set of class labels.

The trajectory of a moving object $d^i \in D$ is a sequence of spatio-temporal pairs: $d^i = \langle (loc_1^i, t_1^i), (loc_2^i, t_2^i), \ldots, (loc_p^i, t_p^i) \rangle : g$

A pair (loc_r^i, t_r^i) where $1 \leq r \leq p$ represents the visited location $loc_r \in LOC$ at timestamp $t_r \in T$ with the class label $g \in G$ such that $t_r^i < t_{r+1}^i$.

Definition 2 *(Subsequence).* Given a sequence $d^i \in D$, let $Q_i = \{q_1, \ldots, q_x\}$ be a set of subsequence of d^i, where $q_j \subset d^i$ and $q_j \in Q_i$.

Definition 3 *(LKC-privacy).* Let L be the maximum background knowledge of the adversary. Let $S = \{s_1, s_2, \ldots, s_v\}$ be a set of sensitive values which specified by the data holder, such that $S \subset G$. The trajectory database D satisfies LKC-privacy conditions if and only if for any subsequence $q_w \in Q_i$ with $1 \leq |q_w| \leq L$, is satisfied [1]:

1. $|D[q_w]| \geq K$, where $|D[q_w]|$ denotes a number of tuples in $D[q_w]$, and $K > 0$ is an integer anonymity threshold.
2. $\frac{|q_w \bigcup s|}{|q_w|} \leq C$, where $1 \leq C \leq L$ is a real number confidence threshold and $|q_w \bigcup s|$ denotes a number of tuples which contains subsequence q_w with sensitive $s \in S$.

2.2   Full-Domain Generalization

Generalization is one of the common anonymization techniques. It was a widely applied technique, i.e., it replaces some selected data with a generalized version of them to preserve the privacy. Generalization is based on a domain generalization hierarchy (DGH) and a corresponding value generalization hierarchy (VGH) on the values in the domains as shown in Fig. 1 which is the DGH and VGH of the location domain. For the full-domain generalization, every quasi-identifier attribute value of all tuples must be replaced by the value of the same level in the distance vector. An example of generating the lattice from the distance vectors for the raw dataset in Table 1 is shown in Fig. 2.

In Fig. 2, we represent the characteristic of the lattice by the two color circles (gray and white color). The gray-color circles represent a generalized dataset which satisfies the LKC-privacy, meanwhile the white-color circles represent

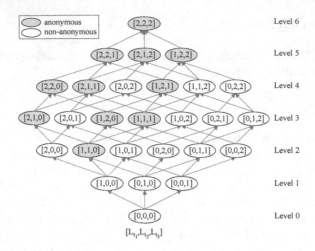

Fig. 2. Example of the corresponding lattices of distance vector.

the non-satisfied dataset. The label on the right-hand side of this lattice is the summation level of the generalization heights of each time stamp. Obviously, there can be more than one circle which satisfies the LKC-privacy. In this work, the well-known general impact on data utility C_{GM} [14] is used to quantify the quality of the generalization which satisfy the LKC-privacy by generalization technique. The impact is defined as follows.

$$C_{GM} = \frac{\sum_j \frac{h_j}{FullGeneralization_j}}{|D|} \tag{1}$$

In this formula, for a timestamp $t_j \in T$, h_j is the height of the generalized value of location at timestamp t_j, and h_j starts from zero when there is no generalization. $FullGeneralization_j$ is the height of the domain generalization hierarchy of location.

For the sake of clarity, the highest data quality C_{GM} of the lattice vectors in Fig. 2 is $[1,1,0]$ with summation level 2. The C_{GM} value of this vector is $\frac{(\frac{1}{2}+\frac{1}{2}+\frac{0}{2})}{7} = 0.14$.

2.3   Problem Statement

After the basic definitions, the full-domain generalization technique, and the data utility C_{GM} are defined, the problem of privacy-preserving for trajectory data publishing is formalized as follows.

Given a trajectory dataset D with a set of sensitive values S of class labels C, DGH and VGH of location domain, find D' which satisfies LKC privacy constraints by full-domain generalization technique such that the impact on data quality C_{GM} is minimized.

3 Algorithm

In this section, we present an LT-BF algorithm to solve the defined problem from the previous section. The algorithm transforms the given trajectory dataset to satisfy LCK privacy constraints and also attempt to minimize the impact $C_G M$.

Algorithm 1. Look-up table Brute-force algorithm

---

input : A trajectory dataset D; Thresholds L, K, C, and sensitive S; Generalization domain of location

output: The output dataset D'_{GM} which satisfies the given LKC-privacy requirement and the general metric C_{GM} impact on data quality is minimal

1   $CS \leftarrow$ create the set of all possible combination sequences in D based on L where sequences size $\leq L$;
2   $CT \leftarrow$ create the set of all possible combination timestamps with size $\leq L$.;
3   **for** *all CT* **do**
4     $LV \leftarrow$ create the set of all corresponding lattice vectors which correspond with timestamp of CT_i.;
5   **for** *all LV* **do**
6   Determine D^* by projection CS with CT_i;
7       $GD^* \leftarrow$ generalized D^* based on LV_j which corresponds with CT_i;
8   **if** *GD^* satisfies K by counting the generalized sequences* **then**
9   **if** *GD^* satisfies C by counting the generalized sequences* **then**
10          $LT \leftarrow LV_j$;
11   **end**
12   **end**
13   **end**
14 **end**
15 $CLV \leftarrow$ create the set of all corresponding lattice vectors.;
16 **for** *all CLV* **do**
17   Initialize $MIN_{GM} = MAX\_VALUE$; ALLCT = true;
18   **for** *all CT* **do**
19   HCT is the height of domain generalization based on CLV_i which corresponds with CT_j.;
20   **if** *HCT is NOT satisfies K and C by LT determining* **then**
21   ALLCT = false;
22   **end**
23   **end**
24   **if** *ALLCT = true* **then**
25   Determine C_{GM};
26   **if** *$C_{GM} < MIN_{GM}$* **then**
27         $MIN_{GM} = C_{GM}$;
28   OptimalLV = CLV_i;
29   **end**
30   **end**
31 **end**
32 D'_{GM} is generalized D by using the *OptimalLV* lattice vector.;

Algorithm 1 shows the pseudo code of the proposed algorithm. It begins with creating the set of all possible combination sequences CS of given dataset. Subsequently, the set of all possible combination timestamps CT with size $\leq L$ will be created. For example, the CT of the dataset in Table 1 when $L = 2$ is $(t_1, t_2), (t_1, t_3)$, and (t_2, t_3). Subsequently, the look-up table LT which keeps all satisfied LKC lattice vectors will be created at Line 5–14. For the look-up table creation, it begins with creating the set of all corresponding lattice of distance vectors LV for each CT_i. The LV of (t_1, t_2) from the running example are $(0, 0)$, $(0, 1), (0, 2), (1, 0), (1, 1), (1, 2), (2, 0), (2, 1)$, and $(2, 2)$. Subsequently, the CS will be projected for generalization with LV_j which corresponds to each CT_i. For each LV_j, if GD^* which corresponds with CT satisfies LKC privacy constraints by counting the generalized sequences, the LV_j will be kept in LT.

For example, all lattice vectors LV of (t_1, t_2), (t_1, t_3), and (t_2, t_3) is shown in Fig. 3(a), (b), and (c), respectively. Note that the gray color lattice vectors in Fig. 3 mean they satisfy LKC privacy constraints. Only the satisfied lattice vector will be kept in the look-up table. Thus, the look-up table of $L = 2$ will show in Table 3. In this case, the number of elements of look-up table is 16. The maximum number of look-up table elements when $L = 2$ and maximum generalization height $= 2$ is $2^3 + 2^3 + 2^3 = 24$ elements.

For the sake of clarity, if the input lattice vector CLV is $[2, 1, 0]$, it will be split into CT. The LV of (t_1, t_2), (t_1, t_3), and (t_2, t_3) is $[2, 1]$, $[2, 0]$, and $[1, 0]$. Each LV will be compared with the element of corresponding look-up table one by one. We can see that all element LV of input vector $[2, 1, 0]$ is satisfied LKC privacy constraints by the look-up table determining.

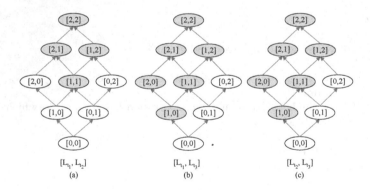

Fig. 3. Example of the corresponding lattices of distance vector when $L = 2$.

Table 3. Example of the look-up tables of $L = 2$

(t_1, t_2)	$[1, 1]$	$[1, 2]$	$[2, 1]$	$[2, 2]$		
(t_1, t_3)	$[1, 0]$	$[2, 0]$	$[1, 1]$	$[1, 2]$	$[2, 1]$	$[2, 2]$
(t_2, t_3)	$[1, 0]$	$[2, 0]$	$[1, 1]$	$[1, 2]$	$[2, 1]$	$[2, 2]$

After the look-up table creation, a bruce-force algorithm will be evaluated at Line 15–32. It begins with creating the set of all corresponding lattice of distance vectors CLV for generalization. The example of all CLV for the raw dataset in Table 1 are shown in Fig. 2. Subsequently, we define the height of generalized dataset HCT of each CLV_i which corresponds to each CT_j. For example, when a CLV_i is $(2, 2, 0)$, the HCT of $(t_1, t_2), (t_1, t_3)$, and (t_2, t_3) are $(2, 2), (2, 0)$, and $(2, 0)$, respectively. If all elements of HCT satisfy LKC privacy constraints by the look-up table LT determining, then the C_{GM} will be determined. Subsequently, we evaluate an optimal lattice vector $OptimalLV$ with minimum C_{GM}. Finally, an $OptimalLV$ is used to generalize dataset D to output dataset D'_{GM}.

4   Experimental Evaluation

In this section, we present the experiments to evaluate the proposed algorithm both in terms of effectiveness and efficiency. The effectiveness of the proposed algorithm is validated by the utility loss, C_{GM}. For the efficiency, the execution time of the proposed algorithm is evaluated.

4.1   Setting

We evaluate our proposed work by using the Metro100K dataset [4,15,16] as in previous literatures. It simulates the routes of 100,000 passengers in the Montreal subway transit system with 65 stations in 60 min, forming 3,900 dimensions. One citizen (or passenger) corresponds to each trajectory data. All the passengers have an average trajectory length of 8 stations. Each record of trajectory data contains a sensitive data with five possible value ("On-welfare", "Part-time", "Full-time", "Self-employed", "Retired"). The sensitive value of a sensitive attribute is "On-welfare".

We pre-process the dataset by removing the tuples with unknown values and discretizing continuous attributes. In addition, the records with less than 3 timestamps are deleted. The records which its timestamps cannot satisfy $K = 50$ are also deleted. This is because we will set up the experiment to evaluate the effect of K value at 10 to 50. After pre-processing, the dataset size remains 85,604 tuples. The number of all possible combination sequences of $L = 1, 2, 3$ are 259,975, 1,944,203, and 3,680,319 sequences, respectively. In the experiment, a number of possible movement timestamps were fixed at 8 and the domain generalization hierarchy was defined as 4 levels. Thus, the number of all corresponding lattices of distance vector is $4^8 = 65,536$.

The experiments are conducted on an Intel(R) Core(TM) i7-6700 CPU @ 3.40 GHz PC with 16 GB of RAM and SPCC Solid State Disk. We compare the result of our LT-BF with a BF algorithm. The BF algorithm is almost the same as our LT-BF except that there is no look-up table is created. More specifically, the difference is the evaluation of LKC privacy constraints of each lattice vector CLV at Lines 19 and 20 in Algorithm 1. The LT-BF algorithm evaluates the constraints by comparing the lattice vector with the created look-up table, but the BF algorithm evaluates by counting the generalized sequences. The BF algorithm will project sequences from CS which corresponds with as CT_j. The projected sequences GD^* will be generalized based on CLV_i which corresponds with CT_j. If all GD^* satisfy LKC privacy constraints by counting the generalized sequences, then the C_{GM}, will be determined. Apparently, the BF can have the high computational expense. However, it can serve us well to present the efficiency of our proposed look-up table structure.

4.2   Effectiveness

In the first section of the experiment, we investigate the effectiveness of the algorithms by the LCK privacy constraints. Both algorithms transform the dataset on a specific timestamp until it reaches a specific L, K, C value. Then, we present the corresponding impact metric of each experiment. Note here that, it is expected that both algorithms will generate the same results in term of effectiveness, the optimal solutions. However, the characteristics of such effectiveness are to be observed in this section.

In Fig. 4(a)–(c), the effect of the K, C, and L to the C_{GM} is shown. In Fig. 4(a), we vary the parameter K from 10 to 50 while fixing $L = 2, C = 0.6$. It is seen that the C_{GM} increased when the value of K is increased. The rationale behind this is because the Metro100K dataset is very dense, so the cost is high when the K value forces the data to be transformed to the higher level sharply.

In Fig. 4(b), we vary the parameter C from 0.2 to 1.0 while fixing $L = 2$, $K = 20$. We can see that the C_{GM} decreased when the value of C increased from

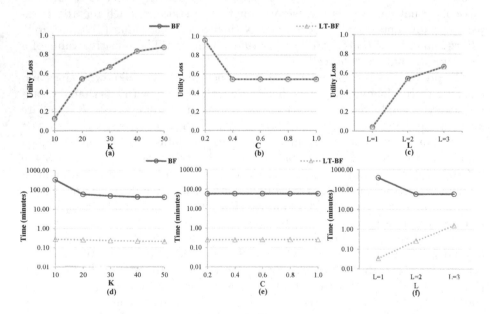

Fig. 4. Effect of the K, C, and L to the utility loss and the execution time

0.2 to 0.4 and then it is stable when the value of C is higher or equal to 0.4. This is because of the value of C affects the generalization to achieving LKC-privacy constraints. For example, from the dataset in Table 1, if we assume K is 2, and C is 0.25, the equivalence class is equal or greater than four records. If C is 0.5, the equivalence class is equal or greater than two records. Thus, the dataset will be more generalization when the C decreases. The C_{GM} is stable when the value of C is higher or equal to 0.4 because the size of equivalence class of generalized dataset of each setting is the same.

The results from both algorithms when parameter L is increased from 1 to 3 is shown in Fig. 4(c), in this experiment, K is fixed at 20 and C is fixed at 0.6. The impact metric C_{GM} of both algorithms are increased when the value of L is increased. As expected, when the adversary's background knowledge represented as L is increased, a number of all possible combination sequences are also increased and affects the cost eventually.

4.3   Efficiency

After the characteristics of the proposed algorithm in term of effectiveness have been demonstrated, subsequently, the efficiency of the algorithms, i.e., the execution time is considered. We investigate the efficiency with regards to the LCK privacy constraints and the dataset size. In these experiments, first, when the effect of the K value is considered, L and C value are fixed at 2 and 0.6, respectively. When the effect of the C value is considered, L and K value are fixed at 2 and 20, respectively. Last, when the effect of the L value is considered, K and C value are fixed at 20 and 0.6, respectively. Note that the Y-axis in these experiment results is in logarithm scale.

In Fig. 4(d), (e), and (f), the execution time of our proposed LT-BF algorithm and the BF algorithm is presented. Obviously, the LT-BF algorithm is much more efficient than the BF algorithm in any setting. This is because of the LT-BF algorithm replaces the redundant tasks by comparing the lattice vector from the pre-created look-up table.

In Fig. 4(d), the effect of the K value is shown. We can see that the execution time of the BF algorithm decreases when the K value increases. This is because of when the K increases, the number of vectors which are satisfied the K is also increased. So the execution time for evaluating C of each K that satisfied vectors is increased. For the LT-BF algorithm, the trend is quite stable, the average execution time is at 14.42 s which is much lower than the execution time of the BF algorithm.

The effect of the C value is shown in Fig. 4(e). We can see that the execution time of the BF algorithm is quite stable when the C value is increased. The reason is that the number of vectors which are satisfied the K condition remains the same, since in this experiment, the K value is fixed at 20. The execution time of the LT-BF also increased from 3.43 s to 15.52 s when the C value is increased from 0.2 to 1.0.

Last, in Fig. 4(f), the effect of the L value is presented. It can be seen that the execution time of the BF algorithm when the L value is set at 1 is very high before it becomes stable. This is because, in this setting, the majority of the vectors satisfy the K value at 20. So the execution time for evaluating the C condition of each K satisfied vector is very high. Meanwhile, the execution time of the LT-BF algorithm also increases from 2.05 s to 93.38 s when the L value is increased from 1 to 3.

5 Conclusion

In this paper, we have addressed the problem of LKC-Anonymization when the input is a trajectory dataset that is published with the sensitive attribute by generalization technique. We have proposed the LT-BF algorithm to preserve privacy and maintain the data quality based on LKC-privacy model. The algorithm has been investigated by the experiments both in terms of effectiveness and efficiency. The experiment results have shown that our proposed algorithm not only generalizes the dataset with optimal data quality the same as the BF algorithm, but also it is very efficient. In our future work, our algorithm will be investigated when the higher-dimensional trajectory data are given as the problem can be more complex [17]. Additionally, our proposed algorithm is still a "one-time" algorithm; i.e., if there is a new set of additional tuples added to the dataset, the algorithm has to reprocess the whole dataset again to preserve the privacy. This may not be an ideal situation in some applications. Thus, we aim at improving our algorithm to perform incremental data transformation in the future.

Acknowledgment. This work was supported by the Graduate School, Chiang Mai University, Thailand.

References

1. Mohammed, N., Fung, B.C.M., Debbabi, M.: Walking in the crowd: anonymizing trajectory data for pattern analysis. In: Proceeding of the 18th ACM Conference on Information and Knowledge Management, pp. 1441–1444 (2009)
2. Fung, B.C.M., Wang, K., Chen, R., Yu, P.S.: Privacy-preserving data publishing: a survey of recent developments. ACM Comput. Surv. **42**, 1–53 (2010)
3. Mohammed, N., Fung, B.C.M., Lee, C.K.: Centralized and distributed anonymization for high-dimensional healthcare data. ACM Trans. Knowl. Discov. Data **4**, 1–33 (2010)
4. Chen, R., Fung, B.C., Mohammed, N., Desai, B.C., Wang, K.: Privacy-preserving trajectory data publishing by local suppression. Inf. Sci. **231**, 83–97 (2013)
5. Ghasemzadeh, M., Fung, B.C.M., Chen, R., Awasthi, A.: Anonymizing trajectory data for passenger flow analysis. Transp. Res. Part C: Emerg. Technol. **39**, 63–79 (2014)
6. Bangkok Insurance: Data security policy. http://www.bangkokinsurance.com/service/service_privacy.php (2015)
7. O'Halloran, M., Glavin, M.: RFID patient tagging and database system. In: International Conference on Networking, Systems, Mobile Communications and Learning Technologies, p. 162 (2006)

8. Robin, D., Saravanan, S., Wanlei, Z.: A practical quadratic residues based scheme for authentication and privacy in mobile RFID systems. Ad Hoc Netw. **11**, 383–396 (2013)
9. Zhu, T., Xiong, P., Li, G.K., Zhou, W.: Correlated differential privacy: hiding information in non-IID data set. IEEE Trans. Inf. Forensics Secur. **10**, 229–242 (2015)
10. Fung, B., Al-Hussaeni, K., Cao, M.: Preserving RFID data privacy. In: 2009 IEEE International Conference on RFID, pp. 200–207 (2009)
11. Fung, B.C.M., Cao, M., Desai, B.C., Xu, H.: Privacy protection for RFID data. In: Proceedings of the ACM Symposium on Applied Computing, pp. 1528–1535 (2009)
12. Al-Hussaeni, K., Fung, B.C., Cheung, W.K.: Privacy-preserving trajectory stream publishing. Data Knowl. Eng. **94**, 89–109 (2014)
13. Harnsamut, N., Natwichai, J.: Privacy preservation for trajectory data publishing and heuristic approach. In: Barolli, L., Enokido, T., Takizawa, M. (eds.) NBiS 2017. LNDECT, vol. 7, pp. 787–797. Springer, Cham (2018). https://doi.org/10.1007/978-3-319-65521-5_71
14. Wong, R., Li, J., Fu, A., Wang, K.: (α, K)-anonymous data publishing. J. Intell. Inf. Syst. **33**, 209–234 (2009)
15. Mohammed, N., Fung, B.C.M., Debbabi, M.: Preserving privacy and utility in RFID data publishing. Technical report 6850 (2010)
16. Komishani, E.G., Abadi, M., Deldar, F.: PPTD: preserving personalized privacy in trajectory data publishing by sensitive attribute generalization and trajectory local suppression. Knowl.-Based Syst. **94**, 43–59 (2016)
17. Aggarwal, C.C.: On K-anonymity and the curse of dimensionality. In: Proceedings of the 31st International Conference on Very Large Databases, pp. 901–909 (2005)

Trajectory Set Similarity Measure:
An EMD-Based Approach

Dan He[1($\boxtimes$)], Boyu Ruan[1], Bolong Zheng[2], and Xiaofang Zhou[1]

[1] The University of Queensland, Brisbane, Australia
{d.he,b.ruan}@uq.edu.au, zxf@itee.uq.edu.au
[2] Aalborg University, Aalborg, Denmark
bolong@cs.aau.dk

Abstract. To address the trajectory sparsity issue concerning Origin-Destination (OD) pairs, in general, most existing studies strive to reconstruct trajectories by concatenating the sub-trajectories along the specific paths and filling up the sparsity with conceptual trajectories. However, none of them gives the robustness validation for their reconstructed trajectories. By intuition, the reconstructed trajectories are more qualified if they are more similar to the exact ones traversing directly from the origin to the destination, which indicates the effectiveness of the corresponding trajectory augmentation algorithms. Nevertheless, to our knowledge, no existing work has studied the similarity of trajectory sets. Motivated by this, we propose a novel similarity measure to evaluate the similarity between two set of trajectories, borrowing the idea of the Earth Mover's Distance. Empirical studies on a large real trajectory dataset show that our proposed similarity measure is effective and robust.

Keywords: Trajectory · Trajectory set similarity
Earth Mover's Distance

1 Introduction

With the proliferation of GPS-enabled devices, a significant increasing volume of trajectories have been collected, which record the mobility of moving objects, e.g., vehicles. Trajectory data offers valuable information for us to discover the intrinsic relationship between the moving objects and specific locations, which foster plenty of applications in location-based social networks and intelligent transportation systems, e.g., personalized routing service. Specifically, given an origin and a destination, the trajectories in between usually offer essential information for us to better understand the diversity of moving behaviours between the origin and destination (OD). However, due to the data sparsity issue, there are always insufficient trajectories to carry out mining algorithms, e.g., classification and clustering, so as to discover the insight properties of OD mobility. To explain, given an origin and a destination, and sometimes, a departure time interval, the number of trajectories could be found from a trajectory dataset

© Springer International Publishing AG, part of Springer Nature 2018
J. Wang et al. (Eds.): ADC 2018, LNCS 10837, pp. 28–40, 2018.
https://doi.org/10.1007/978-3-319-92013-9_3

might be notably small, even though the volume of the entire trajectory set is considerably huge, which hinders the effectiveness of the mining algorithms.

In particular, some existing applications based on the trajectory mining, (e.g., popular route discovery [2], personalized routing [4], destination prediction [17], etc.,) attempt to deal with the sparsity problem by concatenating the sub-trajectories along the specific paths and filling up the sparsity with conceptual trajectory based on probability or popularity of the sub-paths. Nevertheless, none of them gives the robustness validation for their reconstructing trajectories, i.e., how qualified the reconstructed trajectories are to represent the potential mobility. By intuition, the more the reconstructed trajectories similar to the exact ones traversing directly from the origin to the destination, the higher quality the reconstructed trajectories have, which indicates the effectiveness of the corresponding trajectory augmentation algorithms. Motivated by this, consequently, we propose a novel similarity measure for trajectory sets as a robustness validation for trajectory augmentation algorithms, which to the best of our knowledge is the first to explore the similarity between two sets of trajectories, while all existing trajectory similarity measures only focus on two individual trajectories rather than on two trajectory sets.

In our work, borrowing the idea of the Earth Mover's Distance [13] (EMD), we propose an effective and robust similarity measure to evaluate the similarity between two trajectory sets. Our proposed measure captures both spatial and temporal/sequence characteristics of trajectories. Given two set of trajectories, we extract the spatial, temporal/sequence features from trajectory sets respectively, followed by the signature generation for the corresponding features. Note that, the trajectory set we concern shares the same origin and destination, which is defined as *Origin-Destination Set*. Afterwards, we calculate the distance between the two trajectory sets on top of the corresponding signatures. In terms of the computation of the Earth Mover's Distance, we utilize the algorithm proposed in [10], which is the fastest in the state of the art.

Our work has three primary contributions:

- We propose a novel and robust similarity measure, derived from the Earth Mover's Distance, for trajectory set, which measures the distance of the spatial hits distribution between two trajectory sets.
- We further improve the Earth Mover's Distance to the Earth Mover's Distance on Trajectory that not only the spatial but the temporal/sequence properties of trajectory sets can contribute to the set similarity measure.
- We perform the experimental study on a large scale real-world trajectory dataset. And the experimental results suggest the effectiveness of our proposed similarity measure.

The remainder of this paper is organized as follows. In Sect. 2, we introduce the related work and their limitations on our studied problem. Next, in Sect. 3, we present the preliminary concepts. The details of our proposed similarity measure be demonstrated in Sect. 4, followed by the experimental study in Sect. 5. Finally, we conclude and present potential future studies in Sect. 6.

2   Related Work

In this section, we present the existing research work related to our study. In Sect. 2.1, we present existing work on the similarity measures for spatial-temporal data. Then we illustrate the similarity measure for distributions in Sect. 2.2.

2.1   Trajectory Similarity Measures

Measuring the similarity or the distance between two entities is a crucial and fundamental procedure in data mining and knowledge discovering. As for trajectory data, a plethora of research work [1,3,5,6,11,14,16,18] has studied on how to define similarity measures on trajectory data for over decades.

In particular, Euclidean Distance (ED) [14] is a straightforward and intuitive similarity measure with low calculation cost, which computes the distance between the corresponding matched points from two trajectories. However, the ED measure is sensitive to noise. Vlachos et al. introduced the Longest Common Subsequence (LCSS) measure [16], widely used to measure string similarity, to measure the similarity of two trajectories, and is more robust to noise than the ED measure as only the closed matched points would be considered in distance calculation. Chen et al. proposed two versions of similarity measure for two trajectories based on Edit Distance: Edit Distance on Real Sequences (EDR) [1] and Edit Distance with Real Penalty (ERP) [3], which are widely used in trajectory similarity measure. Apart from the above similarity measures, there are many other measures introduced for trajectory data specifically, e.g., Dynamic Time Warping (DTW) [18], One way distance (OWD) [8], Locality In-between Polylines (LIP) [11] etc.

Nevertheless, all the aforementioned similarity measures mainly focus on individual trajectory, aiming to calculate the distance between one trajectory and another. No existing similarity measure is introduced for two sets of trajectories. A naive extension from individual trajectory similarity measure to the trajectory set measure is to calculate the pairwise distances between each pair of trajectories from two different sets respectively. However, such similarity measure is not only time-consuming, but also ineffective, as even for two identical sets of trajectories it might result in a large distance value.

2.2   Distribution Similarity Measures

By extracting some representative features from the corresponding sets and transforming them into distributions, the distribution similarity measure can be easily extended to measure the similarity between two sets of objects. In measuring the similarity between two distributions, which are usually represented by histograms, the Mankowski-Form Distance [15] is the most straightforward one, by simply calculating the L_1-norm distance between each pair of bins. Kullback-Leibler Divergence [7] and Jeffrey Divergence [12] are two distribution measures derived from information theory, that measure how inefficient on average it would be to code one histogram using the other as the code-book. Most of the distribution measures require that the number of bins in two histograms to be the same, and they do not consider the ground distance between each pair of bin.

The Earth Mover's Distance [13] is a well known distribution similarity measure, which is proposed for the image retrieval. Informally, interpreting the distributions as two different ways of piling up a certain amount of dirt over the region, the Earth Mover's Distance is the minimum work flow of moving one pile into the other, where the work is assumed to be the amount of dirt moved multiplying the distance by which it is moved. It takes the ground distance between different bins into account and the numbers of bins in two histograms are unnecessary to be the same.

3   Preliminary

In this section, we first illustrate some formal concepts and definitions. Afterward, we introduce the trajectory retrieval strategy for obtaining a set of origin-destination trajectories with a given OD pair, since in our work, we main focus on the trajectory set that share the same origin and destination.

Definition 1 (Road Network). *A road network is defined as a graph $G = (V, E)$, where V is a set of intersection nodes on the road network and E is a set of road segments $r \in E$, such that $r = (p_s, p_e)$ with $p_s, p_e \in V$ being the two end nodes of r, which is denoted by $<latitude, longitude>$.*

Definition 2 (Trajectory). *A raw trajectory of a moving object is generally recorded by a sequence of spatial-temporal points. Given a road network $G = (V, E)$, each spatial-temporal point from a trajectory can be mapped onto a intersection node of the road network appended with corresponding timestamp. Thus, a trajectory T can be represented by a sequence of time-ordered road network nodes, i.e., $T = \{(p_1, t_1), (p_2, t_2), \ldots, (p_{|T|}, t_{|T|})\}$. Note that p_i here indicates the i-th nodes the trajectory T mapped onto the road network. The length of a trajectory T is the number of constituted nodes, notated as $|T|$. A sub-trajectory of T is a subsequence of road network nodes from T, denoted by $T_{p_j, p_k} = \{(p_j, t_j), \ldots, (p_k, t_k)\}$, where $1 \leq j < k \leq |T|$.*

Definition 3 (Origin-Destination Set). *Given a trajectory database D and a pair of origin and destination nodes (p_o, p_d), the set of trajectories/sub-trajectories traversing from p_o to p_d are notated as $S_{p_o p_d}$. Formally, we have $S_{p_o p_d} = \{T_{p_j, p_k} | T \in D \wedge p_j = p_o \wedge p_k = p_d\}$.*

Definition 4 (Trajectory Inverted List). *Each entry in the trajectory inverted list corresponds to a road intersection nodes, with the form of $<p_{id}, T_{list}>$, where p_{id} indicates the intersection node and T_{list} is the trajectory position list that contains the trajectories occur on that node. The trajectory position list is formed by a list of $<T_{info}, pos>$, where T_{info} consists of both trajectory id and the trajectory address indicating the block where T is stored and the position is the occurrence of the corresponding node on that trajectory.*

Note that the T_{list} is sorted by the trajectory id and the entry list is sorted by the p_{id} for efficient search. Besides, all the trajectory sequences are stored consecutively in the ascending order of the trajectory ids on the disk. Also, the inverted index can be built by a single scan on the trajectory dataset. For each road intersection node that occurs on a trajectory, we create an entry consisting of the occurrence and trajectory information and append this entry to the corresponding trajectory position list of that node.

When given an OD pair of spatial nodes (if they are arbitrary points, find the nearest intersection nodes respectively), we are able to obtain a set of trajectories/sub-trajectories that start from p_o and end at p_d as follow. With the inverted index, we can efficiently return a set of trajectories that traverse across the nodes p_o and p_d. Firstly, we load the corresponding trajectory position lists of p_o and p_d in the memory and scan both synchronously to find out each intersecting trajectory T (i.e. $\{T \in T_{list}(p_o) \bigcap T_{list}(p_d))$. Further, the occurrence of p_o on the intersecting trajectory T should be earlier than that of p_d (i.e. $T(p_o).pos < T(p_d).pos$). This helps find out the Origin-Destination Set of trajectories for the given OD pair with the inverted index.

4   EMD-Based Similarity Measure

In this section, we first introduce a similarity measure to calculate the distance between two set of trajectories, borrowing the idea of an existing distribution similarity measure, the Earth Mover's Distance (EMD). However, it only takes the spatial information of trajectories into consideration. Further, we propose a more robust and effective measure, the Earth Mover's Distance on Trajectory (EMDT) which considers more trajectory characteristics, i.e., temporal/sequence. In our paper, we use the solution proposed in [10] to calculate the Earth Mover's Distance.

4.1   EMD

The Earth Mover's Distance [13] is widely used in image retrieval, which measures the similarity for the distributions of features from two different sets of objects. Given two signatures, EMD calculates the minimum cost to transform one signature to another with the ground distance between each bin into consideration. To consider the similarity of two trajectory sets, intuitively, two similar sets of trajectories *(i)* have higher probability traversing across the same or near locations, *(ii)* go across the same node with similar probabilities. This motivates us to apply the *spatial hits* defined as follows to consider the similarity of two trajectory sets.

Definition 5 (Spatial Hit). *Given a set of trajectories* $\mathbb{T}$ *and a node p, the spatial hit of p w.r.t.* $\mathbb{T}$, *notated as* $sh(p)$, *is defined as the number of occurrence of p in* $\mathbb{T}$. *Correspondingly, we build the spatial hit signature denoted by S =*

$\{(p_1, w_1), (p_2, w_2), \cdots, (p_n, w_n)\}$, where $\{p_1, p_2, \ldots, p_n\}$ is the union set of road network nodes in $\mathbb{T}$, and w_i is the hit ratio for node p_i, formulated by

$$w_i = \frac{sh(p_i)}{\sum_{i=1}^{n} sh(p_i)} \tag{1}$$

The spatial hits captures the above mentioned intuition, and for two similar trajectory sets, the minimum cost to transform one spatial hits signature to another should be small. Hence, based on the spatial hit signature, we introduce the measurement of the distance between two sets of trajectories based on Earth Mover's Distance as follows.

Definition 6 (Earth Mover's Distance (EMD) [13]). *Let two spatial hit signature S_a and S_b be notated as $S_a = \{(p_{a,1}, w_1), (p_{a,2}, w_2), \cdots, (p_{a,n}, w_n)\}$ and $S_b = \{(p_{b,1}, u_1), (p_{b,2}, u_2), \ldots, (p_{b,m}, u_m)\}$, with $p_{a,i}$ (resp. $p_{b,j}$) and w_i (resp. u_j) being the node from the set S_a (resp. S_b) of trajectories and the corresponding hit ratio. Let $\boldsymbol{D} = [d_{ij}]$ be the ground distance matrix where d_{ij} is the ground distance between $p_{a,i}$ and $p_{b,j}$. We aim to find a flow $\boldsymbol{F} = [f_{ij}]$ that minimizes the cost to match S_a to S_b, formulated as below:*

$$EMD(S_a, S_b) = \min\{\sum_{i=1}^{n} \sum_{j=1}^{m} d_{ij} f_{ij}\} \tag{2}$$

subject to the following conditions:

$$f_{ij} \geq 0 \quad 1 \leq i \leq n, 1 \leq j \leq m \tag{3}$$

$$\sum_{j=1}^{m} f_{ij} \leq w_i, \quad \sum_{i=1}^{n} f_{ij} \leq u_j \tag{4}$$

$$\sum_{i=1}^{n} w_i = \sum_{j=1}^{m} u_j = 1 \tag{5}$$

$$d_{ij} = \begin{cases} \frac{d(p_{a,i}, p_{b,j})}{d_{max}}, d(p_{a,i}, p_{b,j}) < d_{max} \\ 1, \quad otherwise \end{cases} \tag{6}$$

Here, $d(p_{a,i}, p_{b,j})$ usually refers to the Euclidean distance or the road network distance between two nodes. According to the experiment, the Euclidean distance is sufficient to display the spatial difference between trajectory sets. For simplification and efficiency, we set the default ground distance measure as the Euclidean distance. In addition, we set a large distance value d_{max} for normalization, s.t. the EMD is bounded by $[0, 1]$.

The flow $\boldsymbol{F} = [f_{ij}]$ is a matrix representing the hit ratio flowing from one signature to another for matching two spatial hit signatures. Constraint (3) confines the amount of $p_{a,i}$ matched to $p_{b,j}$ to be nonnegative. Constraint (4) limits the total amount in S_b matched from $p_{a,i}$ does not exceed w_i, and the total amount in S_a matched to $p_{b,j}$ does not exceed u_j. Take the two spatial hit signatures in Fig. 1 as example, where $S_a = \{(p_1, 0.2), (p_2, 0.3), (p_3, 0.2), (p_4, 0.3)\}$ and

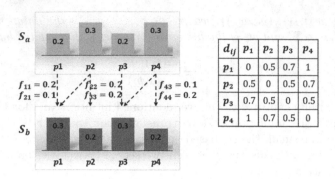

d_{ij}	p_1	p_2	p_3	p_4
p_1	0	0.5	0.7	1
p_2	0.5	0	0.5	0.7
p_3	0.7	0.5	0	0.5
p_4	1	0.7	0.5	0

Fig. 1. EMD example

$S_b = \{(p_1, 0.3), (p_2, 0.2), (p_3, 0.3), (p_4, 0.2)\}$. Given the ground distance matrix d_{ij} shown as Fig. 1, we can obtain the flow with $f_{11} = 0.2, f_{21} = 0.1, f_{22} = 0.2, f_{33} = 0.2, f_{43} = 0.1$, and $f_{44} = 0.2$, such that the $EMD(S_a, S_b)$ is minimum. Eventually, in this case, $EMD(S_a, S_b) = 0.1$.

However, since a trajectory set is a set of spatial-temporal sequences, rather than a multi-set of spatial nodes, simply taking EMD as the measure will discard the temporal/sequence information, and may result in biased results. Take an extreme case as example. Consider two set of trajectories where the first set S_1 contains trajectories going from o to d and the second set S_2 contains trajectories going from d to o. For each trajectory T_i in S_1, there exists a trajectory T_i' such that the nodes going across in T_i are the same as the one in T_i', and vice versa. In this case, the EMD between these two sets should be zero. However, it is clear that the two sets of trajectories differ significantly and the EMD score cannot capture the difference since it ignores the temporal/sequence information.

4.2   EMDT

To capture the temporal/sequence information of trajectories, we further propose the Earth Mover's Distance on Trajectory, an improved version of the EMD to capture more characteristics of trajectory set. In particular, we take into account the time duration information and add it into the signatures. More formally, we define the average delta duration for a node as follow.

Definition 7 (Average Delta Duration). *Given a signature* $S = \{(p_1, w_1),$ $(p_2, w_2), \cdots, (p_n, w_n)\}$ *w.r.t. a set of trajectory* $\mathbb{T}$, *for each node* p, *we define the average delta duration of* p, *denoted as* δ, *to be the average time duration of* p *to the time of the first node in each trajectory in* $\mathbb{T}_p$ *(where* $\mathbb{T}_p \subset \mathbb{T}$ *is the set of trajectories containing* p), *formulated by*

$$\delta = \frac{1}{|\mathbb{T}_p|} \sum_{i=1}^{|\mathbb{T}_p|} (t_{T_i}(p) - t_{T_i}(p_1)) \tag{7}$$

where $T_i \in \mathbb{T}_p$ *is the trajectory traversed through* p, p_1 *is the first node in* T_i *and* $t_{T_i}(p)$ *is the corresponding time stamp of* p *on trajectory* T_i.

Note that the average delta duration indicates not only the temporal information of a signature but also reflects the sequence characteristic of trajectory nodes since the delta duration is an accumulative time used from the starting node of the trajectory. For example, given 3 trajectories $T_1 = \{(p_{11}, 1), (p_{12}, 3), (p_{13}, 6)\}, T_2 = \{(p_{21}, 2), (p_{22}, 5), (p_{23}, 7), (p_{24}, 9)\}$ and $T_3 = \{(p_{31}, 1), (p_{32}, 5), (p_{33}, 8)\}$. Suppose $p = p_{12} = p_{22} = p_{32}$. Then the average delta duration of p in these 3 trajectories equals $(2 + 3 + 4)/3 = 3$. With the average delta duration information on the signature, we propose the *Earth Mover's Distance on Trajectory (EMDT)* as follow.

Definition 8 (Earth Mover's Distance on Trajectory (EMDT)). *Given two trajectory sets S_a and S_b, we have the corresponding spatial hit histograms notated as $S_a = \{(p_{a,1}, \delta_{a,1}, w_1), (p_{a,2}, \delta_{a,2}, w_2), \cdots, (p_{a,n}, \delta_{a,n}, w_n)\}$ and $S_b = \{(p_{b,1}, \delta_{b,1}, u_1), (p_{b,2}, \delta_{b,2}, u_2), \cdots, (p_{b,m}, \delta_{b,m}, u_m)\}$, with δ representing the average delta duration. We define the distance between S_a and S_b as the Earth Mover's Distance on Trajectory (EMDT) formulated by the following:*

$$EMDT(S_a, S_b) = \min\{\sum_{i=1}^{n}\sum_{j=1}^{m} Cost_{ij} f_{ij}\} \qquad (8)$$

with

$$Cost_{ij} = \alpha \times d_{ij} + (1 - \alpha) \times d(\delta_{a,i}, \delta_{b,j}) \qquad (9)$$

$$d(\delta_{a,i}, \delta_{b,j}) = \begin{cases} \frac{dist(\delta_{a,i}, \delta_{b,j})}{dist_{max}}, & dist(\delta_{a,i}, \delta_{b,j}) < dist_{max} \\ 1, & otherwise \end{cases} \qquad (10)$$

where the $dist(\delta_{a,i}, \delta_{b,j})$ is defined as the l_1-norm between $\delta_{a,i}, \delta_{b,j}$ and α is an adjustable linear combination parameter, (which can be defined according to the users' preference, i.e., how to allocate the proportion of the spatial and temporal characteristics in measuring the similarity). Similarly, a large value $dist_{max}$ is set for normalization.

The EMDT differs from the EMD in trajectory set similarity measure by the calculation of the cost for transforming one signature to the other, while the computation of the distance value is similar. As we will see in the experiments in Sect. 5, by capturing the temporal/sequence characteristics of the trajectories, the proposed EMDT is a more robust and effective measure in distinguishing the difference between trajectory sets, than the EMD scores which only considers the spatial information.

5   Experimental Study

In this section, we conduct the experimental study to evaluate the effectiveness and robustness of the proposed similarity measure. Firstly, we present the experimental settings in Sect. 5.1. Afterward, we compare the effectiveness between the EMD and the other distribution similarity measures w.r.t. trajectory sets in Sect. 5.2. Finally, we evaluate the effectiveness of the improved EMDT on trajectory set similarity measure in Sect. 5.3.

5.1 Experiment Setup

The trajectory dataset we use in the experiment is collected from $50K$ taxis in Beijing for 5 days, which consists of more than 2 million trajectories, each of which is represented by a sequence of GPS records. A map-matching [9] algorithm is employed to transform the raw trajectories into a sequence of time-order road intersection nodes (the mapped trajectory set is about 1.6 GB), where the time is estimated by the first GPS point assigned on the corresponding road nodes. We consider the road network of Beijing city that composes of $302,364$ intersections and $387,588$ road segments (60 MB). All of our algorithms are implemented in Java, and we run all the experiments on a Dell R720 PowerEdge Rack Mount Server with two Xeon E5-2690 2.90 GHz CPUs, 192 GB memory running Ubuntu Server 14.04 LTS operating system.

5.2 Effectiveness of EMD

In this subsection, we design a series of experiments to verify the rationality of the EMD-based trajectory set similarity measure. The experiments mainly contain two perspectives. First, we evaluate multiple distribution similarity measures for spatial hit signature, which include Murkowski Form Distance (MFD) [15], Jeffrey Divergence Distance (JDD) [12], and EMD. We aim to verify that among those distribution measures, EMD is the most suitable one for trajectory similarity measure. Secondly, we evaluate the EMD with two different ground distances, Euclidean distance, and road network distance, in order to show the different impact by utilizing different ground distances. In the calculation of similarity measure, we follows the algorithm proposed in [10].

For the comparison of different distribution similarity measures, we randomly select multiple pairs (100 pairs) of OD points, extract the corresponding set of OD trajectories as the sample dataset, and estimate the average distance values. We first compare different distribution similarity measures for the same set of OD trajectories, where each set is divided into two subsets based on different strategies. In particular, we have the self comparison which compares two identical sets, partial comparison that arbitrarily divides a set into two parts, and noise augmentation test which adds noise into a set and compare the noise-added set with the one without noise. In addition, to measure the distance between two different sets of OD trajectories, we divide the sample dataset into 4 subsets and in each subset we arbitrarily pick two OD sets for multiple rounds, calculate the distribution distance, and show the average distance scores. In self-comparison, as the contrastive two subsets are derived from the same set, the distance scores are supposed to be very small. From Fig. 2, we can observe that these three distribution similarity measures are robust to noise in self-comparison, as the distance scores are all very small. Also, the self-self distances are all zero, which is superior to the pairwise individual trajectory similarity measure (discussed in Sect. 2.1). However, when comparing the similarity between two different sets of trajectories, as shown in Fig. 3 apart from the EMD, the other two distribution similarity measures cannot distinguish the difference between two different sets

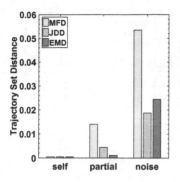

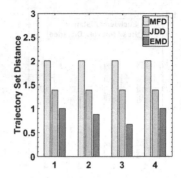

Fig. 2. Self comparison   **Fig. 3.** Different set comparison

of trajectory, as the distance scores of the MFD and JDD are both identical in different sets' comparison, which is in line with our analysis, since the EMD will take the ground distance of the signatures into consideration.

Regarding the different ground distance comparison, we use the Euclidean distance and road network distance respectively in the calculation of the EMD. The data settings in this part are the same as the one for the comparison of different distribution similarity measures. From the Fig. 4, we can find out that, the variation of two ground distances is insignificant, which indicates that changing the ground distance from road network distance to Euclidean distance exert little effect on the measurement of EMD. Thus, for the rest of our experiment, we use the Euclidean distance as the ground distance for EMD calculation. Applying the Euclidean distance, we can either reduce the time on ground distance calculation or eliminate the space consumption to store the ground distance matrix for road network distance.

5.3 Effectiveness of EMDT

In this subsection, we discover the difference between EMD and EMDT to show that how EMDT can capture the temporal/sequence information. The parameter α denotes the percentage of spatial characters for trajectory set similarity measure in EMDT, where $\alpha = 1$ indicates only the spatial distance is considered for the cost computation, while $\alpha = 0$ indicates that only average delta duration is taken into account.

We test the parameter α for EMDT calculation. The datasets used in this experiment are from a single set of trajectories (i.e., the trajectories from the same origin to the same destination). We evaluate the average distance scores from 100 OD pairs, where each pair corresponds to a set of trajectories. For each set, we divide the trajectories into two subsets as follow. We first reverse the sequence of trajectories (as discuss in Sect. 4) and compare it with the origin set (denoted as reverse). Furthermore, we partition the set of trajectories based on temporal information, namely peak time (7:00–9:00am, 5:00–7:00pm) and off-peak time, weekday and weekend. We compare the peak (resp. weekday) set

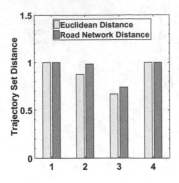

Fig. 4. Ground distance

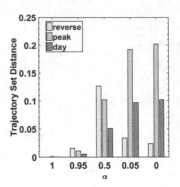

Fig. 5. Temporal contribution

with the off-peak (resp. weekend) set, denoted as peak (resp. day) in Fig. 5. And the parameter α varies from 1-0 indicating the spatial character contribution for cost computation. The result is shown in Fig. 5. As we can see, when $\alpha = 1$, which means we only consider the spatial character, the distance between the reverse set and origin set is zero. When the contribution of temporal character increases, the EMDT values also increase. For the comparison between the reverse set and the original set, taking the spatial and temporal/sequence evenly results in largest distinction since considering only one type of characteristics, the difference between reverse set and original set of trajectories is insignificant. In terms of the other two scenario, the distance scores increase with the higher proportion of the temporal characteristics. By intuition, the speed of trajectory during the peak (resp. weekday) time might be lower than the one during the off-peak time (resp. weekend). Thus, we can infer that EMDT can capture the speed information of trajectories sharing the same spatial routes, as the distances between peak set and off-peak set, weekday set, and weekend set, are notable. Consequently, we conclude that (1) EMDT can display the sequence information since the original set is different from the reversed set. (2) EMDT can distinguish the difference between two set of trajectories with different speed, and indicates the temporal feature in trajectory sets.

6   Conclusion

In this paper, we proposed a novel similarity measure towards origin-destination trajectory sets, as a validation method for trajectory augmentation algorithm to evaluate whether the reconstructed trajectories are similar to the exact one traversing from an origin to a destination. We borrow the idea from the Earth Mover's Distance to measure the similarity between two trajectory sets on top of the generated feature (i.e., spatial hit) signatures. Then we improved the similarity measure by taking the temporal characteristics into consideration. From the experiment, we observed that, the proposed measures are effective and robust in trajectory set similarity evaluation. In future work, we will strive to address the sparsity issue w.r.t. OD pairs by developing a practical trajectory augmentation algorithm, in which the reconstructed trajectories are supposed to be similar to the exact OD trajectories.

References

1. Chen, L., Özsu, M.T., Oria, V.: Robust and fast similarity search for moving object trajectories. In: Proceedings of the 2005 ACM SIGMOD International Conference on Management of Data, pp. 491–502. ACM (2005)
2. Chen, Z., Shen, H.T., Zhou, X.: Discovering popular routes from trajectories. In: 2011 IEEE 27th International Conference on Data Engineering (ICDE), pp. 900–911. IEEE (2011)
3. Chen, Z., Shen, H.T., Zhou, X., Zheng, Y., Xie, X.: Searching trajectories by locations: an efficiency study. In: Proceedings of the 2010 ACM SIGMOD International Conference on Management of Data, pp. 255–266. ACM (2010)
4. Dai, J., Yang, B., Guo, C., Ding, Z.: Personalized route recommendation using big trajectory data. In: 2015 IEEE 31st International Conference on Data Engineering (ICDE), pp. 543–554. IEEE (2015)
5. Kassidas, A., MacGregor, J.F., Taylor, P.A.: Synchronization of batch trajectories using dynamic time warping. AIChE J. **44**(4), 864–875 (1998)
6. Kruskal, J.B.: An overview of sequence comparison: time warps, string edits, and macromolecules. SIAM Rev. **25**(2), 201–237 (1983)
7. Kullback, S.: Information Theory and Statistics. Courier Corporation, North Chelmsford (1997)
8. Lin, B., Su, J.: Shapes based trajectory queries for moving objects. In: Proceedings of the 13th Annual ACM International Workshop on Geographic Information Systems, pp. 21–30. ACM (2005)
9. Newson, P., Krumm, J.: Hidden Markov map matching through noise and sparseness. In: Proceedings of the 17th ACM SIGSPATIAL International Conference on Advances in Geographic Information Systems, pp. 336–343. ACM (2009)
10. Pele, O., Werman, M.: Fast and robust earth mover's distances. In: 2009 IEEE 12th International Conference on Computer Vision, pp. 460–467. IEEE (2009)
11. Pelekis, N., Kopanakis, I., Marketos, G., Ntoutsi, I., Andrienko, G., Theodoridis, Y.: Similarity search in trajectory databases. In: 14th International Symposium on Temporal Representation and Reasoning, pp. 129–140. IEEE (2007)
12. Puzicha, J., Hofmann, T., Buhmann, J.M.: Non-parametric similarity measures for unsupervised texture segmentation and image retrieval. In: Proceedings of the 1997 IEEE Computer Society Conference on Computer Vision and Pattern Recognition, pp. 267–272. IEEE (1997)
13. Rubner, Y., Tomasi, C., Guibas, L.J.: The earth mover's distance as a metric for image retrieval. Int. J. Comput. Vis. **40**(2), 99–121 (2000)
14. Sanderson, A.C., Wong, A.K.: Pattern trajectory analysis of nonstationary multivariate data. IEEE Trans. Syst. Man Cybern. **10**(7), 384–392 (1980)
15. Swain, M.J., Ballard, D.H.: Color indexing. Int. J. Comput. Vis. **7**(1), 11–32 (1991)
16. Vlachos, M., Kollios, G., Gunopulos, D.: Discovering similar multidimensional trajectories. In: Proceedings of the 18th International Conference on Data Engineering, pp. 673–684. IEEE (2002)

17. Xue, A.Y., Zhang, R., Zheng, Y., Xie, X., Huang, J., Xu, Z.: Destination prediction by sub-trajectory synthesis and privacy protection against such prediction. In: 2013 IEEE 29th International Conference on Data Engineering (ICDE), pp. 254–265. IEEE (2013)
18. Yi, B.-K., Jagadish, H., Faloutsos, C.: Efficient retrieval of similar time sequences under time warping. In: Proceedings of the 14th International Conference on Data Engineering, pp. 201–208. IEEE (1998)

Histogram Construction for Difference Analysis of Spatio-Temporal Data on Array DBMS

Jing Zhao[1]([⊠]), Yoshiharu Ishikawa[2], Chuan Xiao[3], and Kento Sugiura[1]

[1] Graduate School of Information Science, Nagoya University, Nagoya, Japan
{zhao,sugiura}@db.ss.is.nagoya-u.ac.jp
[2] Graduate School of Informatics, Nagoya University, Nagoya, Japan
ishikawa@i.nagoya-u.ac.jp
[3] Institute for Advanced Research, Nagoya University, Nagoya, Japan
chuanx@nagoya-u.jp

Abstract. To analyze scientific data, there are frequent demands for comparing multiple datasets on the same subject to detect any differences between them. For instance, comparison of observation datasets in a certain spatial area at different times or comparison of spatial simulation datasets with different parameters are considered to be important. Therefore, this paper proposes a *difference* operator in spatio-temporal data warehouses, based on the notion of histograms in the database research area. We propose a *difference histogram* construction method and they are used for effective and efficient data visualization in difference analysis. In addition, we implement the proposed algorithms on an array DBMSs SciDB, which is appropriate to process and manage scientific data. Experiments are conducted using mass evacuation simulation data in tsunami disasters, and the effectiveness and efficiency of our methods are verified.

1 Introduction

As big data attracts attention in a variety of fields, research on data analytics for sophisticated analytic processing of a large amount of data in a database has gained popularity [10]. As for spatio-temporal databases, there are growing demands for analyzing large-scale spatio-temporal data in various domains such as mobility data, moving trajectory data, and scientific data [2,7]. In scientific fields, a lot of simulations are conducted for the purpose of predictions, decision making, etc. For instance, disaster simulations like human evacuation simulations and tsunami simulations are conducted for effective humanitarian relief and disaster management [19]. Analysis of disaster simulation data can achieve various objectives, such as interesting patterns discovery, and decision support like suggesting an appropriate location as a shelter of disasters [9]. Moreover, since large amounts of simulation data are generated by those simulations with different conditions and parameters, *data warehouse* techniques that enabling massive data storage and exploration are in demand.

ⓒ Springer International Publishing AG, part of Springer Nature 2018
J. Wang et al. (Eds.): ADC 2018, LNCS 10837, pp. 41–52, 2018.
https://doi.org/10.1007/978-3-319-92013-9_4

This paper specifically examines differences as one of the basic analytic requirements for *spatio-temporal data warehouses*, in which detection of temporal changes, as well as differences between observation datasets with different parameters or conditions should be required. Consider that an earthquake analyst intends to explore the evacuation simulation data after an earthquake. In this case, a query like "Return the major change in the distribution of evacuees between the first hour and the second hour after the earthquake occurs." is considered to be useful to understand the variation trend in the movement of evacuees.

Various types of difference operators are possible, depending on the properties or application purposes of the target data. However, it is not clear which types of difference operators are appropriate for the above-mentioned data analysis. In this paper, we define a general-purpose operator based on the notion of histograms [1,5,11,12], which are widely studied for the purpose of query optimization and selectivity estimation in database systems. Different from the main focus of those work, which is to improve the accuracy of estimations, our work aims to enable exploratory and interactive analysis of big simulation data. The difference operator studied in this paper focuses on both usability in visual analytics and accuracy of histograms.

An intuitive example of the difference operator is shown in Fig. 1. The left and middle ones represent the aggregate results of evacuees in time intervals T_1 and T_2, respectively. The intensity of cells correspond to the aggregate values (the number of moving users in the cell during the specified period of time). The figure on the right side of Fig. 1 approximately represents the differences between the aggregate results of T_1 and T_2. In the heat map representation, the more the color of the cell is "hot" (red is the extreme one), the larger the increase of aggregate values from T_1 to T_2. Meanwhile, the "cold" (blue in the extreme case) regions correspond to large decrease from T_1 to T_2. In order to represent a rough trend of differences, any adjacent cells with a similar trend of differences are merged into one cell. Presentation of such output results enables users to easily grasp any differences between two different time segments.

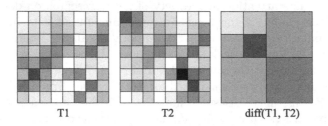

T1   T2   diff(T1, T2)

Fig. 1. Image of difference operator (Color figure online)

On the other hand, due to the challenges in detecting any remarkable changes within a large amount of data, it is necessary to develop efficient algorithms by effectively using the latest database system technology. As scientific data is usually represented as 2-D (or 3-D) array structure, array-based representation is more appropriate for the representation [15]. In this paper, we propose difference histogram construction methods, and implement the algorithms on SciDB [16–18], which is an open source array-oriented DBMS for the efficient storage and manipulation of large array data.

Our contributions can be summarized as follows:

- We study the problem of detecting differences among massive spatio-temporal data, and define the difference operator in a spatio-temporal data warehouse (Sect. 2).
- We propose both exact and heuristic histogram construction algorithms based on the structure of quadtree (Sect. 3).
- We discuss the implementation of the difference operator on SciDB, the state-of-the-art array DBMS (Sect. 4).
- We conduct extensive experiments on massive simulation data to verify the effectiveness and efficiency of the proposed methods (Sect. 5).

2   Preliminaries

In this section, we introduce some basic definitions of spatio-temporal arrays before we formulate the difference histogram studied in this paper.

2.1   Spatio-Temporal Array

Definition 1 (Spatial Cell). *We assume that the target two dimensional space has a $2^d \times 2^d$ grid structure. Each grid cell is represented by $cell(x, y)$, where $1 \le x, y \le 2^d$. The rectangle area corresponding to $cell(x, y)$ is denoted by $area(x, y)$.*

We call each $area(x, y)$ a *base area* because it is a smallest spatial unit considered in the following.

Definition 2 (Spatio-Temporal Array). *A spatio-temporal array $\mathcal{A}$ is a three dimensional array with numeric element values. The dimensions x and y correspond to the two dimensional spatial grid structure and the dimension t is a temporal dimension. The temporal dimension is represented by a series of time stamps with equal time difference τ.*

Note that τ can be one minute, one hour, etc., and depends on the dataset and the analysis.

2.2   Problem Definition

For the purpose of analyzing spatio-temporal data, we focus on the variation of data distribution by time and spatial dimensions, which is considered as one of the most important requirements of data analytics. Therefore, we formulate the problem of detecting differences at both spatial and temporal scales as below.

We define some notions before the problem definition.

Definition 3 (Aggregated Array). *Given a spatio-temporal array $\mathcal{A}$ and a time interval T, an aggregated array for $T, \mathcal{A}[T]$, is a two-dimensional array such that each (x, y) element value of $\mathcal{A}[T], \mathcal{A}[T](x, y)$, is obtained by applying the aggregate function to all the (x, y, t) element values of $\mathcal{A}$ $(t \in T)$.*

The aggregate function depends on the target dataset and application, but the difference operation, applied next, should be meaningful. In our example of tsunami disaster simulation, $\mathcal{A}(x, y, t)$ corresponds to the number of evacuees within the spatial cell $cell(x, y)$ for time t. Therefore, the *sum* aggregate function is used, and $\mathcal{A}[T](x, y)$ is the total number of evacuees within $cell(x, y)$ while time interval T.

Definition 4 (Difference Array). *Given a spatio-temporal matrix $\mathcal{A}$ and two time intervals T_i and T_j, the difference array of $\mathcal{A}[T_i]$ and $\mathcal{A}[T_j], \mathcal{DA}_{ij}$, is defined by $\mathcal{DA}_{ij}(x, y) = \mathcal{A}[T_j](x, y) - \mathcal{A}[T_i](x, y)$ for each (x, y) element.*

In order to catch an insight of difference arrays, we use the notion of *histograms* from the studies on selectivity estimation and query optimization in the database area. As the most of histogram construction problems in the literature of database are proved to be NP-hard [13], we exploit a *quadtree-based hierarchical structure* to construct a difference histogram. Next, we formulate the notion of a difference histogram. It is based on hierarchical space partitioning applying the idea of quadtree [8].

Definition 5 (Difference Histogram). *Given a spatio-temporal array $\mathcal{A}$, two time intervals T_i and T_j, an integer B defining the size of a bucket, and an error metric $E()$, the difference histogram H of the difference array $\mathcal{DA}_{ij}$ consists of a set of buckets $\{b_1, b_2, \ldots, b_B\}$, generated by partitioning the whole spatial region of $\mathcal{DA}_{ij}$ into B non-overlapping buckets based on the quadtree-based partitioning. Each bucket b_l $(1 \le l \le B)$ has a corresponding rectangle area $b_l.area$, and an aggregated value $b_l.val$. The set of elements that belong to a bucket b_l is represented as $Elem_l$, which satisfies the following conditions: $\{\forall e \in Elem_l \mid e \in \mathcal{DA}_{ij} \wedge e.area \in b_l.area\}$. The value of $b_l.val$ is calculated by averaging elements in $Elem_l$:*

$$b_l.val = \frac{\sum_{e \in Elem_l} e}{|b_l.area|} \tag{1}$$

Next, we define the error function. It is based on the notion of *sum squared error* (SSE), which is a common error metric for measuring difference between two data distributions.

Definition 6 (Error Function). *The error function E of a difference histogram H is defined as*

$$E_B(H) = \sum_{l=1}^{B} \sum_{e \in Elem_l} (e - b_l.val)^2. \tag{2}$$

3   Quadtree-Based Histogram Construction Methods

In this section, we propose histogram construction methods based on a *quadtree-based hierarchical structure*. The overall spatial region corresponds to the root of the quadtree at depth 0, and each leaf node at the largest depth represents an element in the difference array. In addition, every internal node in the quadtree contains four child nodes. Every partitioning of an internal node generates four child nodes if they are non-empty cells.

We assume that the target space is partitioned in a $2^d \times 2^d$ grid structure and we are given the parameter B, the number of buckets used in the difference histogram. In the following, we describe an exhaustive bottom-up algorithm to construct a difference histogram. Since its cost is prohibitively large, we also propose a greedy algorithm which can be efficiently implemented. In addition, we present a hybrid approach of the exhaustive and the greedy algorithms for taking trade-offs of two algorithms.

3.1   Exhaustive Bottom-Up Approach

We briefly describe a baseline algorithm for constructing a histogram. It is based on the *bottom-up* approach and finds the *optimal* histogram exhaustively. The reason to select the bottom-up approach is that our implementation described later is based on an array DBMS—we assume that the dataset is already available in the DBMS with a grid structure. The input of the algorithm is a *complete quadtree*, a quadtree in which all the leaf nodes are in the level d. In the leaf nodes, the quadtree stores the count information (the number of evacuees in our example).

The algorithm starts from the nodes in level $d-1$ of the given complete quadtree. For each level $d-1$ nodes, it considers two options: (1) create four buckets for four children in the leaf level with error 0, and (2) create one bucket by combining four children with some error. Then we move to the upper level $d-2$ and consider possible candidates of bucket arrangement. This process continues to the root level, but we can omit intermediate candidates when (a) the cost (the number of buckets) exceeds B and (b) the error of the candidate is worse than other one with the same or smaller cost. Finally, at the root level (level 0), we select the best candidate with the lowest error within the budget B.

In this approach, the number of candidates is $O(2^d)$ because we need to consider all the possible combinations. We can reduce the cost using the pruning intermediate candidates using strategies (a) and (b) above, but the cost is still prohibitively huge. Note that we can also reduce the computation cost of the error function, which is called many times in the process. We temporally store computed aggregated values for each nodes and compute required statistics values for the error function incrementally.

3.2   Greedy Approach

As described above, the computational cost of the exhaustive algorithm is quite expensive. To improve the response time, we propose an efficient *greedy* approach. The algorithm is also based on the bottom-up approach for the implementation on the array DBMS.

The basic idea is to iteratively partition the target region of a given node n into k subregions, where $k \in \{1, \ldots, b_{max}\}$. The value of b_{max} is the maximum number of buckets the node is able to contain, which is computed by the smaller value of limit number of buckets (B) and the number of leaf nodes covered by the node $(size(n))$. For each partition of the node, we choose the one with the maximum error reduction from the candidate results of its child nodes. The process finishes when the number of buckets is larger than k. Note that, we store the candidate results of nodes to compute the candidate results of its parent node, in order to reduce the computation cost of multiple accesses of covered leaf nodes.

3.3 Hybrid Approach

The *hybrid* approach is based on the following observation: In general, the larger the depth of a given node in a histogram, the smaller the error of the node compared to its ancestor nodes. Which means that if we employ the greedy approach for the deep level of the complete quadtree, the quality of the resulting histogram would be less effected. We empirically set a depth threshold δ. We use the exhaustive approach when the depth is less than δ and use the greedy approach otherwise. The depth threshold δ is chosen to take trade-offs of the two proposed algorithms, the larger the δ is, the more accuracy the result histogram is, vice versa. The experimental evaluation is shown in the experiment part (Sect. 5).

4   Implementation on Array DBMS

Since scientific data typically have spatio-temporal structure, indexed arrays are often used to represent scientific data, while the traditional relational model cannot handle such array data [15]. Some array database management systems are developed to support scientific computing and online analytical processing (OLAP), such as RasDaMan [4], ArrayDB [3], SciDB [16–18], etc. In this paper, we implement the proposed histogram construction methods on SciDB, one of the state-of-the-art array DBMSs.

4.1   Overview of SciDB and Our Configuration

SciDB is a parallel database system based on the shared nothing architecture, and designed specifically for scientific data management and analysis. In SciDB, array data is organized on disks as *chunks*, which also work as the I/O units. Chunking ensures that logically co-located cell values are clustered into the same physical block, and enables efficient query processing. Chunks are distributed among all instances of a SciDB cluster. SciDB uses a variety of functions for chunk mapping, and the default is the hash-based distribution. During query execution, each instance node executes query locally with the partial array data, and transfers intermediate results across nodes when global computing is necessary.

SciDB supports a variety of operators for array data, such as data extraction (e.g., *slice, between*) and aggregation (e.g., *aggregate, regrid*). For aggregate operators, a lot of aggregate functions (e.g., sum, min, and max) are supported. In addition to built-in operators and aggregate functions, users are also allowed to implement user-defined operators (UDOs) and user-defined aggregates (UDAs) using C++ language based on the plugin mechanism. Once a plugin operator is loaded into the SciDB library system, it can perform in the similar way with the built-in operators of SciDB for data processing.

Our experiments are performed on a SciDB cluster, which consists of a coordinator server (CPU: Intel Xeon E5-2637 v4 @ 3.50 GHz × 2, RAM: 128 GB, OS: Ubuntu 14.04 LTS 64bit) and 3 worker servers (CPU: Intel Xeon E5620 @ 2.40 GHz × 2, RAM: 32 GB, OS: Ubuntu 14.04 LTS 64bit), each with 2 servers. There are totally 10 SciDB instances that work in parallel. The used version of SciDB is 16.9.

4.2 Implementation Details

We implement the three algorithms described in Sect. 3 on SciDB. The pseudocode of implementing the optimal difference histogram construction algorithms on SciDB is shown in Algorithm 1, which can be easily extended to implement other merging strategies. The inputs of the difference operator contain a difference array A, the desired number of buckets B, and the maximum depth of the quadtree. The algorithm returns a result histogram, which is stored as an array with only one element, i.e., the solution of the root node.

In the implementation, we realize the proposed histogram construction algorithms by implementing the histogram initialization phase as a UDO and merging phases as UDAs. In details, we implement a UDO *initialize* for the initial-

---

Algorithm 1. Implement histogram construction methods on SciDB

Input: A: input array, B : number of buckets, dep_{max}: the maximum depth of the quadtree

Result: H: output array of result histogram

1 $H_0 \leftarrow initialize(A, dep_{max})$;   // Histogram initialization
2 $H \leftarrow$ regrid($H_0, 2, 2, leafMerge$(leafNode) as interNode) ;   // Merge leaf nodes
3 $dep_{cur} \leftarrow dep_{max} - 1$;   // Depth of parent nodes
4 **while** $dep_{cur} - 1 > 0$ **do**
5 | $H \leftarrow$ regrid($H, 2, 2, internalMerge$(interNode) as interNode) ;   // Merge internal nodes
6 | $dep_{cur} - -$;
7 **end**
8 **return** H;

---

ization phase to transfer the numeric attribute values to leaf nodes (Line 1). The proposed histogram construction methods conduct merging in a bottom-up style until reaching the root node. The merging strategies are implemented as UDAs, *leafMerge* and *internalMerge* for merging leaf nodes and internal nodes, respectively (Lines 4–7).

The UDAs are executed by the built-in operator `regrid` of SciDB. For example, `regrid(H_0, 2, 2, leafMerge(leafNode) as interNode` in Line 2 conducts merging with block size of 2×2 on leaf nodes. Built-in operators such as `regrid` are executed efficiently on SciDB. Using the bottom-up construction approach, we can fully utilize the query processing power of SciDB.

5   Experiments

5.1   Datasets

The target data sets used in the experiments are evacuation simulation results in the event of large-scale earthquakes in Kochi City and Kantou area in Japan, respectively. Dataset-1 is the sample evacuation simulation data of six hours compiled under the conditions in which an earthquake occurs at 9 a.m., and the evacuations peak is set as sixty minutes after its occurrence. The simulation data is about 40,000 people's evacuations based on person trip data. Dataset-2 contains 194,226,288 records of evacuees' mobility data during 24 h after an earthquake occurs.

Each simulation data is a collection of records in the format of $(id, time, x, y)$, where *id* denotes user ID, *time* is a time stamp, and (x, y) is the location of a user at *time*. We preprocess the simulation data by dividing the spatial region with a maximum grid size of $2^{12} \times 2^{12} = 4,096 \times 4,096$ (i.e., $d = 12$), and the number of evacuees in each cell is aggregated every minute. The aggregated datasets resulting after the preprocessing are loaded into SciDB and they are used as the targets of query processing of the difference operator.

5.2   Experimental Results

We conduct experiments to evaluate the effectiveness and efficiency of the proposed methods. For the evaluation of efficiency, the total execution time for generating difference arrays and constructing histograms, as well as the histogram construction time are considered. For the evaluation of effectiveness, we used the ratio of error values of a histogram computed by the greedy (or hybrid) method with an "optimal" histogram computed by the exhaustive method—the ratio is computed as $(E - E^*)/E^*$, where E is the error value of a greedy (or hybrid) histogram and E^* is the error of an exhaustive histogram.

In what follows, experimental results are presented by varying the array size $2^d \times 2^d$ and the number of buckets B. *Exact* represents the exhaustive algorithm, and *Greedy* is the greedy-based approach. For the hybrid approach, *Hybrid_3*, *Hybrid_4*, *Hybrid_5* correspond to the approaches when threshold δ is set as 3, 4, and 5, respectively.

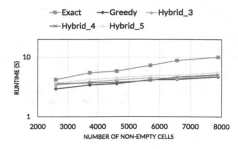

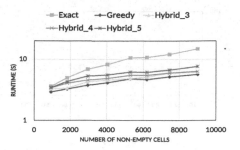

Fig. 2. Runtime: varying array size (Dataset-1, $B = 50$)

Fig. 3. Runtime: varying array size (Dataset-2, $B = 50$)

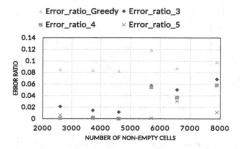

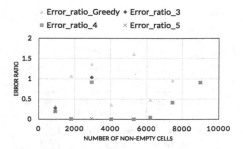

Fig. 4. Error ratio: varying array size (Dataset-1, $B = 50$)

Fig. 5. Error ratio: varying array size (Dataset-2, $B = 50$)

Varying the Array Size ($2^d \times 2^d$). Using different granularity of time intervals to aggregate Dataset-1 and Dataset-2, difference arrays with different numbers of non-empty cells are generated. Figures 2 and 3 show that the execution time increases as the array size increases. The execution time of the exhaustive algorithm is larger than the execution time of other two algorithms.

In Figs. 4 and 5, the corresponding error ratios are presented. The quality scores of resulting histograms follow the ordering of Hybrid_5 > Hybrid_4 > Hybrid_3 > Greedy (greater is better). This is because that the larger the depth threshold of the hybrid approach, the more accurate the result is. We can conclude that the execution time of the hybrid algorithm is close to that of the greedy algorithm, while the quality of the hybrid algorithm is better than the greedy algorithm when δ is 4 or 5.

Varying the Number of Buckets (B). Next, we conduct experiments on two arrays of size $2^{12} \times 2^{12} = 4,096 \times 4,096$ with different densities. The two arrays called diffArray_sparse and diffArray_dense contain 8,460 and 15,248 non-empty cells, respectively.

Figures 6 and 7 show the execution time and error ratio when varying B for diffArray_sparse. We can see that both of execution time and error ratio

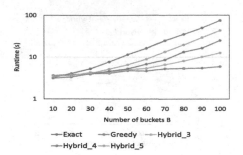

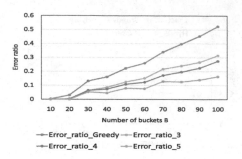

Fig. 6. Runtime: varying B (diffArray_sparse)

Fig. 7. Error ratio: varying B (diffArray_sparse)

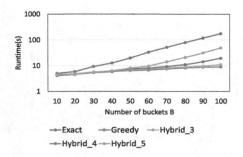

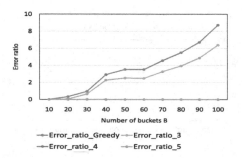

Fig. 8. Runtime: varying B (diffArray_dense)

Fig. 9. Error ratio: varying B (diffArray_dense)

increases when B increases. Also, the effectiveness of the greedy algorithm is the best, while the quality of the hybrid algorithm is good even when B is large.

The results for diffArray_dense are shown in Figs. 8 and 9. The execution time follows the similar trend as in Fig. 6, while Hybrid_4 performs similarly with the greedy algorithm. Meanwhile, the quality of Hybrid_4 and Hybrid_5 are good even the number of buckets increases. Comparing to diffArray_sparse, both the effectiveness and efficiency of Hybrid_4 are good for diffArray_dense, in the case when the data density is higher.

6   Related Work

A *histogram* is one of the popular approach in summarizing the large datasets and often used in database systems [11]. One of the application area of histograms is query cost estimation based on cardinality estimation of a query result. Another popular usage of histograms is visualization since they can present the overview of data distribution in a summarized way. In our paper, we have used histograms for summarizing the overall structure of the differences between two 2-D arrays. Since construction of accurate multi-dimensional histograms are prohibitively large [1,5,12], we consider a restricted quadtree-like structure for summarizing difference arrays.

Another feature of our approach is the use of an array DBMS, such as Ras-DaMan [4], ArrayDB [3], SciDB [16–18]. Since array DBMSs are now becoming popular in scientific computing and online analytical processing (OLAP), their effective use is an important issue in the database research area. We have used SciDB for implementing the proposed three algorithms. Using the feature of user-defined operators, we could easily implement our operators.

As data analytics has recently attracted increasing attention, data visualization is found effective in supporting interactive analyses and many studies on the subject are now underway. From the database perspective, technologies that can instantly visualize large-scale data or select data to be visualized are important. For example, MuVE [6] visualizes data by bar graphs as a result of their consideration on the viewpoints that will concentrate data into specified conditions remarkably different from the whole data. SEEDB system for the visualization of databases, though intended for category attributes, is also closely related to this study [14].

7   Conclusions

In this paper, aiming at realizing the advanced analysis functionality of large-scale spatio-temporal data, we have proposed the difference operator and the algorithms to realize the operator. We evaluate the proposed algorithms implemented on SciDB, and conduct experiments on massive evacuation simulation data to verify the effectiveness and efficiency of our methods. Experimental results demonstrate the efficiency as wells as the effectiveness of the proposed approaches.

Acknowledgements. This study was partly supported by the Grants-in-aid for Scientific Research (16H01722) and CREST: "Creation of Innovative Earthquake and Tsunami Disaster Reduction Big Data Analysis Foundation by Cooperation of Large-Scale and High-Resolution Numerical Simulations and Data Assimilations".

References

1. Acharya, S., Poosala, V., Ramaswamy, S.: Selectivity estimation in spatial databases. In: SIGMOD, pp. 13–24 (1999)
2. Andrienko, G., Andrienko, N., Wrobel, S.: Visual analytics tools for analysis of movement data. SIGKDD Explor. Newsl. 9(2), 38–46 (2007)
3. Arunprasad, K.S., Marathe, P.: Query processing techniques for arrays. VLDB J. 11(1), 68–91 (2002)
4. Baumann, P., Dehmel, A., Furtado, P., Ritsch, R., Widmann, N.: The multidimensional database system RasDaMan. In: SIGMOD, pp. 575–577 (1998)
5. Bruno, N., Chaudhuri, S., Gravano, L.: STHoles: a multidimensional workload-aware histogram. In: SIGMOD, pp. 211–222 (2001)
6. Ehsan, H., Sharaf, M.A., Chrysanthis, P.K.: MuVE: efficient multi-objective view recommendation for visual data exploration. In: ICDE, pp. 731–742 (2016)

7. Eldawy, A., Mokbel, M.F., Al-Harthi, S., Alzaidy, A., Tarek, K., Ghani, S.: SHA-HED: a mapreduce-based system for querying and visualizing spatio-temporal satellite data. In: ICDE, pp. 1585–1596 (2015)
8. Finkel, R.A., Bentley, J.L.: Quad trees: a data structure for retrieval on composite keys. Acta Informatica 4(1), 1–9 (1974)
9. Hristidis, V., Chen, S.-C., Li, T., Luis, S., Deng, Y.: Survey of data management and analysis in disaster situations. J. Syst. Softw. 83(10), 1701–1714 (2010)
10. Idreos, S., Papaemmanouil, O., Chaudhuri, S.: Overview of data exploration techniques. In: SIGMOD, pp. 277–281 (2015)
11. Ioannidis, Y.: The history of histograms (abridged). In: VLDB, pp. 19–30 (2003)
12. Jagadish, H.V., Koudas, N., Muthukrishnan, S., Poosala, V., Sevcik, K.C., Suel, T.: Optimal histograms with quality guarantees. In: VLDB, pp. 275–286 (1998)
13. Muthukrishnan, S., Poosala, V., Suel, T.: On rectangular partitionings in two dimensions: algorithms, complexity and applications. In: Beeri, C., Buneman, P. (eds.) ICDT 1999. LNCS, vol. 1540, pp. 236–256. Springer, Heidelberg (1999). https://doi.org/10.1007/3-540-49257-7_16
14. Parameswaran, A., Polyzotis, N., Garcia-Molina, H.: SeeDB: visualizing database queries efficiently. PVLDB 7(4), 325–328 (2013)
15. Rusu, F., Cheng, Y.: A survey on array storage, query languages, and systems. CoRR, abs/1302.0103 (2013)
16. Paradigm4: Creators of SciDB a computational DBMS. http://www.paradigm4.com/
17. Stonebraker, M., Brown, P., Poliakov, A., Raman, S.: The architecture of SciDB. In: Bayard Cushing, J., French, J., Bowers, S. (eds.) SSDBM 2011. LNCS, vol. 6809, pp. 1–16. Springer, Heidelberg (2011). https://doi.org/10.1007/978-3-642-22351-8_1
18. Stonebraker, M., Brown, P., Zhang, D., Becla, J.: SciDB: a database management system for applications with complex analytics. IEEE Comput. Sci. Eng. 15(3), 54–62 (2013)
19. Xuan, S., Quanshi, Z., Yoshihide, S., Ryosuke, S., Jing, Y.N., Xing, X.: A simulator of human emergency mobility following disasters: knowledge transfer from big disaster data. In: AAAI, pp. 730–736 (2015)

Location-Aware Group Preference Queries in Social-Networks

Ammar Sohail[✉], Arif Hidayat, Muhammad Aamir Cheema,
and David Taniar

Faculty of Information Technology, Monash University, Melbourne, Australia
{ammar.sohail,arif.hidayat,aamir.cheema,david.taniar}@monash.edu

Abstract. With the recent advances in location-acquisition techniques and *GPS*-embedded mobile devices, traditional social networks such as Twitter and Facebook have acquired the dimension of location. This in result has facilitated the generation of geo-tagged data (e.g., check-ins) at unprecedented scale and have essentially enhanced the user experience in location-based services associated with social networks. Typical location-based social networks allow people to `check-in` at a location of interest using smart devices which then is published on social network and this information can be exploited for recommendation. In this paper, we propose a new type of query called *Geo-Social Group preference Top-k* ($SG\text{-}Top_k$) query. For a group of users, a $SG\text{-}Top_k$ query returns top-k places that are most likely to satisfy the needs of users based on spatial and social relevance. Finally, we conduct an exhaustive evaluation of proposed schemes to answer the query and demonstrate the effectiveness of the proposed approaches.

1 Introduction

A location-based social network (LBSN) is usually represented as a complex graph where nodes represent various entities in the social network (such as users, places or pages) and the edges represent relationships between different nodes. These relationships are not only limited to friendship relations but also contain other types of relationships such as `works-at`, `born-in` and `studies-at` etc. [1]. In addition, the nodes and edges may also contain spatial information such as a user's check-ins at different locations [2]. Consider the example of a Facebook user Sarah who was born in USA, works at Monash University and checks-in at a particular restaurant. Facebook records this information by linking Facebook pages for *Monash University* and *USA* with Sarah [3], e.g., Sarah and Monash University are connected by an edge labelled `works-at` and, Sarah and USA are connected with an edge labelled `born-in`. The check-in information records the places the user has visited.

Inarguably, social connections play a vital role in our daily lives to enable us in making right decisions in various activities and events and thus impose some influence on us. For instance, previous work [4] explores the effects of social influence on recommendation and their experiments show that a user adopts a suggestion from people socially connected to her which may or may not be derived from her own preference. In recent years, several works on social network analysis [5] have observed that a user's behaviour indeed often correlates to the behaviour of her friends.

In many applications, a group of users may want to plan an activity to find a point of interest (POI) for example, some conference attendees would like to go out for dinner together. For this purpose, we may consider their respective locations and social circles to recommend required POIs. In this paper, we study a problem of finding top-k places considering their distance from the group of query users Q and popularity of the place among each query user $q_i \in Q$'s social connections (e.g., the number of check-ins at the place by each q's friends).

Consider an example of a group of tourists visiting Melbourne. The group consists of tourists from various countries e.g., conference attendees from Italy, Germany and Denmark. They may want to find a nearby pub which is popular (e.g., frequently visited) among people from their respective countries. This involves utilizing spatial information (i.e., near by pub, check-ins) as well as social information (i.e., people who were born-in Italy, Germany and Denmark).

The applications of such queries are not only limited to traditional location-based social services. These can also be used in disaster management, public health, security, tourism, marketing etc. For example, in public safety and crime prevention, law enforcement agencies may be keen on finding frequently visited places by users who have tweeted about *Drugs, Burglary and Extortion* and have also joined some pages/groups containing/sharing information related to those crimes on social networks. The users are socially connected through an edge (entity) e.g., a tweet, a page or a group in social network and then agencies can exploit one-hop neighbours of the entities to find frequently visited places to raid and prevent drugs dissemination.

Although several types of queries have been investigated on LBSNs [6–8], to the best of our knowledge, none of the existing methods can be applied to answer the queries like the above that aim at finding near by places that are popular in social circles of the query users satisfying social and spatial constraints. Motivated by this, in this paper, we formalize this problem as a *Geo-Social Group preference Top-k (SG-Top$_k$)* query and propose efficient query processing techniques. Specifically, a *SG-Top$_k$* query retrieves top-k places (points of interest) ranked according to their spatial and social relevance to the group of query users where the spatial relevance is based on how close the place is to the location of each group member and the social relevance is based on how frequently it is visited by the one-hop neighbors of each query user $q_i \in Q$. A formal definition is provided in Sect. 3.1.

First we present *Branch-and-Bound* approach to solve our problem and then we propose some optimization techniques to further improve its performance. Our experimental study shows that our optimized algorithm outperforms the other one.

We make the following contributions in this paper.

1. To the best of our knowledge, we are the first to study the *SG-Top$_k$* query that retrieves near by places popular among a particular group of users w.r.t. each query user $q_i \in Q$ in the social network.

2. We present *Branch-and-Bound* algorithm followed by some optimizations made to it to process the query which enable flexible data management and algorithmic design.
3. We conduct an exhaustive evaluation of the proposed schemes using real dataset and demonstrate the effectiveness of the proposed approaches.

2 Related Work

Geo-Social query processing is an emerging field and is getting attention of research community these days [7,9]. Huang and Liu [10] studied a Geo-Social query that retrieves the set of nearby friends of a user that share common interests, without providing concrete query processing algorithms. Yang et al. [11] introduced a group query namely, *Social-Spatial Group Query* (SSGQ) which is useful for impromptu activity planning. In addition, nearest neighbour queries have been widely applied in location-based social networks recently [12,13].

Similarly, top-k queries retrieve top-k objects based on a user defined scoring function and have been well studied [1,14]. Ilyas et al. [15] give a comprehensive survey of top-k query processing techniques. [16] propose some of the top-k processing algorithms for example Fagins Algorithm and No-Random Access algorithms. Another work is presented by Jiang et al. [17] in which they propose a method to find *top-k* local users in geo-social media data. However, their social scoring criteria is not applicable to our problem definition. There are some related works on group queries and community search but they focus on different scenarios and objectives [18,19].

Group (aggregate) nearest neighbour queries are first presented by Papadias et al. [20] and proposed three different methods MQM (multi query method), SPM (single point method) and MBM (minimum bounding method). The proposed methods are designed for Euclidean space and are not suitable for criteria involving users' preference. In 2007, Yiu et al. [21] introduces a new query called *top-k* spatial preference query which returns top-k objects whose ranking is defined by other objects around them. Yuan et al. [6] proposed a new query which returns top-k objects based on distance and objects ratings. Many previous studies [21,22] have proposed to integrate POI properties into POI recommendations however, these works do not consider user preferences.

3 Preliminaries

3.1 Problem Definition

Location Based Social Network (LBSN): A *location-based social network* consists of a set of entities U (e.g., users, Facebook Pages etc.) and a set of places P. The relationship between two entities u and v is indicated by a labelled edge where the label indicates the type of relationship (e.g., `friend`, `lives-in`) [1]. A LBSN also records check-ins where a check-in of a user $u \in U$ at a particular place $p \in P$ indicates an instance that u had visited the place P at a particular time.

Score of a place p [1,2]: Given a query user q_i, the score of a place $p \in P$ is the weighted sum of its spatial score (denoted as $spatial(p, q_i)$) and its social score (denoted as $social(p, q_i)$).

$$Score(p, q_i) = \alpha \times spatial(p, q_i) + (1 - \alpha) \times social(p, q_i) \qquad (1)$$

where α is a parameter used to control the relative importance of spatial and social scores. The social score $social(p, q_i)$ is computed as follows. Let F_{qi} denotes the one-hop neighbors of any of the query users $q_i \in Q$ considering a particular relationship type, e.g., if the relationship is `works-at`, the query entity is a Facebook Page for the company Samsung, then F_{qi} is a set of users who work in Samsung. Although our techniques can be used on any type of relationship, for the ease of presentation, in the rest of the paper we only consider the friendship relationships. In this context, F_{qi} contains the friends of the query user q_i. Let V_p denotes the set of all users that visited (i.e., checked-in at) the place. The social score $social(p, q_i)$ of place p is computed as follows:

$$social(p, q_i) = 1 - \frac{|F_{qi} \cap V_p|}{|F_{qi}|} \qquad (2)$$

where $|X|$ denotes the cardinality of a set X. Intuitively, $social(p, q_i)$ is the proportion of the friends of a query user $q \in Q$ who have visited the place p.

The spatial score $spatial(p, q_i)$ is based on how close the place is to the query user $q_i \in Q$. Formally, $spatial(p, q_i) = ||p, q_i||$, where $||p, q_i||$ indicates Euclidean distance between the query user and p. Note that $social(p, q_i)$ is always between 0 to 1 and the smaller social score is considered better. In addition, we also normalize $spatial(p, q_i)$ such that it is also between 0 to 1, e.g., the data space is normalized such that $||p, q_i|| \leq 1$.

Aggregate Score of a Place p: Given a set of query users $Q = \{q_1, q_2, \ldots, q_n\}$, the aggregate score of a place p (denoted as $aggScore(p)$) is computed using a monotonic scoring function f which takes as input each $Score(p, q_i)$ for every $q_i \in Q$.

$$aggScore(p) = f(Score(p, q_i), \ldots, Score(p, q_n)) \qquad (3)$$

For example, if f is *average*, the aggregate score corresponds to $\sum_{i=1}^{i=n} Score(p, q_i)/n$. Similarly, if f is *min*, the aggregate score corresponds to minimum of $Score(p, q_i)$ for $q_i \in Q$.

Geo-Social Group Preference Top-k (SG-Top_k) Query: Given a set of places $P = \{p_1, p_2, \ldots, p_n\}$ in a LBSN, a SG-Top_k query Q returns k places with smallest aggregate score $aggScore(p)$. The $aggScore(p)$ of each place $p \in P$ is computed as described above depending on the function f used. Some examples of the function f are *min, max* and *avg*. For instance, if f corresponds to *min*, the aggregate score will be $aggScore(p) = min(Score(p, q_i), \ldots, Score(p, q_n))$ that is, $aggScore(p) = \arg\min_{i:1 \ to \ n} Score(p, q_i) \ \forall \ q_i \in Q$. As an example, consider a dataset containing a set of places i.e., $P = \{p_1, p_2, p_3, p_4, p_5\}$ and Q is a set of query users i.e., $Q = \{q_1, q_2, q_3\}$. Table 1 illustrates spatial score, social score, and score for each place p for each query user q_i and it also shows the aggregate score.

Table 1. Sample dataset and aggregate scores

P	$\|p, q_i\|$	$Social(p, q_i)$	$Score(p, q_i)$	$aggScore(p)$
p_1	$q_1 = 0.10$	$q_1 = 0.6$	$q_1 = 0.35$	$Avg = 0.36$
	$q_2 = 0.14$	$q_2 = 0.4$	$q_2 = 0.27$	$min = 0.27$
	$q_3 = 0.12$	$q_3 = 0.8$	$q_3 = 0.46$	$max = 0.46$
p_2	$q_1 = 0.09$	$q_1 = 0.8$	$q_1 = 0.445$	$Avg = 0.345$
	$q_2 = 0.05$	$q_2 = 0.6$	$q_2 = 0.325$	$min = 0.265$
	$q_3 = 0.13$	$q_3 = 0.4$	$q_3 = 0.265$	$max = 0.445$
p_3	$q_1 = 0.22$	$q_1 = 1.0$	$q_1 = 0.61$	$Avg = 0.495$
	$q_2 = 0.20$	$q_2 = 0.6$	$q_2 = 0.40$	$min = 0.40$
	$q_3 = 0.15$	$q_3 = 0.8$	$q_3 = 0.475$	$max = 0.61$
p_4	$q_1 = 0.20$	$q_1 = 0.2$	$q_1 = 0.20$	$Avg = 0.245$
	$q_2 = 0.17$	$q_2 = 0.4$	$q_2 = 0.285$	$min = 0.20$
	$q_3 = 0.10$	$q_3 = 0.4$	$q_3 = 0.25$	$max = 0.285$
p_5	$q_1 = 0.17$	$q_1 = 0.6$	$q_1 = 0.385$	$Avg = 0.363$
	$q_2 = 0.12$	$q_2 = 0.8$	$q_2 = 0.46$	$min = 0.245$
	$q_3 = 0.09$	$q_3 = 0.4$	$q_3 = 0.245$	$max = 0.46$

If f corresponds to $avg, \alpha = 0.5$ and $k = 2$, the corresponding $SG\text{-}Top_2$ query reports places (p_4 and p_2) that minimizes the average aggregate score $aggScore(p)$. Similarly, if f corresponds to max, the $SG\text{-}Top_2$ query reports places (p_4 and p_2) that minimizes the maximum aggregate score ($aggScore(p)$). On the other hand, if f corresponds to min, the $SG\text{-}Top_2$ query reports places (p_4 and p_5) that minimizes the minimum aggregate score ($aggScore(p)$).

4   Techniques Overview

Before presenting our approaches to solve $SG\text{-}Top_k$ query in detail, first we provide a brief overview of the approaches and to the best of our knowledge, there does not exist any technique in literature that can be adopted to answer the proposed query. First we present *Branch-and-Bound* approach and then we present optimization techniques to further improve its performance. The *Branch-and-Bound* approach uses R-tree to process places in ascending order of their aggregate distance from each query user $q_i \in Q$ and then computes social score of each place p to finally compute aggregate score i.e., $aggScore(p)$. Since computation of $aggScore(p)$ of each $p \in P$ is computationally expensive, we design a specialized index structure associated with each user $u \in U$ to pre-process her friends' check-in information. Our Optimized approach leverages the proposed index structure to offer efficient pruning techniques to prune such candidate places that cannot be a part of top-k places.

Next, we briefly describe three indexes used by our algorithms.

Facility R-Tree: We create an R-tree where all places ($p \in P$) in the dataset are indexed based on their location coordinates.

Check-in R-Tree: For each user u, we create a *Check-In R-Tree* which indexes all check-ins of the u. This is a 2 dimensional R-tree containing the location coordinates information of each check-in. If a place p is visited by a user multiple times, it will be indexed as many times it was visited hence, *Check-in R-Tree* contains duplicate entries for the place p since many applications (e.g., which include ranking and recommendation of places) do require complete check-in information of users.

Friendship Index: For each user, her friends are indexed using B^+-*Tree* sorted on their IDs. This is used to efficiently retrieve the friends based on their IDs.

4.1   Branch-and-Bound (B&B) Algorithm

Before presenting our *Optimized* approach, we first discuss $B\&B$ approach to process $SG\text{-}Top_k$ query. The B&B approach is to traverse *Facility R-Tree* in *best-first* manner. For this purpose, we use a *min-heap* where the key for each entry E is $minAggDist(Q, E)$. To compute $minAggDist(Q, E)$, the algorithm computes minimum distance of E from each query user $q_i \in Q$ and then according to the aggregate function f provided, the algorithm finalises the value of $minAggDist(Q, E)$. For example, if $f = min$, the $minAggDist(Q, E)$ is the smallest minimum distance between E and any of the q_i. Then, we initialize *min-heap* with the root of *Facility R-Tree*.

Further, the algorithm starts de-heaping entries in ascending $minAggDist(Q, E)$ order. If a de-heaped entry E is a node, it computes its lower-bound aggregate score (denoted as $LBaggScore(E)$) based on its $minAggDist(Q, E)$ only, assuming that its social score i.e., $social(E)$ is minimum. Further, if the de-heaped entry E is an object (a place p), it computes its exact aggregate score $aggScore(p)$ and updates *top-k* places. Finally, at any point, if an entry E having lower-bound aggregate score worse than current k_{th} best place score (denoted as $aggScore_k$) is de-heaped, the algorithm terminates. The reason is, every subsequent entry E in *min-heap* will have worse aggregate score than the current $aggScore_k$.

4.2   Optimized Algorithm

This section focuses on our *Optimized* approach to process $SG\text{-}Top_k$ queries and before presenting the technique in detail, first we describe a specialized index specifically designed for the technique.

Friends Check-Ins R-Tree: In addition to the previous indexes, for each user u, we propose another index called *Friends Check-Ins R-tree (FCR-Tree)* which maintains the *summary* of check-ins of all friends of u. Specifically, *FCR-Tree* stores check-in information of each friend of u by indexing only one MBR (minimum bounding rectangle) for each friend, thus constitutes the summary of all friends check-ins. Since we index only one object per friend therefore, the size of the index is proportional to the number of friends of u. Note that the indexed objects are the root MBRs of each friend's *Check-in R-Tree*.

Let's assume a user $u \in U$ where the friends of u are $F_u = \{u_1, u_2, u_3 \ldots u_{19}, u_{20}\}$. Figure 1 illustrates the idea behind the *FCR-Tree*.

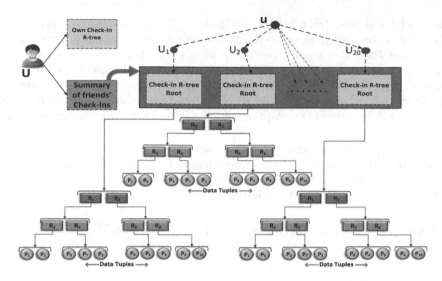

Fig. 1. Summary of Friends' check-ins

4.2.1 Computation Module

In B&B algorithm, since lower-bound of *Facility R-tree* nodes is computed based only on $minAggDist(Q, E)$, it is loose which results in high computation cost. To develop an efficient approach to computing solution for $SG\text{-}Top_k$ query, we propose few improvements in the algorithm. First, we present highlights of the improvements we made.

1. First we compute tighter lower-bound on aggregate score of a node entry E i.e., $LBaggScore(E)$ using better estimate of its social score. For this purpose, the algorithm exploits *FCR-Tree* of each query user $q_i \in Q$.
2. Then, the algorithm computes a region (denoted as region bounded rectangle, *RBR*) based on current $aggScore_k$ to quickly check the entries that can be pruned.
3. Finally, while en-heaping an entry E, we make an observation to avoid computing its lower-bound on social score by associating its parent node's lower-bound on social score with it as an initial estimate.

The details of the above mentioned improvements are provided next.

1. Computing Lower Bound on Aggregate Score

Recall that in B&B approach, to estimate best possible aggregate score $LBaggScore(E)$ of an entry E, we assume that its social score i.e., $social(E)$ is maximum and therefore, its lower-bound is loose. To overcome this limitation, the *Optimized* algorithm leverages *Friends Check-ins R-Tree* (FCR-Tree) to estimate social score of the E (denoted as $LBSocial(E)$) which in return, tightens the lower-bound on aggregate score $LBaggScore(E)$.

Specifically, to compute $LBSocial(E)$ of an entry E of *Facility R-tree*, the algorithm traverses specialized index i.e., *FCR-Tree* of a query user q_i to compute number of its objects (root MBRs of Check-In R-trees of friends) intersecting with E. Let's consider an example in Fig. 2 where we have a *Facility R-tree* entry E and some *FCR-Tree* objects belonging to q_i's friends ranging from u_1 *to* u_5. Since only u_1, u_4 *and* u_5 overlap with E, they might have checked-in at any place p in E. Therefore, the maximum number of friends who might have visited a place in E is 3, which can be used to obtain the lower-bound on social score. Let's denote the number of overlapping objects as $numOverlap$, the lower-bound on social score is computes as $1 - \frac{numOverlap}{|F_{qi}|}$.

In addition, once the lower-bound on social score against a query user q_i is computed, the lower-bound on score (denoted as $LBScore(E, q_i)$) is computed against the query user q_i using Eq. 4. The pseudocode of computing $LBScore(E, q_i)$ is given in Algorithm 1.

$$LBScore(E, q_i) = \alpha \times minDist(E, q_i) + (1 - \alpha) \times \left(1 - \frac{numOverlap}{|F_{qi}|}\right) \quad (4)$$

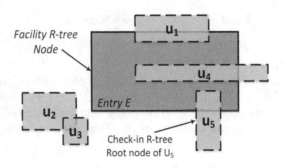

Fig. 2. MBR social score bound

Algorithm 1. Get-$LBaggScore(mbr, Q)$

---

1 $numOverlap = \emptyset$;
2 **foreach** *user* $q_i \in Q$ **do**
3 $\quad$ Issue a range query on FCR-Tree;
4 $\quad$ $numOverlap =$ Compute number of objects overlapping with the mbr;
5 $\quad$ $LBSocial(mbr, q_i) = 1 - \frac{numOverlap}{|F_{qi}|}$;
6 $\quad$ $LBScore(mbr, q_i) = \alpha \times minDist(mbr, q_i) + (1 - \alpha) \times LBSocial(mbr, q_i)$;
7 **end**
8 $LBaggScore(mbr) = f(LBScore(mbr, q_i), ..., LBScore(mbr, q_n))$;
9 **return** $LBaggScore(mbr)$

---

2. Optimal MBR Based Search Regions

Recall that in B&B, we need to compute $minDist(E, q_i)$ n times to compute $minDist(E, Q)$. For this purpose, we require to compute minimum distance from the entry E to each q_i and if this distance is greater than $\frac{aggScore_k}{\alpha}$, we can ignore E. However, this requires computing $minDist(E, q_i)$ n times. To overcome this problem, we create a *Region Bounding Rectangle* (denoted as *RBR*) such that if an entry E does not overlap with it, it is pruned.

In particular, *RBR* is defined by corresponding aggregate function f and its size depends on current $aggScore_k$ and α i.e., $\frac{aggScore_k}{\alpha}$. The algorithm only accesses those entries which intersect with it. Figure 3 demonstrates two *RBRs* for *min, max and average* aggregate functions.

- **Min:** Consider $SG\text{-}Top_k$ query with $Q = \{q_1, q_2, q_3\}$ in Fig. 3(a). The shaded area corresponds to the RBR for *min* (where $n = 3$) which is a minimum bounding rectangle of union of three circles (centred at q_1, q_2, q_3) each with radius $\frac{aggScore_k}{\alpha}$. Entry E for example, should be not visited since it is not intersecting with the RBR and cannot contain a place p whose smallest score w.r.t. any of the $q_i \in Q$ is smaller than current $aggScore_k$ i.e., for any place p in E, $aggScore(p) > aggScore_k$.

- **Max:** The RBR corresponds to the intersection of three minimum bounding rectangles (shaded area) for each circle (centred at corresponding q_i) with radius $\frac{aggScore_k}{\alpha}$ as illustrated in Fig. 3(b). Let's take an example of an entry E intersecting with the circle of q_3. This entry E should not be visited because for any place p in E, which is outside this intersected area, $dist(q_i, p) > aggScore_k$ for at least one q_i. Therefore, $aggScore(p) > aggScore_k$.

- **Average:** For $f = Average$, the RBR is same as $f = min$ because a place p for which $aggScore(p)$ regarding $f = min$ is greater than $aggScore_k$, its $aggScore(p)$ regarding $f = Average$ is also greater than $aggScore_k$. Note that a place p that is outside RBR, has $aggScore(p) > aggScore_k$ because its average distance is greater than $\frac{aggScore_k}{\alpha}$. For example, an entry E should not be visited since it is not intersecting with the RBR as shown in Fig. 3(a). Therefore, it cannot contain a place p whose average score (aggScore(p)) w.r.t. all $q_i \in Q$ is smaller than current $aggScore_k$.

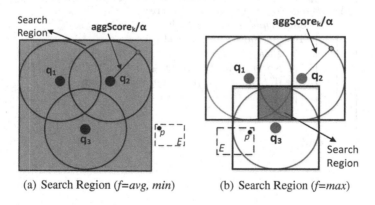

(a) Search Region (*f=avg, min*)   (b) Search Region (*f=max*)

Fig. 3. MBR based search space

3. Observation on Social Score

Recall that in step 1, to compute lower-bound aggregate score of an entry E, it requires traversing *FCR-Tree* another time while inserting it in priority queue for the first time. To avoid this overhead, we consider its parent's social score lower-bound as an initial estimate of $E's$ social score lower-bound which is a valid lower-bound on a child's social score.

We next describe the algorithm in detail with pseudocode given in Algorithm 2.

4.2.2   Algorithm Overview

Algorithm 2 starts traversing *Facility R-tree* in best-first approach. For this purpose, a *min-heap* is initialized with the root node with $LBaggScore(root)$ as a sorting key (at line 3). To compute $LBaggScore$, it first invokes *Get-LBaggScore(mbr, Q)* (Algorithm 1). Then in first loop (at line 4), algorithm starts de-heaping entries iteratively and examines whether or not it intersects with RBR, if it does not, it is immediately pruned along with all the entries lie inside (at line 6). Further, if the entry E overlaps and is a place p (an object), the algorithm computes its $aggScore(P)$ (at line 8) and update current k_{th} best place score $aggScore_k$ and RBR (at line 9).

Algorithm 2. Optimized Algorithm

---

1 $min\text{-}heap = \emptyset$, $aggScore_k = \infty$;
2 $LBaggScore = $ Get-$LBaggScore(root, Q)$;
3 Initialize min-heap with root of Facility R-tree with $LBaggScore$ as a key ;
4 **while** $min\text{-}heap \neq \emptyset$ **do**
5   De-heap entry E;
6   **if** E *overlaps with RBR* **then**
7   **if** E *is an object* **then**
8   Compute $aggScore(E)$;
9   Update $aggScore_k$ and RBR;
10   **else**
11          $LBaggScore(E) = $ Get-$LBaggScore(E, Q)$ // Algorithm 1
12   **if** $LBaggScore(E) < aggScore_k$ **then**
13   **foreach** *child node c of E* **do**
14   **if** *c overlaps with RBR* **then**
15                   $LBaggScore(c) = $
   $\alpha \times minAggDist(c, Q) + (1 - \alpha) \times LBsocial(E)$;
16   **if** $LBaggScore(c) < aggScore_k$ **then**
17   insert c in *min-heap*;
18
19
20   **end**
21
22
23
24 **end**
25 **return** *Return Top-k Places*

Otherwise, the algorithm invokes *Get-LBaggScore(mbr, Q)* (Algorithm 1) to compute $LBaggScore(E)$ (at line 11). Subsequently, if $LBaggScore(E)$ is better than current $aggScore_k$, in second loop, it starts en-heaping its child nodes provided that they overlap with RBR (at line 14). Moreover, if a child node c qualifies, the algorithm computes its $LBaggScore(c)$ by inheriting its social score from its parent. Consequently, if the estimated $LBaggScore(c)$ of c is less than the current $aggScore_k$, it is finally en-heaped for further processing (at line 17). Once *min-heap* is emptied, the algorithm terminates and reports top-k places (at line 20).

5   Experiments

5.1   Experimental Setup

To the best of our knowledge, this problem has not been studied before and no previous algorithm can be trivially extended to answer $SG\text{-}Top_k$ queries therefore, we evaluate the proposed algorithms on their performance by comparing them with each other.

Each method is implemented in C++ and experiments are run on Intel Core $I5$ 2.4 GHz PC with 16 GB memory running on 64-bit Ubuntu Linux. We use real dataset of *Gowalla* [23] and various parameters used in our experiments are shown in Table 2 where *Query MBR Size* represents the size of the region in which query users are spread. *Gowalla* dataset contains 196,591 users, 950,327 friendships, 6,442,890 check-ins and 1,280,956 checked-in places across the world. The node size of *Facility R-tree* index is set to 4096 Bytes and 1024 Bytes for *Check-In R-Tree* and *FCR-Tree* indexes because they have fewer objects as compared to *Facility R-tree*. For each experiment, we randomly choose 10 groups of query users and consider them as query groups Q.

Table 2. Parameters (Default shown in bold)

Parameters	Values
Group Size (n)	2, **4**, 6, 8
f	*min, max, avg*
Query MBR Size (km)	50, **100**, 200, 400
Average Friends	200, 400, **600**, 800
k	5, **10**, 15, 20

5.2   Performance Evaluation

Effect of k: In this evaluation, we test our proposed algorithms for various values of k for *min, max and avg* function. Note that for $f = min$ in Fig. 4(a), *Optimized Algorithm* (OA) is upto 10 times faster and the performance is not significantly affected by the value of k. The reason is that, the main cost depends on traversing *Facility R-tree* and then computing lower bounds of the nodes and this dominant cost is not affected by k. Similarly, in Fig. 4(b) for $f = max$, *Branch-and-Bound Algorithm* (B&B) takes little bit longer to process the query due to more number of places being qualified as candidates. However, for $f = avg$ both the algorithms performs better as compared to other functions where OA outperforms $B\&B$ by atleast 8 time as shown in Fig. 4(c).

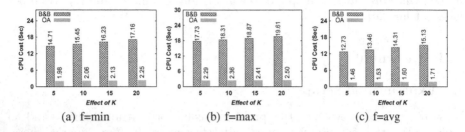

(a) f=min   (b) f=max   (c) f=avg

Fig. 4. Effect of varying number of requested places (k)

Effect of Average Number of Friends: In this experiment, we study the effect of number of friends on $B\&B$ and OA algorithms in Fig. 5. Note that the size of *FCR-Tree* relies on number of friends of a query user $q_i \in Q$. Also, the distribution of each friend's check-ins in search space determines the size of root node of *Check-in R-Tree*. This in return, affects the lower-bound on social score of *Facility R-tree* entries in OA Algorithm. In $B\&B$ algorithm, CPU cost mainly depends on computing the social score of the places $p \in P$ and as we increase the number of friends, the CPU cost increases. On the other hand, OA algorithm is less affected due to the optimization techniques. Note that, if f = avg, both the algorithms perform better than *min and max* functions due to lower $aggScore_k$ which aids in pruning more places.

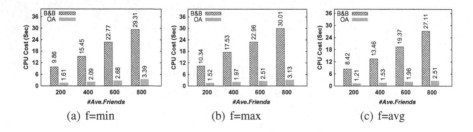

(a) f=min   (b) f=max   (c) f=avg

Fig. 5. Effect of varying number of Friends

Effect of Query MBR Size: Next in Fig. 6, we evaluate the performance of our algorithms on query MBR size. For this purpose, we randomly spread the query users in the region of size between 50 to 400 km. Note that, as we increase the size, it does not affects the query processing to great extent since the main cost involves traversing *Facility R-tree*, computing lower-bounds and social score of the query. Note that for $f = min$ and $f = max$ in Fig. 6(a) and (b) respectively, *Optimized Algorithm* (OA) is upto 10 times faster than *B&B* algorithm. However, if $f = average$, the algorithms perform relatively better as illustrated in Fig. 6(c).

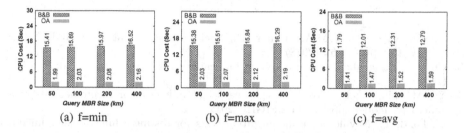

(a) f=min   (b) f=max   (c) f=avg

Fig. 6. Effect of varying query MBR size

Effect of Group Size: In this evaluation, we test our proposed algorithms for different group sizes ranging from 2 to 8 for *min, max and avg* aggregate functions in Fig. 7. As we increase the group size, it greatly affects the performance of the two algorithms because the algorithms have to process spatial and social information for more query users. However, for larger groups, *OA* performs better than the other one. In addition, if $f = avg$, both the algorithms perform relatively better than *min and max* as shown in Fig. 7(c).

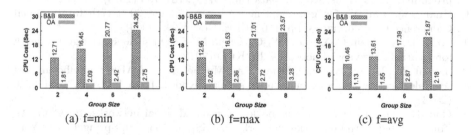

(a) f=min   (b) f=max   (c) f=avg

Fig. 7. Effect of varying group size (n)

6 Conclusions

In this paper, we formalized a problem namely, *Geo-Social Group preference Top-k (SG-Top$_k$)* query and proposed efficient query processing techniques. First we presented *Branch-and-Bound* approach to solve our problem and then we proposed some optimization techniques to further improve its performance. For this purpose, we introduced a specialized index structure, a region bounding rectangle and an observation to efficiently process the query. Our experimental study showed that our optimized algorithm outperforms the other one.

Acknowledgements. Muhammad Aamir Cheema is supported by DP180103411.

References

1. Sohail, A., Murtaza, G., Taniar, D.: Retrieving top-k famous places in location-based social networks. In: Cheema, M.A., Zhang, W., Chang, L. (eds.) ADC 2016. LNCS, vol. 9877, pp. 17–30. Springer, Cham (2016). https://doi.org/10.1007/978-3-319-46922-5_2
2. Sohail, A., Cheema, M.A., Taniar, D.: Social-aware spatial top-k and skyline queries. Comput. J. **62** (2018)
3. Curtiss, M., et al.: Unicorn: a system for searching the social graph. In: PVLDB (2013)
4. Ye, M., Liu, X., Lee, W.-C.: Exploring social influence for recommendation: a generative model approach. In: SIGIR (2012)
5. La Fond, T., Neville, J.: Randomization tests for distinguishing social influence and homophily effects. In: WWW (2010)
6. Tian, Y., Jin, P., Wan, S., Yue, L.: Group preference queries for location-based social networks. In: Chen, L., Jensen, C.S., Shahabi, C., Yang, X., Lian, X. (eds.) APWeb-WAIM 2017. LNCS, vol. 10366, pp. 556–564. Springer, Cham (2017). https://doi.org/10.1007/978-3-319-63579-8_42
7. Armenatzoglou, N., Ahuja, R., Papadias, D.: Geo-social ranking: functions and query processing. VLDB J. **24**, 783–799 (2015)
8. Qian, Y., Lu, Z., Mamoulis, N., Cheung, D.W.: P-LAG: location-aware group recommendation for passive users. In: Gertz, M., et al. (eds.) SSTD 2017. LNCS, vol. 10411, pp. 242–259. Springer, Cham (2017). https://doi.org/10.1007/978-3-319-64367-0_13
9. Mouratidis, K., Li, J., Tang, Y., Mamoulis, N.: Joint search by social and spatial proximity. IEEE Trans. Knowl. Data Eng. **27**(3), 781–793 (2015)
10. Huang, Q., Liu, Y.: On geo-social network services. In: 2009 17th International Conference Geoinformatics, pp. 1–6. IEEE, New York (2009)
11. Yang, D.-N., Shen, C.-Y., Lee, W.-C., Chen, M.-S.: On socio-spatial group query for location-based social networks. In: KDD (2012)
12. Sarwat, M., Levandoski, J.J., Eldawy, A., Mokbel, M.F.: LARS*: an efficient and scalable location-aware recommender system. Knowl. Data Eng. **26**, 1384–1399 (2014)
13. Gao, H., Liu, H.: Data analysis on location-based social networks. In: Chin, A., Zhang, D. (eds.) Mobile Social Networking. CSS, pp. 165–194. Springer, New York (2014). https://doi.org/10.1007/978-1-4614-8579-7_8
14. Wu, D., Li, Y., Choi, B., Xu, J.: Social-aware top-k spatial keyword search. In: MDM (2014)
15. Ilyas, I.F., Beskales, G., Soliman, M.A.: A survey of top-k query processing techniques in relational database systems. ACM Comput. Surv. **40**, 11 (2008)
16. Fagin, R., Lotem, A., Naor, M.: Optimal aggregation algorithms for middleware. J. Comput. Syst. Sci. **66**, 614–656 (2003)
17. Jiang, J., Lu, H., Yang, B., Cui, B.: Finding top-k local users in geo-tagged social media data. In: ICDE (2015)
18. Lappas, T., Liu, K., Terzi, E.: Finding a team of experts in social networks. In: SIGKDD, pp. 467–476 (2009)
19. Li, C.-T., Shan, M.-K.: Team formation for generalized tasks in expertise social networks. In: IEEE, SocialCom/IEEE, PASSAT (2010)

20. Papadias, D., Shen, Q., Tao, Y., Mouratidis, K.: Group nearest neighbor queries. In: Data Engineering. IEEE (2004)
21. Yiu, M.L., Dai, X., Mamoulis, N., Vaitis, M.: Top-k spatial preference queries. In: ICDE (2007)
22. Attique, M., Cho, H.-J., Jin, R., Chung, T.-S.: Top-k spatial preference queries in directed road networks. ISPRS Int. J. Geo-Inf. **5**, 170 (2016)
23. Eunjoon, C., Myers, S.A., Leskovec, J.: Friendship and mobility: user movement in location-based social networks. In: ACM SIGKDD (2011)

Social-Textual Query Processing on Graph Database Systems

Oshini Goonetilleke[1], Timos Sellis[2], and Xiuzhen Zhang[1(✉)]

[1] RMIT University, Melbourne, Australia
{oshini.goonetilleke,xiuzhen.zhang}@rmit.edu.au
[2] Swinburne University of Technology, Melbourne, Australia
tsellis@swin.edu.au

Abstract. Graph database systems are increasingly being used to store and query large-scale property graphs with complex relationships. Graph data, particularly the ones generated from social networks generally has text associated to the graph. Although graph systems provide support for efficient graph-based queries, there have not been comprehensive studies on how other dimensions, such as text, stored within a graph can work well together with graph traversals. In this paper we focus on a query that can process graph traversal and text search in combination in a graph database system and rank users measured as a combination of their social distance and the relevance of the text description to the query keyword. Our proposed algorithm leverages graph partitioning techniques to speed-up query processing along both dimensions. We conduct experiments on real-world large graph datasets and show benefits of our algorithm compared to several other baseline schemes.

1 Introduction

The graph data model supported by graph database management systems are able to capture labeled, attributed, multi-graphs emerging from the real-world [16,19]. Apart from the traditional nodes, edges and other attributes, these graphs may have free text associated to the nodes. For example in Twitter, users are connected via the "follow" relationship and those nodes may be associated with tweets or hashtags they generate. Queries performed on these unstructured text items can be more complex involving relevance ranking than simple predicates on other attributes returning exact answers.

Standard graph database systems such as Neo4j [16] and Titan [19] are optimized for graph traversals with index-free adjacencies. There have been no detailed investigations on how other dimensions stored within a graph can work well together with graph traversals. These dimensions are fundamentally supported very well by different storage models—queries on the topology by graph database systems and specialised indices, and queries on text by specialized full-text indexing schemes. Our goal is to investigate how a full-text search can be seamlessly integrated into graph traversals within a graph database system.

J. Wang et al. (Eds.): ADC 2018, LNCS 10837, pp. 68–80, 2018.
https://doi.org/10.1007/978-3-319-92013-9_6

Existing systems such as Neo4j and Titan provide support for indexing on both node and edge properties for exact search on graphs, while full-text search capabilities are supported by an external text search engine such as Lucene (http://lucene.apache.org). Recently, APOC procedures in Neo4j also provided enhanced features to access the indexes. Full-text searches are not first-class citizens of graph systems and thus are not yet fully integrated into the graph schema. Real-world graphs and practical queries on them demand graph database systems that can facilitate the integration of text search with graph traversals. We introduce a query that retrieves k objects that are both socially close to a query user u and are textually relevant to a query keyword w, denoted as a *Social Textual Ranking Query* (kSTRQ).

Example 1. kSTRQ example. A user may be interested in finding friends who are interested in going to the 'Australian Open'. In a Twitter network, this translates to finding the top-10 users of u_5 (perhaps from his close neighbourhood) who have mentioned terms relevant to the query hashtag #AusOpen. The objective of the query is to suggest 10 users who are socially close to the query user (more likely to be friends) and who have used terms relevant to keyword #AusOpen. This can be answered with kSTRQ where $u = u_5, w =$ AusOpen and $k = 10$.

Related work on social media platforms such as Facebook's Unicorn system [5] and Twitter's real-time EarlyBird engine [3] are specifically tailored for different types of social query workloads and are not focused on graph traversals beyond a 1- or 2-step neighborhood. Our solution is more generic, involving a user's n-step neighborhood with the ability of varying the preference to each dimension thereby perfectly complementing these prior works. Graph keyword search has also been studied on RDF and XML graphs [6,8] exhibiting specific characteristics returning substructures while kSTRQ returns a ranked list of nodes. Specialised indexes have been proposed [2,12,17] solving approximate and other variations to our problem (More details in Sect. 2). Different from these approaches, we propose our algorithm PART_TA to efficiently answer kSTRQ queries in a graph database setting, aiming at a general solution based on the graph data model. We wish to construct a combined index along the graph and text dimensions similar to an IR-tree [4] designed for answering spatial-textual queries. Since there is no ubiquitous graph index, we believe that a good graph partitioning can represent a generic solution for a graph index and we combine this with text lists that map to the partitions. These smaller partitions of the graph enable us to run kSTRQ locally, searching for k results, traversing and expanding as few partitions as possible. Then we assemble to results from the locally generated partitions to construct the final answer to the kSTRQ.

Contributions. To the best of our knowledge, we are the first to conduct a detailed investigation on running the kSTRQ in a graph database system; we designed an algorithm PART_TA to efficiently process kSTRQ by introducing graph partitioning to optimize the use of existing techniques on a decomposed graph. We conducted experiments on three real-world datasets with different characteristics. Our proposed solution performs well on large graphs demonstrating performance gains up to 76% compared to other baselines.

2 Related Work

In this section, we discuss several categories of existing work that are closely related to the graph keyword search problem.

Social Graph Queries. Existing research from Twitter and Facebook is related, but are not focused on performing graph traversals. The EarlyBird [3] engine provides a search framework at Twitter enabling text to be immediately available for real-time search. Personalization to retrieve the most relevant results is done by adding some static and dynamic information about the user but only considers the user's local social graph. Unicorn [5] describes the system providing the primary infrastructure for Facebook's 'typeahead' search enabling users to find other users by typing the first few characters of the person's name. Focused on either direct friends or friends-of-friends, this essentially provides set-based primitives highly customized for the specific prefix search query.

Keyword Search on Graphs. Keyword search has been studied with a focus on specific type of graphs such as RDF and XML [6,8]. The output of these queries are different, retrieving triplets and snippets of XML documents for RDF and XML respectively. A category of related works [9,22] studied search with keywords over graphs to efficiently retrieve the sub-structures with distinct roots containing query keywords. The focus of these previous work is returning subgraphs, while we want to retrieve an ordered set of graph nodes. The literature on answering the *nearest* keyword search query where an approximate distance between two users/nodes [2,17] is possibly more relevant to our work as they do not necessarily operate on specialised graphs such as RDF and XML. The approximate distances in the Partitioned Multi-Indexing (PMI) scheme [2] are calculated based on 'distance oracles' which is used to estimate the distance between two nodes. A major drawback in this approach as observed in later studies [12,17] is that the distance estimation error is large in practice, thus affecting the ranked result list. Problem-specific indexes are proposed in some studies [12,17] and they are not easily extensible to the generic graph database system scenario we address.

Orthogonal Work in Multiple Domains. There have been related studies that combine the efficient processing of queries in other domains such as spatial-textual and spatial-social [1,4,13,15]. IR-tree [4] is an index introduced to efficiently perform a query that is composed of a keyword and a location, and retrieves documents that are both geographically and textually close to the query object. In the IR-tree, a traditional spatial R-tree index is augmented with an inverted index having the posting lists at each level of the tree. There are studies on graph indexing focusing on other types of queries such as subgraph matching, shortest path or reachability [18,20]. Many of these graph indexes involved a large pre-computation overhead [18] and was focused on efficient processing of specific queries.

3   Problem Definition

Let $G(V, E)$ be a social graph with a set of users represented as vertices $v \in V$ and a set of edges $e \in E$ connecting them. An edge can represent any social interaction among users. Each node $v \in V$ contain a set of zero or more keywords associated with it, denoted by $D(v)$. The set of vertices containing a given keyword w is denoted by $V(w)$ where $V(w) \subseteq V$. A user v is ranked based on the combination of distance to query user $q.u$ and textual descriptions relevant to query term $q.w$ as illustrated next.

Social Proximity. A path $p = (v_1, \dots v_l)$ is a sequence of l vertices in V such that for each v_i $(1 \leq i \leq l)$, $(v_i, v_{i+1}) \in E$. The length of the path is the number of edges along the path. Social proximity between any two users v_i and v_j, denoted as $s(v_i, v_j)$ is based on their shortest path distance:

$$s(v_i, v_j) = \frac{sdist(v_i, v_j)}{sdist_{max}} \qquad (1)$$

where $sdist(v_i, v_j)$ is the length of the shortest path connecting v_i and v_j. The $sdist_{max}$ is the largest shortest path length between any pair of vertices, used to normalise $s(v_i, v_j)$ to $[0, 1]$. We adopt the shortest path approach as a measure of social proximity as previous work [21] has shown that it effectively captures the proximity between two users. A higher value of social proximity $(1 - s(q.u, v))$ for node v indicates better social relevance to query node $q.u$.

Textual Relevance. A user v is considered relevant iff v contains the query term $q.w$ at least once, i.e. $q.w \in D(v)$. The textual relevance $t(q.w, D(v))$ denotes the similarity between a query term $q.w$ and $D(v)$. We adopt the standard tf-idf model from previous work [4,13] normalised by the maximum score for the term, $tdist_{max} = \max_{v \in V} t(q.w, D(v))$. A higher value of textual relevance $t(q.w, D(v))$ for node v indicates better textual relevance to query keyword $q.w$.

Overall Ranking Function. Following common practice [4,15], we apply a linear function over the normalized social and textual proximity to rank objects. Given a query user $q.u$ and a keyword $q.w$, the ranking of $v \in V$ is determined by function f as:

$$f(v) = \alpha \cdot (t(q.w, D(v))) + (1 - \alpha) \cdot (1 - s(q.u, v)) \qquad (2)$$

where $0 \leq \alpha \leq 1$ denotes the relative significance of the individual components in the two domains.

Definition 1 (kSTRQ). Top-k Social-Textual Ranking Query is expressed as a triple $q = (u, w, k)$ where $u \in V$ is the query vertex, w is a keyword and k is a positive integer denoting the number of output records. kSTRQ query returns a result set R containing k users $v \in V - \{q.u\}$ with the highest $f(v)$ values.

4   Baseline Algorithms

In this section we describe algorithmic approaches forming our baselines.

4.1 Text First and Social First Algorithms

A kSTRQ query q can be processed using a Text First Algorithm (TFA) that iterates through the posting list for $q.w$, in decreasing text relevancy. For each user
$v \in V(q.w)$, TFA calculates the social proximity $s(v, q.u)$ and it turn computes
$f(v)$. For social proximity, we rely on the graph system to efficiently calculate
the shortest path between two users. The TFA approach works well when the
frequency of the query keyword is relatively low. Similarly Social First Algorithm
(SFA) iterates through users in increasing social distance to $q.u$ (via a BFS). For
every encountered user v, combined score $f(v)$ is calculated by a random access
to the postings list $V(q.w)$ (if v exists in $V(q.w)$). Time complexity of TFA and
SFA is $O(|V(q.w)|*(|E|+|V|*log(|V|)))$ and $O(|V|*|V(q.w)|)$ respectively.

Early termination conditions on TFA (named TFA_ET) and SFA (named
SFA_ET) allows traversing the corresponding lists partially by keeping track of
the score of the k-th object in the result set, denoted by f_k. In TFA_ET (or
SFA_ET), the right (left) of the '+' operand in Eq. 2, can be upper bounded by
the maximum social (textual) score $maxSS$ ($maxTS$). $maxSS$ and $maxTS$ are
calculated by the best possible social score with $sdist = 1$ (i.e. direct neighbor)
and text score with $tdist_{max}$ respectively. For a new object, if f_k exceeds the
text relevance (or social proximity) score combined with $maxSS(maxTS)$ (from
Eq. 2), the algorithm can terminate.

The drawback of both TFA- and SFA-based algorithms is that they are igno-
rant of the social or the textual dimension respectively. To overcome this limitation, the threshold algorithm we describe next, iterates through both dimensions
simultaneously for efficient pruning of results.

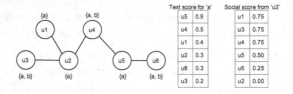

Fig. 1. Social network and ranked lists for term a and distance to u_2.

4.2 Threshold Algorithm (TA)

Threshold algorithm [7] (TA) maintains two decreasing lists: one with social
proximity to $q.u$ and another with text relevance to $q.w$ denoted by $S(q.u)$ and
$T(q.w)$ respectively. In order to calculate a combined score f, for every sorted
access in one ranked list it requires a random access to the other, probing lists
in a round robin fashion. It maintains an interim result of top-k tuples seen so
far and keeps a threshold θ computed as the value of f over the last attribute
value pulled from each of the ranked lists. TA terminates when θ is no smaller
than any of the f values in the interim results.

Example 2. Threshold algorithm: Let us consider Fig. 1 where query user is u_2, query term is a and $\alpha = 0.5$. TA retrieves the top-2 as follows. TA first accesses u_1 in the social domain (u_1's text score from random access) with f value 0.575 and places into the interim result, $R = \{u_1\}$. Sorted postings list gives u_5 with f value of 0.7 (social score from random access) and sets $R = \{u_5, u_1\}$. Next, u_3 with $f = 0.475$ and u_4 with $f = 0.625$ is added to the list $R = \{u_5, u_4, u_1, u_3\}$. At this point the threshold values for social and textual domain are 0.75 and 0.5 yielding a threshold $\theta = 0.625$. The current top-2 results are no smaller than θ, the algorithm terminates returning top-2 $\{u_5, u_4\}$ with the highest scores.

Random access in the social domain requires that, given any user v, the shortest distance between query node $q.u$ and v is found (retrieved by the graph database system). Random access in the textual domain means that, given a term w, and a user v, we need to find its score, in the worst case, a full scan of the postings list $T(q.w)$. The shortest path between two random nodes further apart may be a more expensive operation compared to finding the text score of a user in the sorted text list. The number of iterations in TA is upper bounded by $|T(q.w)|$ as $|T(q.w)| \le |S(q.u)|$.

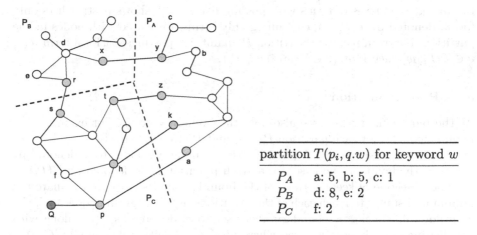

partition $T(p_i, q.w)$ for keyword w	
P_A	a: 5, b: 5, c: 1
P_B	d: 8, e: 2
P_C	f: 2

Fig. 2. A partitioned social network with corresponding postings lists for keyword w. The edges crossing partitions are in blue and the boundary nodes are highlighted in grey. Query node is Q. (Color figure online)

5 Proposed **PART_TA** Algorithm

Our main idea is to decompose the social graph by partitioning, and the text indexes are also maintained to map the social partitions. The rationale behind graph partitioning is to enable users who are socially close, to be placed within the same partition. This way, for a given query user, most of this user's n-step neighbourhood will be found by traversing only a few partitions. Our algorithm

---

Algorithm 1. PART_TA

Input: query user $q.u$, keyword $q.w$, requested number of users k, $S(P_i, q.u)$ ranked social list,
$\quad T(P_i, q.w)$ ranked text list
Output: Result set R containing the top-k users
1: $R \leftarrow \{\}$, Queue $\leftarrow$ getNewPriorityQueue()
2: **for** partition $p_i \in P$ **do**
3: $\quad f \leftarrow$ TRAVERSE($p_i, 1$)   ▷ f is the max. score for p_i
4: $\quad$ Queue.Enqueue(p_i, f)   ▷ type='partition'
5: **end for**
6: **while** —R— $\leq k$ **do**   ▷ Processing the Queue
7: $\quad$ element $\leftarrow$ Queue.Dequeue()
8: $\quad$ **if** $type$(element) == 'partition' **then**
9: $\quad\quad x \leftarrow k$—$R$—   ▷ Remaining no. of elements to find
10: $\quad\quad$ localQueue $\leftarrow$ TRAVERSE(id(element), x)   ▷ partition id
11: $\quad\quad$ Queue $\leftarrow$ Queue $\cup$ localQueue   ▷ add x elements
12: $\quad$ **else**
13: $\quad\quad R \leftarrow R \cup \{id$(element)$\}$
14: $\quad$ **end if**
15: **end while**

---

is inspired by the threshold algorithm running on partitions, hence the name
PART_TA. Figure 2 shows the social network of users decomposed in three partitions. The edges crossing the partitions (*edgecuts*) and nodes that have edges
cut by partitions (*boundary nodes*) are marked. Each partition maintains separate inverted indexes of terms with posting lists, Fig. 2 shows posting lists only
for w, denoted by $T(P_i, w)$, containing only terms associated with nodes in the
partition. For example, each partition P_i maintains postings list for a term w, if
$v \in T(P_i, w)$ such that $\{v \in V(w) \cap v \subset P_i\}$.

5.1 Precomputation

At the partitioning phase, we also note the boundary nodes. For example, the
boundary nodes for each partition P_A, P_B and P_C in Fig. 2 are $\{a, k, y, z\}, \{r, x\}$
and $\{h, p, s, t\}$ respectively. A partition that a node v belongs to is denoted by
$p(v)$ and the boundary node set for a given partition P_i is denoted by $B(P_i)$.

The objective of keeping track of the boundary nodes is to pre-calculate the
minimum distance to reach each of the partitions from any given node $v \in V$. For
each node v, the closest boundary nodes set to v, denoted as $C(v)$, along with
the distance to v is precomputed where $C(v) \in B(p(v))$ and generally $|C(v)| <$
$|B(p(v))|$. In Sect. 5.2 we explain why we do not require maintaining the distance
to all boundary nodes. For a specific node v, any node $c \in C(v)$ and $c \in p(v)$,
the minimum distance to reach any other partition P_i is $sdist(v, c) + 1$. This
feature allows us to precompute and store a small subset of only the boundary
nodes in the partition that v belongs to $B(p(v))$, instead of calculating distances
to all the boundary nodes in other the partitions. The node sets along with their
social scores, denoted by $S(P_i, v)$ for each partition P_i, specific to a node v, act
as the closest entry point to reach each of the partitions from v. $S(p(v), v)$ is
calculated via a BFS from node v.

Example 3. Boundary node pre-computation: For query node Q in the example
Fig. 2, $P(Q) = P_C$. The boundary nodes $B(P_C) = \{p, h, s, t\}$. The closest bound-

ary nodes with their distances are {p:1, h:2, s:4, t:4}. From this we can derive the closest entry points to reach each of the partitions: $P_A = \{a : 2, k : 3, z : 5\}$ and $P_B = \{r : 5\}$ denoted by $S(P_A, Q)$ and $S(P_B, Q)$ respectively.

5.2   Query Processing Algorithm

The intuitive idea of PART_TA (Algorithm 1) is to run a variation of the threshold algorithm locally on each partition until the global top-k results are found. An element in the priority queue to keep track of results can either represent a score (f) for a partition (*type* = 'partition') or represent a score for a user (*type* = 'user') in the network.

The algorithm starts by enqueuing partition elements with f scores representing the top-1 scores for each partition calculated by running the threshold algorithm locally (lines 2–5 in Algorithm 1). The TRAVERSE function runs a modified threshold algorithm locally within the partition to find the top-x elements. TRAVERSE requires two sorted lists: $T(P_i, q.w)$ is a ranked postings list record for partition P_i filtered by the query keyword $q.w$ and $S(P_i, q.u)$ is a ranked list of social proximity from user $q.u$ to enter a partition P_i (ref. Sect. 5.1). Each partition also records its local queue, and an iteration position. After this step, the initial queue will consist of maximum f scores of only partition elements which quide the order in which the query will be processed. Partition with the highest score will be expanded first. As such, the first element is dequeued, and is expanded (Line 8) to find x elements where initially, $x = k$. The algorithm continues to expand partitions in the order they appear in the queue, until k users are found.

The complexity of TA is upper bounded by the size of the postings list, i.e. $|T(q.w)|$. Assuming a similar distribution of keywords among all partitions, a partition on average has a postings list of size $l = \frac{|T(w)|}{|P|}$. Using this heuristic, the size of the social list in a partition, $|(S(P_i, q.u))|$ or the subset of boundary nodes to be maintained $(|C(q.u)|)$, can be upper bounded to l where w above is a non-stopword term with the highest frequency.

kSTRQ algorithm can be terminated early using a few strategies. Algorithm can terminate if top-x positions are found where $x = k - |R|$ or the local threshold in TRAVERSE goes below the x-th position of the global queue as it is guaranteed that an element below the local threshold cannot be part of the top-k elements in the global queue. The result set $|R|$ is then populated with the top-x elements in the local queue. The PART_TA algorithm guarantees that only the partitions that appear in the top-k result set will be expanded.

5.3   Graph Partitioning Strategy

We perform a n-way graph partitioning algorithm using METIS [11]. Partitioning algorithms such as METIS create n partitions similar in size, enabling a balanced workload for each partition, but n may not represent the natural clusters within the graph. Alternatively, we can adopt community detection or clustering algorithms, but they are not guaranteed to generate equal sized partitions. As another improvement on the decomposition, existing clustering approaches can be extended that take into account the homogeneity of attribute values along with the graph topology when deciding its clusters [23,24]. This may yield a better final result (expanding even fewer partitions) as the graph is essentially partitioned in both dimensions, however comes at a much higher pre-processing cost. These are two trade-offs to be considered in selecting algorithms to decompose the graph. In this paper, we resort to graph partitioning methods that are known to be efficient and effective in terms of reducing edge cuts on large graphs. We choose n to be dependent on $|V|$, i.e. $n = log(|V|)$. As seen in other work [10,14] the idea is that, to take advantage of a decomposition, we need to consider reductions that are an order of magnitude less than the original graph.

6 Experiments

6.1 Datasets, Setup and Graph Database System

We used three real-world datasets from AMiner (https://aminer.org/data) that demonstrate different characteristics of graphs and text associated with the nodes. Table 1 shows a summary of each of the datasets considered. The experiments were conducted on a Intel Core i7-4790K at 4.00 GHz with 16 GB RAM and 60 GB SSD.

Table 1. Dataset description

Dataset	Nodes	Edges	Avg/Max Degree, Diameter	No. of unique keywords	Description	Text content
Twitter	87,349	306,249	7.8/230, 15	1.3M	Who-follows-whom	Hashtag
AMiner	1,057,194	3,634,124	4.9/551, 24	2.9M	Academic co-authorship	Interests
Flickr	424,169	8,475,790	39.6/11930, 8	340K	Friendship	Interests

Neo4j (v3.1) is selected as the graph database system as it is optimized for graph traversals, allows manipulation of text via a Lucene index facilitating our kSTRQ. We construct the inverted index with keywords as terms, node ids corresponding to the document ids, and we made use of the tf-idf based similarity measures provided by Lucene. The partitions created from METIS have been modeled in the graph as a node attribute ranging from 1 to $|P|$. As PART_TA requires the inverted indexes to be partitioned; we simulate this behaviour in Neo4j by storing different Lucene indexes corresponding to each partition. The local similarity measures of each partition were configured to match the similarity of a global inverted index – otherwise, PART_TA operating on partitions would yield a different result set to the baseline algorithms. For all experiments page cache in Neo4j was set to 4 GB.

6.2 Performance Evaluation

To generate a query, we randomly pick a user v in the dataset and randomly pick a term out of the keywords attached to this user to be the query keyword. The reported timing measurements is an average timing of running 100 such queries. We first investigate the effect of the parameters by varying α (default: 0.3), and the number of objects k (default: 10) returned from the query.

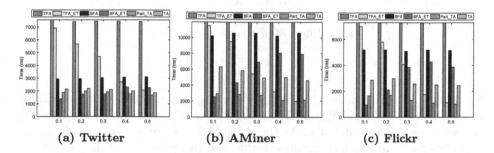

(a) Twitter   (b) AMiner   (c) Flickr

Fig. 3. Effect of preference parameter α.

Varying α. Figure 3 shows the results of varying the preference parameter value α from 0.1 to 0.5; this setting is following existing work [3,5] where preference is given to social proximity. A smaller value of α indicates that more preference is given to the social proximity of a user v. In all the datasets, TFA and SFA approaches do not vary much, as these baselines require traversing their respective textual and social lists, irrespective of the α. We retain their performance to observe the relative difference in their respective early termination variations.

Let us first discuss some observations across the datasets. A larger value in α leads to better and worse performance in the TFA_ET and SFA_ET algorithms respectively. As we have noted in Sect. 4, a random unit operation in TFA_ET (i.e. shortest path calculation) is much more expensive than a random unit operation in SFA_ET (i.e. retrieving a text score in a list) which helps to explain the large timing difference between TFA_ET and SFA_ET in lower α values.

Averaging across varying α values, the performance improvement of PART_TA compared to TA is 10.2%. SFA_ET performs better than PART_TA and TA for small α values operating on the graph with only 87 K nodes. A possible reason could be that, due to the small size of the graph, it does not fully utilize the benefits of partitioning the graph. For larger graphs, PART_TA demonstrates better performance irrespective of the changing α. For the Aminer and Flickr datasets, the best performance (compared to TA) is observed at $\alpha = 0.4, \alpha = 0.5$ with a performance improvement of 57.8% and 59.1% respectively. PART_TA performs even better compared to TFA- and SFA- based early termination variations (upto 76% improvement), with the exception of the two edge cases in AMiner. Although the early termination algorithms perform better for the edge cases, the unstable behaviour, makes them not suitable for the general case.

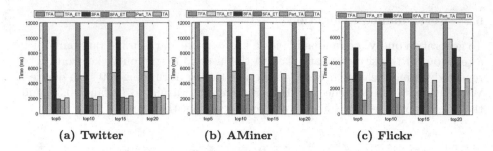

(a) Twitter   (b) AMiner   (c) Flickr

Fig. 4. Effect of preference parameter k.

Varying k. Figure 4 shows the results of varying the number of output records k from 5 to 20. The TFA and SFA baselines are about the same as they are not sensitive to the value of k. As the value of k is increased, more processing and traversals are required to retrieve the final result set. In all datasets, with increasing k, the rate of growth for TFA_ET and SFA_ET algorithms is higher than TA and PART_TA. The Twitter graph (Fig. 4a) does not show significant increase in the methods, as the costly shortest path calculation step can be efficiently executed on a smaller graph.

Partitions Expanded. For each dataset, we investigate the percentage of partitions expanded in PART_TA with increasing α. As the graphs are of different characteristics, we want to examine the effect the density of the graphs have on the percentage of expanded partitions. For smaller α values, socially close users would be found by expanding only a few partitions. For the AMiner and Twitter graphs, the percentage of partitions expanded is increased with α, however it stabilises at around 48% when $\alpha = 0.5$. For the denser Flickr graph, the percentage of partitions expanded is much higher at first, however do not increase much with a growing α. When α was increased to $\alpha = 0.9$, the percentage only increased to 66.3, 54.5 and 49.8 for the Flickr, Twitter and Aminer graphs respectively, which is acceptable, not expanding all partitions.

Discussion. In our experiments we observe better performance and robustness of our algorithms, especially on larger graphs, which are desired in many applications. We believe that if graph systems had support to manage the partitions physically in storage, we would reap more benefits of our approaches, dealing with much smaller, autonomous graphs for computation. However the platform should ideally not incur much overhead (i.e. communication costs) for processing parts of the graph spanning multiple partitions. The percentage of partitions expanded above is indicative of the fraction of partitions that would have to be processed in order to retrieve the final result set k. In future work, one can also investigate the effects of using different social and text relevance metrics and the effects of varying number of partitions has on the final result.

7   Conclusions

We investigated the kSTRQ query in a graph database system which requires ranking of users measured as a combination of their social distances to query user u and text relevance to a query keyword w. Based on existing work, we proposed a novel algorithm PART_TA that leverages graph partitioning strategies to efficiently answer the kSTRQ. We conducted experiments on real graphs exhibiting diverse characteristics. We observed that our PART_TA algorithm did in fact lead to improved query performance over the baselines and it also demonstrated robust behaviour under changing parameters.

References

1. Armenatzoglou, N., Papadopoulos, S., Papadias, D.: A general framework for geo-social query processing. PVLDB **6**(10), 913–924 (2013)
2. Bahmani, B., Goel, A.: Partitioned multi-indexing: bringing order to social search. In: WWW 2012, pp. 399–408. ACM, New York (2012)
3. Busch, M., Gade, K., Larson, B., Lok, P., Luckenbill, S., Lin, J.: Earlybird: real-time search at Twitter. In: ICDE 2012, pp. 1360–1369 (2012)
4. Cong, G., Jensen, C.S., Wu, D.: Efficient retrieval of the top-k most relevant spatial web objects. PVLDB **2**(1), 337–348 (2009)
5. Curtiss, M., Becker, I., et al.: Unicorn: a system for searching the social graph. PVLDB **6**(11), 1150–1161 (2013)
6. Elbassuoni, S., Blanco, R.: Keyword search over RDF graphs. In: CIKM 2011, pp. 237–242. ACM (2011)
7. Fagin, R., Lotem, A., Naor, M.: Optimal aggregation algorithms for middleware. J. Comput. Syst. Sci. **66**(4), 614–656 (2003)
8. Guo, L., Shao, F., Botev, C., Shanmugasundaram, J.: XRANK: ranked keyword search over XML documents. In: SIGMOD 2003, pp. 16–27 (2003)
9. He, H., Wang, H., Yang, J., Yu, P.S.: BLINKS: ranked keyword searches on graphs. In: SIGMOD, pp. 305–316 (2007)
10. İnkaya, T.: A parameter-free similarity graph for spectral clustering. Expert Syst. Appl. **42**(24), 9489–9498 (2015)
11. Karypis, G., Kumar, V.: Multilevel k-way partitioning scheme for irregular graphs. J. Parallel Distrib. Comput. **48**(1), 96–129 (1998)
12. Li, Y., Bao, Z., Li, G., Tan, K.: Real time personalized search on social networks. In: ICDE, pp. 639–650 (2015)
13. Li, Z., Lee, K.C.K., Zheng, B., Lee, W., Lee, D.L., Wang, X.: IR-tree: an efficient index for geographic document search. TKDE **23**(4), 585–599 (2011)
14. Liu, J., Wang, C., Danilevsky, M., Han, J.: Large-scale spectral clustering on graphs. In: IJCAI 2013, pp. 1486–1492. AAAI Press (2013)
15. Mouratidis, K., Li, J., Tang, Y., Mamoulis, N.: Joint search by social and spatial proximity. In: ICDE, pp. 1578–1579 (2016)
16. Neo4j: Neo4j Graph Database (2017). https://neo4j.com/product/
17. Qiao, M., Qin, L., Cheng, H., Yu, J.X., Tian, W.: Top-k nearest keyword search on large graphs. Proc. VLDB Endow. **6**(10), 901–912 (2013)
18. Sun, Z., Wang, H., Wang, H., Shao, B., Li, J.: Efficient subgraph matching on billion node graphs. PVLDB **5**(9), 788–799 (2012)

19. Titan: Titan (2017). http://thinkaurelius.github.io/titan/
20. Trißl, S., Leser, U.: Fast and practical indexing and querying of very large graphs. In: SIGMOD, pp. 845–856 (2007)
21. Vieira, M.V., Fonseca, B.M., Damazio, R., Golgher, P.B., de Castro Reis, D., Ribeiro-Neto, B.A.: Efficient search ranking in social networks. In: CIKM, pp. 563–572 (2007)
22. Wang, H., Aggarwal, C.C.: A survey of algorithms for keyword search on graph data. In: Aggarwal, C., Wang, H. (eds.) Managing and Mining Graph Data. Advances in Database Systems, vol. 40, pp. 249–273. Springer, Boston (2010). https://doi.org/10.1007/978-1-4419-6045-0_8
23. Yang, J., McAuley, J.J., Leskovec, J.: Community detection in networks with node attributes. CoRR abs/1401.7267 (2014)
24. Zhou, Y., Cheng, H., Yu, J.X.: Graph clustering based on structural attribute similarities. PVLDB 2(1), 718–729 (2009)

Using SIMD Instructions to Accelerate Sequence Similarity Searches Inside a Database System

Sidath Randeni Kadupitige$^{(\boxtimes)}$ and Uwe Röhm

The University of Sydney, Sydney, NSW 2006, Australia
{sidath.randenikadupitige,uwe.roehm}@sydney.edu.au

Abstract. Database systems are optimised for managing large data sets, but they face difficulties making an impact to life sciences where the typical use cases involve much more complex analytical algorithms than found in traditional OLTP or OLAP scenarios. Although many database management systems (DBMS) are extensible via stored procedures to implement transactions or complex algorithms, these stored procedures are usually unable to leverage the inbuilt optimizations provided by the query engine, so other optimization avenues must be explored.

In this paper, we investigate how sequence alignment algorithms, one of the most common operations carried out on a bioinformatics or genomics database, can be efficiently implemented close to the data within an extensible database system. We investigate the use of single instruction, multiple data (SIMD) extensions to accelerate logic inside an DBMS. We also compare it to implementations of the same logic outside the DBMS.

Our implementation of an SIMD-accelerated Smith Waterman sequence-alignment algorithm shows an order of magnitude improvement on a non-accelerated version while running inside a DBMS. Our SIMD accelerated version also performs with little to no overhead inside the DBMS compared to the same logic running outside the DBMS.

Keywords: Sequence databases · Stored procedures
SIMD acceleration

1 Introduction

Modern DBMS have to handle more than traditional online transaction-processing (OLTP) workloads. The capability to efficiently process analytical workloads, either stand-alone or intermixed with OLTP transactions is becoming more and more important. This is particularly important in the scientific and biological databases area [18].

To satisfy these new use cases, we need to provide functionality that is outside the scope of common database systems - which usually rely on relational algebra and relational query execution operators. However, we do not want to add

© Springer International Publishing AG, part of Springer Nature 2018
J. Wang et al. (Eds.): ADC 2018, LNCS 10837, pp. 81–93, 2018.
https://doi.org/10.1007/978-3-319-92013-9_7

another system layer but rather strive to implement any analytical operations close to the data inside the database. Luckily, many modern DBMS allow the integration of complex logic using user-defined functions or stored procedures.

One drawback of user-defined functions inside a database is that they typically have limited supported by optimizations provided by the DBMS (such as the query optimizer), so other optimization approaches must be investigated.

In looking for faster performance, we chose to explore the use of hardware optimizations, particularly SIMD-based optimizations. Most commodity workstation and server hardware nowadays exposes some level of SIMD optimizations, typically in the form of the SSE or AVX API.

Using these starting points of SIMD acceleration and complex logic provision via stored procedures, we aim to answer the following questions: How difficult is it to integrate hardware-specific SIMD instructions into general stored procedure code? What scalability benefits does SIMD-enabled stored procedure code offer? What overhead penalty do we have to pay as compared to standalone, outside-DBMS implementation?

In order to answer the above questions, we restrict our focus to a common bioinformatics use case of providing a sequence similarity search for a database of gene sequences. We chose two state-of-the-art extensible DBMS in PostgreSQL and a commercial DBMS which we refer to as DBMS X. PostgreSQL is an extensible database system that supports user-defined functions via dynamically linked native, compiled code. DBMS X offers user-defined functions via an integrated .NET runtime and has an established history of extensibility for scientific workloads [14, 15].

In this paper we implement stored procedures that perform accelerated bioinformatics logic inside a DBMS. We do this by leveraging the SIMD instructions made available through the .NET System.Numerics library for DBMS X and the Intel SIMD Instrinsics C library for PostgreSQL. First we develop a C# and C implementation using a similar method to the Striped Smith Waterman introduced by Farrar [4] and also implemented in [1,17,20]. Then we integrate the assembly into the DBMS as a stored procedure.

2 Background

In the following, we will give a brief description of how SIMD works in most commodity hardware and how the dynamic programming algorithm for sequence similarity searches works.

2.1 SIMD

In order to facilitate parallelism for common functions, CPU vendors began to include special instructions that allow a single operation to be carried out on a prepared set of multiple data items. These instruction sets were bundled as extensions and tagged under the common headline - *Single Instruction Multiple Data* or *SIMD*. The most common extension set in existing CPUs is Intel's

SSE v4.2 with modern CPUs that were released after 2014 supporting a new set of extensions under the moniker AVX. The primary difference (apart from certain supported instructions) between these two extension sets is the size of the register upon which these extensions are executed. In SSE v4.2, the register size is 128 bits, whereas from AVX2 onwards, the register size is 256 bits. The register size determines how many data points can be operated on at once. E.g. if your data is based on 32 bit integers, then a 128 bit register would allow you to carry out operations on four 32 bit integers, while a 256 bit register would allow you to carry out operations on eight 32 bit integers.

As seen in the related work, SIMD usage has been limited inside DBMS. However, extensible DBMS logic can be added via stored procedures. Our first chosen environment is DBMS X. The primary reasoning for this was the ease of adaption of logic into the DBMS based on previous work in this domain [15]. DBMS X uses the .NET Common Language Runtime (CLR) for it's stored procedures which makes it very straight forward to adapt code written in a .NET language such as C# to be used as stored procedures. Our second environment was PostgreSQL as it is widely used to test concepts. PostgreSQL extensions written in C have an easily usable extension framework in PGXS to be integrated into the DBMS. However, due to the speed for complexity trade-off in using C, the development and integration time is somewhat increased compared to C# and DBMS X.

2.2 Dynamic Programming

Dynamic programming is a technique used in many fields to solve complex problems by dividing the problem into several smaller problems and computing and storing the solutions to each of the smaller sub-problems. The solutions for the sub-problems are then combined and a solution to the initial complex problem is then found. In bioinformatics, it is used for sequence alignment. It's primary representation is in the Smith and Waterman [16] sequence alignment algorithm.

Smith Waterman. The Smith Waterman algorithm is a local alignment algorithm that finds the optimal local alignment between two sequences based on a given scoring matrix.

The algorithm itself rests on the use of a two dimensional scoring matrix H with one axis being the reference sequence d and one axis being the query sequence q. Each sequence string is pre-pended with a zero character which allows the first row and first column of the scoring matrix to be set to zero. Then each position in the matrix is calculated based on the following equation:

$$H_{i,j} = max \begin{cases} 0 \\ H_{i-1,j} - G_{init} \\ H_{i,j-1} - G_{init} \\ H_{i-1,j-1} + W(q_i, d_j) \end{cases}$$

Each horizontal or vertical movement computation is based on a gap score $G_{(init)}$. Each diagonal movement computation is based on a score profile W

which contains all the characters found in the alphabet of q and d. A common set of score profiles are the BLOSUM DNA and protein profiles and the PFAM protein profiles [6]. We used a truncated BLOSUM62 scoring profile that only used the values for a DNA alphabet of {A, C, G, T, N}.

Once the scoring matrix has been fully computed, a traceback operation is carried out from the maximum score until a score of zero is reached. Figure 1 shows a completed score matrix H and Fig. 2 shows an example traceback operation on the same completed score matrix H.

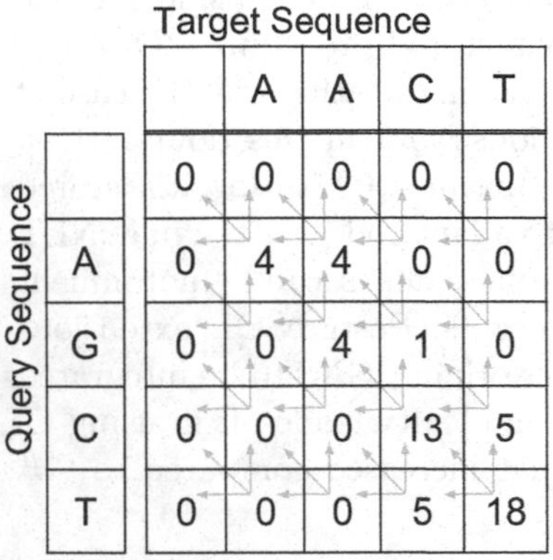

Fig. 1. The score matrix and required computations for each cell

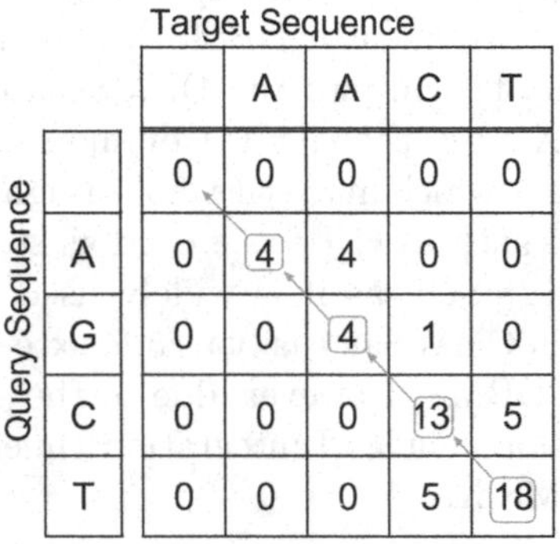

Fig. 2. A completed score matrix with the traceback operation carried out to find the best alignment

3   Related Work

While there are some uses of SIMD inside DBMS for applications in the storage layer and query engine, nothing has been done in the space of stored procedures. Utilization of available SIMD extensions has seen widespread adoption for efficient processing of OLAP workloads:

SIMD-Aware Reorganising of Basic DBMS Architecture. Based on the work of [10] for designing in-memory column store databases, the work of [5, 22] form the core of the X100 engine of the Vectorwise database engine. While they do not focus on the use of SIMD, their entire design of Vectorized Query Execution in itself means that any operations run on their engine will leverage SIMD extensions for query execution.

In-Memory Column Store DBMS with SIMD in Mind. [21] is the seminal paper discussing the use of commodity SIMD extensions in the database query execution engine. They look into using SIMD to improve table scans, indexing methods and join process algorithms. Their results show 2-5x performance gain (depending on the SIMD register bit depth). The authors of [21] went on to develop this field of research in the contending companies of Microsoft and Oracle, so we will look at how this research further developed in those two companies:

Microsoft SQL Server. [8] uses SIMD for performing scan operations on column store index. Their scan code contains SIMD variants of the following column operations: bit unpacking, comparison filters, bitmap filters, compaction, and aggregation. Their comparative results showed a 2.35x to 11.77x speed improvement between code using SIMD and code not using SIMD for proposed inclusion into SQL Server 2016. [3] shows the overall aspects where SIMD was actually integrated into SQL Server 2016: Column Store index scan operations as mentioned in [8]; Numeric from String operations. Usually a numeric character string is processed by taking a difference to a numeric character string of all zeros. SIMD allows for the vectorization of each string for this operation. This use-case occurs often in bulk insert cases which results in overall bulk insert operations having a 1.2x speedup; Encryption using the underlying OS Cryptos API. The Cryptos API on the OS layer is leveraged by SQL Server to increase encryption speed through the use of SIMD instructions.

Oracle Improvements. [11] introduces two fundamental operations - selective load and selective store that were proposed to be used for an Oracle in-memory column store database engine. These constitute how to pre-process table data to make it SIMD ready and all other operations in the paper are built on these two. They implement SIMD aware code for the following operations: Selection scans; Hash tables with Linear probing, double hashing and cuckoo hashing; bloom filters; partitioning for radix, hash and range histograms, un/buffered shuffling; sorting; hash joins. Interestingly, they tested the code on both commodity Intel Haswell cores that were AVX2 capable and also on Intel Xeon Phi cores that were AVX-512 capable (as well as having more smaller registers than the normal core series). Investigations [9] show that the SIMD instructions that are actually being called inside the Oracle 12c In-Memory Compression Unit (ICMU) for general purpose compression and decompression as well as predicate filtering.

Full Text Search Engine. [2] investigated the internals of the SQL Server 2012 Full Text Engine and found that it was using SIMD aware functions to accelerate it's ranking function.

4   Approach

Given that our focus is on determining the feasibility of using SIMD to accelerate stored procedure logic, we implemented existing SIMD-accelerated logic first as a stand-alone console program, then integrated the same logic into a stored procedure. By toggling the accelerations on and off, we were then able to measure the impact of the SIMD-acceleration on the logic and the overhead incurred by the DBMS.

4.1   SIMD Accelerated Dynamic Programming

Since Wozniak [19] first introduced the idea back in 1997, several different attempts to speed up the dynamic programming algorithms for sequence alignment have come into existence (outlined in Fig. 3). All of them use the concept of a pre-computed query profile for matching every possible character in the target sequence alphabet. Currently the best intrasequence (comparing one sequence to the target sequence) is based on Farrar's method described in [4]. Our implementation is based on a modification of Farrar's method that uses the same query profile calculation but a modified score matrix calculation.

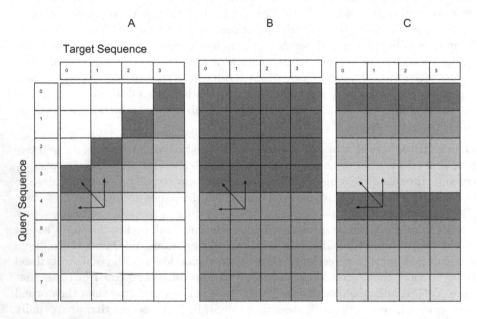

Fig. 3. Examples of various query profiles with their dependencies. A: Vectors along a diagonal [19]; B: Vectors along the query [13]; C: Striped Vectors along the query [4];

Farrar Method. The Farrar method [4] for carrying out a SIMD accelerated striped Smith Waterman algorithm is still the most efficient for *intrasequence* sequence alignment (some better methods exist for *intersequence* sequence alignment [12]). The key innovation of Farrar's approach over previous methods such as Wozniak [19] and Rognes [13] was the use of a striped query profile. Figure 3 outlines the various different query profiles that were considered for SIMD-accelerated SW. Farrar's approach is shown in example C of Fig. 3. By compiling SIMD vectors from every t-th character in the query, Farrar was able to uncouple the dependencies within the two nested loops for iterating across the score matrix. A query profile is a set of pre-computed alignment scores of the query against the alphabet of the target sequence. Usually the alphabet for both the query and the target sequence are the same. In our (and most other) implementation, our expected alphabet is {**A, C, G, T, N, -**} (where - represents a gap) for DNA sequences. So, our query profile would take the form of the reference alphabet size of 6 times t vectors. The size of each vector is determined by the expected query size. We use Farrar's method of query profile creation, but we propose our own method for Score Matrix calculation shown in Algorithm 1.

4.2   Data Organisation

All of our sequence data was stored in a database table as `varchar(max)` attribute together with several meta-data attributes about the position and meaning of each sequence, such as the organism and chromosome from which the reference sequence came from. This is a distinct advantage of this approach that bio-data and meta-data are closely related. An `id` field was used a primary key to identify each sequence. In this instance we only have the single profile so we also created a hard coded two-dimensional int array where each index corresponded to a specific character: 0, 1, 2, 3, 4 to A, G, C, T respectively. In future work, we expect multiple likely score profiles, so we used a user defined type (UDT) called ScoreProfile and a table with the schema *(uint16:id, varchar(100):scoreprofiledescription, ScoreProfile:scoreprof)* to store our score profiles. When we run our implementation, we begin by loading all the sequence data from tables into main memory to remove any table scan/loading bias from our testing process.

4.3   Our Implementation

Our implementation follows Farrar's approach, but has a few differences due to the limitations imposed by the System.Numerics library in .NET 4.6 onwards. In order to maintain parity between comparisons, we used the same implementation in C for PostgreSQL. We use the same query profile generation as Farrar but our particular approach for completing the score matrix is outlined in Algorithm 1 on the following page. We also keep track of the maximum valued cell position to reduce the time required in the traceback step of Smith Waterman.

The algorithm operates in a nested *for* loop iterating down the query profile for each character in the target sequence. Initially we designate two vectors that perform baseline operations for comparison to all zeros (*vZero* in line 2 of Algorithm 1) and the subtraction of the gap penalty (*vGap* in line 3). Then lines 5 to 20 deal with performing most of the standard comparisons for each cell in the score matrix *matrixProf* - i.e. for this cell at position (i, j): compare with cell $(i-1, j)$ with a subtraction of the gap cost (line 16); and cell $(i-1, j-1)$ with an addition of the appropriate score cost from the score matrix W (line 12 and 14); and make sure all values are zero or above (lines 7, 12, 14). Given the striped query profile introduces possible errors when doing the comparison to cell $(i, j-1)$, we add another *for* loop (lines 22 to 38) with a change flag (line 21) to check for inconsistencies by performing a gap penalty correction (lines 26, 28).

It is in this region where our code differs from Farrar's approach. He uses a single Intel Intrinsics SIMD instruction *AnyElement()* to perform lines 21, 30 to 34 in a single instruction. Whereas we use the .NET-available SIMD instruction *greaterThanAny()* (Line 30) combined with vector assignments and the vectorized *max* instruction to check for inconsistencies.

Once it completes this nested *for* loop, then the entire score matrix is completely filled and the traceback can begin from the previously tagged maximum score cell position.

Algorithm 1. Our Score Matrix Calculation Implementation

1: **function** TRAVERSESCOREMATRIXNEW(Query, Ref, vQProf, segLen, gapPenalty)
2:     $vZero \leftarrow < 0, ..., 0 >$ ▷ Zero Vector
3:     $vGap \leftarrow < gapPenalty, ..., gapPenalty >$ ▷ GapCost Vector
4:     **for** $i = 0..Reference.length$ **do**
5:         **for** $j = 0..segLen$ **do**
6:             **if** $i == 0$ **then**
7:                 $vH \leftarrow \mathbf{max}(vZero, vQProf[j][Ref[i]])$
8:             **else**
9:                 **if** $j == 0$ **then**
10:                    $vH \leftarrow matrixProf[segLen - 1][i - 1]$
11:                    $vH \leftarrow vH >> 1$
12:                    $vH \leftarrow \mathbf{max}(vZero, vH + vQProf[j][Ref[i]])$
13:                **else**
14:                    $vH \leftarrow \mathbf{max}(vZero, matrixProf[j - 1][i - 1] + vQProf[j][Ref[i]])$
15:                **end if**
16:                $vE \leftarrow matrixProf[j][i - 1] - vGap$
17:                $vH \leftarrow \mathbf{max}(vH, vE)$
18:            **end if**
19:            $matrixProf[j][i] \leftarrow vH$
20:        **end for**
21:        $cFlag \leftarrow \mathbf{false}$ ▷ change flag
22:        **for** $j = 0..segLen$ **do**
23:            **if** $j == 0$ **then**
24:                $vH \leftarrow matrixProf[segLen - 1][i]$
25:                $vH \leftarrow vH >> 1$
26:                $vF \leftarrow vH - vGap$
27:            **else**
28:                $vF \leftarrow matrixProf[j - 1][i] - vGap$
29:            **end if**
30:            $gtFlag \leftarrow \mathbf{greaterThanAny}(vF, matrixProf[j][i])$
31:            $cFlag \leftarrow cFlag || gtFlag$
32:            $vH \leftarrow \mathbf{max}(vF, matrixProf[j][i])$
33:            $matrixProf[j][i] \leftarrow vH$
34:            **if** $(j == (segLen - 1)) \wedge cFlag$ **then**
35:                $j \leftarrow -1$
36:                $cFlag \leftarrow \mathbf{false}$
37:            **end if**
38:        **end for**
39:    **end for**
40:    **return** matrixProf
41: **end function**

4.4   DBMS Integration

DBMS X: DBMS X is a commercial database engine that features a tight integration with the .NET CLR such that stored procedures can execute within .NET inside the same DBMS process. As we carried out our implementation in C# (which runs on the .NET CLR), porting our solution into a stored procedure was straight-forward. The original console based library function was moved to a stored procedure class *StoredProcedures.DBSIMDSW()*, only 5 lines of code needed to be changed to implement the stored procedure.

One can build and publish the stored procedure via Visual Studio to DBMS X, which creates a script file that injects *two* assemblies into DBMS X. The first assembly is the .NET CLR SIMD Instructions library: System.Numerics. This is what allows the DBMS to access SIMD instructions. The second assembly adds the logic we have programmed as well as defining any stored procedures we encoded (*DBSIMDSW()* and *DBNOSIMDSW()* in this case). Once this is done, we can call the stored procedure by using the commanda *exec DBSIMDSW()* or *exec DBNOSIMDSW()*.

PostgreSQL: PostgreSQL integration is somewhat more complex. However, there are existing extensions such as the PGXS framework to ease the deployment of our functionality to the DBMS. Our C code needed a few wrapper functions and PGXS needed some definitions to alert the DBMS that we are defining new objects. The extra code was approximately 50 lines of code per function. Some change of the makefiles was also required to ensure AVX2 compatibility. We combined all the deployment instructions into a short script and our final tally for extra code came to 142 lines to go from C code to an executable set of two stored procedures: *SELECT PGSIMDSW()* and *SELECT PGNOSIMDSW()*.

5   Evaluation

We evaluate the performance benefits and trade-offs of SIMD extensions inside stored procedure code using a use case from bioinformatics.

Evaluation Setup. We implemented our approach with DBMS X on .NET Framework 4.7.1 and Postgres 11devel on top of Windows 10 (v1709, Build 16299.98). The hardware used was as follows: Intel Core i7-4710HQ (4 physical cores, 8 logical cores, running at a locked speed of 2.50 GHz with AVX2 Instruction sets available), 16 GB RAM (DDR3L 1600 MHz), SSD Samsung 850 EVO SATA M.2 500 GB (expected read/write of 540 Mbps/500 Mbps with a SATA 3 bus).

Scenario. Our dataset was generated from the reference genome for *homo sapiens* (vGRCh38.p7) [7] chromosome 1. We took random samplings of length 35, 50, 75, 100, 150, 200, 250, 300, 500, 1000, 1500, 2000, 2500, 3000, 5000 (measured in base pairs or bp) from the region between positions 1 million and 1.1 million bp from the beginning of the chromosome to reduce the chance of N regions.

We chose these sizes as they are the most likely sizes found in genome assembly for short read sequence alignment which is high frequency use-case for sequence similarity searches. These samplings were classified as our query sequences. For each sample, we also gathered a surrounding region of length 50 both upstream and downstream for use as a corresponding target sequence (i.e. if we took an initial query sequence sample at position 1023728 of length 100, then our corresponding target sequence would begin at position 1023678 and end at 1023877 and be of length 200). Once we had our *(query sequence, target sequence)* pairs, we then also generated a set of *(mutated query sequence, target sequence)* based on various edit distances (ED). The retrieved sequences were bulk loaded into memory to remove any I/O bias from our experiments.

Evaluation of Scalability and Overhead. We ran our baseline Smith-Waterman and SIMD aware Smith Waterman implementation in three modes: As a console program executed from Windows PowerShell; as a DBMS X stored procedure executed from a query window inside a DBMS X associated GUI tool; as a PostgreSQL stored procedure from the psql interface. When we chart the values in log scale as seen in Fig. 4, we can see that the SIMD improvements are resulting in an order of magnitude improvement at the higher query lengths. Since read sizes are continually increasing, this does bode well for the performance of our solution when measured against upcoming read sizes. We can also observe that as expected, our C implementation runs an order of magnitude faster than our C# implementation. Furthermore, the benefits of SIMD instructions in C result in greater benefits, sometimes even up to a 40x performance improvement as compared to the C# code. This is because the C implementation has direct access to the Intel Intrinsics library, while the C# implementation uses the System.Numerics library wrapper.

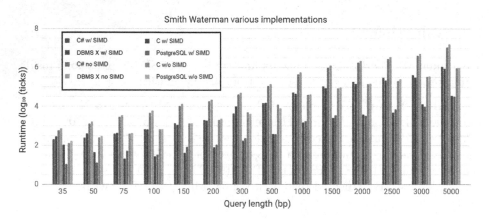

Fig. 4. Smith Waterman algorithm runtime with and without SIMD, and either in console or inside a DBMS (DBMS X - left set of 4 bars in each group or PostgreSQL - right set of 4 bars in each group).

For each mode, we ran our implementation five times for each different edit distance and query length. The selected edit distances of 0, 5 and 10. Our suppositions for these choices were as follows: the longer the sequence length, the longer the runtime as a dynamic programming is bound at $O(n.m)$ where n is the query sequence length and m is the target sequence length; and the greater the edit distance, the greater the computation required for the backtrace algorithm. This could become relevant for implementation of pruning approaches to further limit the required calculations (especially relevant for larger query lengths going forward). Figure 5 shows the impact of edit distance on the runtime of SW running with SIMD inside a DBMS. While no trend is immediately apparent, it seems to indicate that with longer sequences, we see a edit distance impacting our search time as expected.

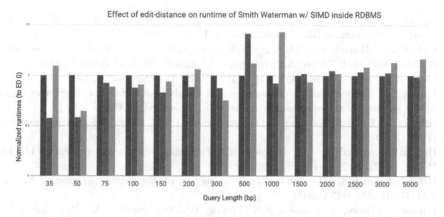

Fig. 5. Smith Waterman algorithm runtime with SIMD with edit distances 5 (middle bar in each group) and 10 (right bar in each group) normalized against edit distance of zero (left bar in each group).

6   Conclusions

In this paper, we demonstrated the performance benefits of integrating SIMD instructions in stored procedure code of computation-intensive algorithms. The required implementation effort is small: We were able to integrate a full-fledged, SIMD-enabled sequence alignment algorithm within a commercial-grade DBMS using extensible .NET stored procedures with only few code changes of its C# code. Similarly, we were able to implement a faster C-based approach into PostgreSQL with an extra 142 lines of code.

Because such complex stored procedures are basically black boxes to the database engine, we further investigated on how to accelerate the sequence alignment code inside the DBMS using hardware extensions, specifically SIMD instructions as available in many modern CPUs. In our experiments we could demonstrate an order of magnitude faster execution of sequence alignment searches due to SIMD acceleration.

We were also able to show that the overhead of running SIMD-enabled code within a DBMS as compared to executing the same code standalone is very small; in fact, at times the SIMD accelerated code ran faster inside both DBMS systems than in the console, though the difference is within the measuring variance.

6.1 Future Work

As a next step, we plan to investigate the capabilities of GPGPU accelerations for sequence alignment searches inside a DBMS, as those offer an even higher degree of data and code parallelism, though requiring specific additional hardware.

References

1. Daily, J.: Parasail: SIMD C library for global, semi-global, and local pairwise sequence alignments. BMC Bioinform. **17**(1), 81 (2016)
2. Delaney, K., Beauchemin, B., Cunningham, C., Kehayias, J., Randal, P.S., Nevarez, B.: Microsoft SQL Server 2012 Internals. Microsoft Press, Redmond (2013)
3. Dorr, R.: How It Works: SQL Server 2016 SSE/AVX Support (2016)
4. Farrar, M.: Striped smith-waterman speeds database searches six times over other SIMD implementations. Bioinformatics **23**(2), 156–161 (2006)
5. Héman, S.: Updating compressed column stores. Ph.D. thesis, Informatics Institute (IVI) (2009)
6. Henikoff, S., Henikoff, J.G.: Amino acid substitution matrices from protein blocks. PNAS **89**(22), 10915–10919 (1992)
7. IHGRC: Finishing the euchromatic sequence of the human genome. Nature **431**(7011), 931–945 (2004)
8. Larson, P., Birka, A., Hanson, E.N., Huang, W., Nowakiewicz, M., Papadimos, V.: Real-time analytical processing with SQL server. PVLDB **8**(12), 1740–1751 (2015)
9. Leturgez, L.: SIMD outside and inside Oracle 12c (2015)
10. Manegold, S., Boncz, P.A., Kersten, M.L.: Optimizing database architecture for the new bottleneck: memory access. VLDB J. **9**(3), 231–246 (2000)
11. Polychroniou, O., Raghavan, A., Ross, K.A.: Rethinking SIMD vectorization for in-memory databases. In: ACM SIGMOD, SIGMOD 2015, pp. 1493–1508. ACM, New York (2015)
12. Rognes, T.: Faster Smith-Waterman database searches with inter-sequence SIMD parallelisation. BMC Bioinform. **12**, 221 (2011)
13. Rognes, T., Seeberg, E.: Six-fold speed-up of Smith-Waterman sequence database searches using parallel processing on common microprocessors. Bioinformatics **16**(8), 699–706 (2000)
14. Röhm, U., Blakeley, J.A.: Data management for high-throughput genomics. In: Fourth Biennial Conference on Innovative Data Systems Research, CIDR 2009, Asilomar, CA, USA, 4–7 January 2009, Online Proceedings (2009)
15. Röhm, U., Diep, T.-M.: How to BLAST your database — a study of stored procedures for BLAST searches. In: Li Lee, M., Tan, K.-L., Wuwongse, V. (eds.) DAS-FAA 2006. LNCS, vol. 3882, pp. 807–816. Springer, Heidelberg (2006). https://doi.org/10.1007/11733836_58
16. Smith, T.F., Waterman, M.S.: Identification of common molecular subsequences. J. Mol. Biol. **147**(1), 195–197 (1981)

17. Sosic, M.: An SIMD dynamic programming C/C++ library. Master's thesis, University of Zagreb (2015)
18. Stonebraker, M., Brown, P., Zhang, D., Becla, J.: SciDB: a database management system for applications with complex analytics. Comput. Sci. Eng. **15**(3), 54–62 (2013)
19. Wozniak, A.: Using video-oriented instructions to speed up sequence comparison. Comput. Appl. Biosci. **13**(2), 145–150 (1997)
20. Zhao, M., Lee, W.P., Garrison, E.P., Marth, G.T.: SSW library: an SIMD Smith-Waterman C/C++ library for use in genomic applications. PLoS ONE **8**(12), e82138 (2013)
21. Zhou, J., Ross, K.A.: Implementing database operations using SIMD instructions. In: Proceedings of the 2002 ACM SIGMOD International Conference on Management of Data, Madison, Wisconsin, 3–6 June 2002, pp. 145–156 (2002)
22. Żukowski, M.: Balancing vectorized query execution with bandwidth-optimized storage. Ph.D. thesis, Informatics Institute (IVI) (2009)

Renovating Database Applications
with DBAutoAwesome

Jonathan Adams[✉] and Curtis E. Dyreson

Department of Computer Science, Utah State University, Logan, USA
jadams@outlook.com, Curtis.Dyreson@usu.edu

Abstract. Renovating a database application is the act of significantly reprogramming the application to meet new needs, extend functionality, or re-design to foster maintainability. It can be costly to manually renovate a database application so techniques for automating the renovation are needed. Previous research in renovation has focused on methods to improve performance, such as autonomic database research to automatically tune a DBMS or manage indexes. But there has been little previous research on how to improve *functionality*. There are several ways in which the functionality can be improved such as interfaces to other tools (*e.g.*, data mining with Weka), content management system integration (*e.g.*, Wordpress plugins), an enhanced set of forms and scripts to query and manage the data, and database mediation and migration scripts. We focus on the final category in this paper: management of the data. We propose an approach, which we call *DBAutoAwesome*, that adopts Google's Auto Awesome philosophy: automatically improve an existing artifact and let the user (developer) decide whether to keep and use the improved artifact. The DBAutoAwesome approach ingests a database application to produce an enhanced application. In this paper we describe how DBAutoAwesome enhances data modification and query forms.

1 Introduction

Auto Awesome is an app that automatically enhances photos uploaded to Google Photos.[1] Photos are enhanced in various ways such as by adding special effects or by combining photos to create animations and panoramas. For instance, a picture of a dog in snow may be enhanced with a falling snow effect, or combined with other photos of the dog to create an animated scene. Auto Awesome also creates slide shows with music and can geo-locate (non-gps tagged) photos via photo matching. All of these enhancements are completely automatic. The only human input is to decide whether to keep or discard the enhanced photos. Not every photo is enhanced only some within a collection are chosen for enhancement.

We propose adapting the Auto Awesome philosophy to relational database applications (DBApps). A DBApp is a collection of forms and processing scripts

---

[1] Google re-branded the app as "Photo Creations" in 2015.

© Springer International Publishing AG, part of Springer Nature 2018
J. Wang et al. (Eds.): ADC 2018, LNCS 10837, pp. 94–106, 2018.
https://doi.org/10.1007/978-3-319-92013-9_8

to manage and query data stored in a relational database; typically in a three-tier architecture (client, web server, and database server). A scientific DBApp is usually set up and run by people, typically domain scientists, who did not develop or maintain the software. We will refer to the people who set up and run the software as *administrators*, and those who develop the DBApp software as *developers*.

Administrators often want to modify, improve, or extend some aspects of the software to better suit their needs, but administrators usually have limited programming skill or time. Tools are needed to help administrators modify database applications, without having to become experts in software development.

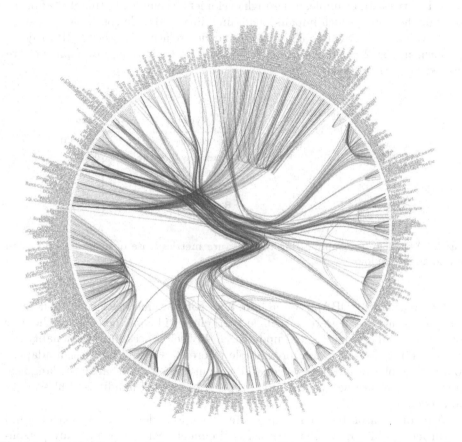

Fig. 1. A graph of class relationships. Classes are listed around the circle. An edge between a pair of classes indicates that a method in one class calls a method in another, computed by PHPMetrics.

As a canonical DBApp, consider the Symbiota project [7]. At the heart of many scientific pursuits is the gathering and cataloging of data. Modern technologies allow this data to be stored in online databases, allowing for greater ease of access and collaboration. Symbiota is an open-source, software platform for creating voucher-based biodiversity information portals and communities. Symbiota, as of May 2016, was written in 148,533 lines of PHP code spanning 394 classes (typically one class per file) and 3545 methods (functions or procedures). There are also some Javascript and CSS files. The PHP classes are inter-related as depicted in Fig. 1. Each class is listed around the outside of the circle. An edge connects a class that calls (invokes a method) in another class. Symbiota's biodiversity data is stored in a MySQL database with 143 tables.

Software metrics can be used to estimate the complexity of software and the difficulty of extending it, maintaining it, and fixing bugs [5]. We computed the software metrics for Symbiota using PHPMetrics [1]. Symbiota scores poorly on several metrics, for example, it has high cyclometric complexity (number of paths through the code), which impairs maintainability and code correctness. A summary evaluation of Symbiota's software metrics relative to other PHP projects is shown in Fig. 2 where the metrics related to a topic (*e.g.*, development) are plotted on a radiograph.

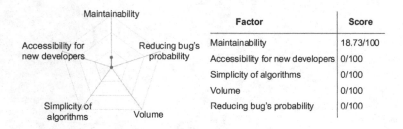

Factor	Score
Maintainability	18.73/100
Accessibility for new developers	0/100
Simplicity of algorithms	0/100
Volume	0/100
Reducing bug's probability	0/100

Fig. 2. A radiograph summarizing the software metrics; ease of maintainability and development are low.

One reason why DBApps often have poor software metrics is that their functionality is highly integrated. A single PHP class will combine code for the user interface, database queries and updates, and other processing functionality. So to change the user-interface, for example to create a responsive design adapted to a mobile platform or internationalize the interface (*e.g.*, change the language in the forms from English to Arabic), reprogramming of hundreds of files might be needed.

A second reason is that DBApps often have long development lifetimes and are prone to shifting project needs. Development teams expend many person-years to code a DBApp at a cost of thousands to hundreds of thousands of dollars to support the development team. The development investment means that an organization is more willing to extend a DBApp than dump the existing code and start again to meet new user needs or incorporate new software techniques and platforms. Hence, DBApps are frequently extended and updated.

The cost of redesigning and reprogramming a DBApp raises the need for *techniques to automatically, or with limited manual effort, improve or augment an existing DBApp.* Previous research has focused on techniques that enhance *performance*, such as research in autonomic databases to automatically tune a DBMS (*c.f.*, [12]) or manage indexes (*c.f.*, [15]). There has also been research on improving code *design* by refactoring (*c.f.*, [6]). Our focus is on *functionality*. *DBApp renovation* is the process of repairing and improving the functionality of an existing DBApp. There are several ways in a DBApp can be renovated such as: creating tool interfaces (*e.g.*, to facilitate data mining with Weka or search with Sphinx), integrating with a content management system (*e.g.*, through Wordpress plugins), generating database mediation and migration scripts, and enhancing a set of forms and scripts to query and manage the data. We focus on the final category in this paper: forms and scripts to manage the data.

We propose an approach, which we call *DBAutoAwesome*, that adopts Google's Auto Awesome philosophy: automatically improve an existing artifact and let the user (developer) decide to keep and use the improved artifact. The Auto Awesome approach will ingest a DBApp to produce an enhanced app. Our approach can help to lower the cost of extending and updating a DBApp.

2   Related Work

A taxonomy of previous research in DBApp renovation is shown in Fig. 3. At the top level of the taxonomy we distinguish research that targets the *database* rather than *applications* that interact with the database. In the database side of the taxonomy, renovation can impact the *schema* or *data*. On the data side, usability can be improved through better *queries* or by enhancing data *quality*. Usability can also be improved through *refactoring* the schema, *extending* it to support a wider range of data, or *migrating* to a different DBMS. On the application side of the taxonomy, a tool may target *performance*, or it may offer ways to modify the application's *code*. These modifications come in the form of *generating* new code, *refactoring* existing code, or offering *better user interfaces*.

There have been many attempts to use the data and schema to improve database applications.

Database/Data/Queries. Error-correcting compilers for query construction are present in many graphical query builders and IDEs, *c.f.*, [11].

Database/Data/Quality. Many techniques have been proposed to automatically impute missing values or repair erroneous values, *e.g.*, by mining attribute correlations and building classifiers to predict values [17]. Specific to relational databases, there are also systems to find and use (approximate or soft) functional dependencies to improve data quality, *c.f.*, [8,10].

Database/Schema/Migration. The plethora of DBMSs has spurred research in automating database migration [16] and led to the development of migration tools, *c.f.*, [2].

Database/Schema/Extension. An et al. [3] propose extending a database schema automatically to include attributes specified in a newly created form.

Database/Schema/Refactor. Vial [14] discusses many of the challenges of analyzing and improving a database schema, as well as techniques they found valuable in performing database refactoring, and present an automated, schema refactoring tool.

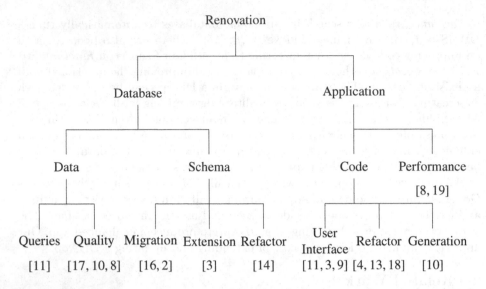

Fig. 3. Taxonomy of database renovation research

The application that interacts with the underlying database can also benefit from renovation. Key aspects that may need improvement are the user interface, the quality and structure of underlying code, and performance. These all have a significant impact on the usability of a DBApp.

Application/Code/User Interface. Jagadish et al. [9] identified several usability pain points and created and tested alternative interfaces appealing to a range of novice to expert users. Nandi and Jagadish [11] augment an interface with a text box, which combines guided query building with search, and so that one form essentially supports many different kinds of queries.

Application/Code/Refactor. Cedrim [4] propose a machine learning system to automate the identification of code refactoring opportunities. Sharma [13] takes a different approach in order to identify extract-method refactoring. This type of refactoring involves reorganizing existing code into new methods without altering the overall application behavior of the code segment. Xin et al. [18] created the MEET DB2 tool to find database operations in the code that may need to be modified in a database migration, and estimates how much work will be required to migrate the database.

Application/Code/Generation. Jayapandian and Jagadish [10] show how to automatically identify important relationships in a database, and using these relationships, generate forms and processing code that will cover the majority of queries that are likely to be performed on the data.

Application/Performance. Zisman and Kramer [19] propose a system to automatically create indexes to improve information retrieval and discovery. Ilyas et al. [8] use soft functional dependencies to optimize queries.

We also automate the improvement of DBApps in the **Application/ Code/User Interface** area; we provide ways to improve the user interface by creating new forms that better suit administrators' needs. A key piece missing from previous research is that we harvest and reuse existing validation code when building forms. Our system refactors the code related to a form. A form and the code to process the form are analyzed to determine which database attributes are tied to the form fields. We then use the relevant database schema information to determine which types of validation scripts are likely to be valuable for each field and the overall form. This allows us to guide a DBApp administrator through generating new form validation code. Having better form validation allows us to improve the messaging presented to a user of the form when data is not properly entered into the form, as well as to validate data entry and query boxes.

3 DBAutoAwesome

DBAutoAwesome is a framework that applies a suite of techniques. This section describes the techniques.

3.1 Getting Started

DBAutoAwesome inputs forms, processing scripts, and a database schema to produce enhanced forms and processing scripts. The DBApp ingestion process parses the PHP, Javascript, HTML, and database operations into the class structure shown in Fig. 4. The parsing identifies relationships between parts of the application and the database. The series of PHP functions called when a form is submitted is traced. The database fields that are interacted with, when a form or function is used, are identified. The characteristics of the data in the database, including data type, length, nullability, and constraints, are gathered.

3.2 Generate Database Code Templates

A DBApp's usefulness centers around being able to access or update data. To make beneficial enhancements to the application, DBAutoAwesome needs to be capable of generating code, which we call a *template*, to allow for these data interactions. The templates are generated from a set of building blocks. An example of block is shown in the context of a generated insert template in Figure 5. First the code to connect to the DBMS is generated. Next the SQL statement or statements are built for the tables being used. Then the query processing code is generated for binding the submitted values, executing the SQL statement, and handling the results.

To properly generate the value binding code, DBAutoAwesome learns the data type of each column the query interacts with from the schema. When the form input data is bound to the SQL statement, a binding function of the MySQLi class is inserted to matc the data type taken from the database.

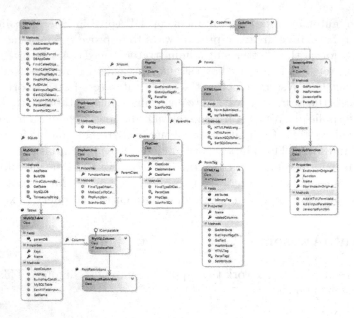

Fig. 4. The schema for storing parsed DBApp information.

There are four classes of templates that can be generated by DBAutoAwe-some: (1) insert data into a table, (2) check if specific data values currently exist in a table, (3) retrieve data from one or more tables, and (4) delete data from a table. The simplest interaction type is inserting data into the database. To build a code snippet the tool needs to know which database table and which columns in that table the data goes in. The template will take the appropriate values, attempt to insert them into the database, and then return a Boolean to indicate whether it succeeded.

The most common interactions found in Symbiota are the two data retrieval types. The interaction to check if data values currently exist in the table is typi-cally used to check if data being inserted into the table will meet constraints on the values, like uniqueness or a foreign key constraint. The information required to generate this template is the table and columns to check against and what type of value comparison to do. Typically, this type of interaction is based on the equality operator, to ensure that the submitted values exactly match existing values. However, if the need arises, any standard SQL comparator can be used. The template will return true or false to indicate whether the provided values match any existing values in the database.

The other data retrieval operation is used to retrieve a set of data matching a set of input values. This template is a bit more complicated to generate, depend-ing on the desired use, than the previous two. If a single table is desired, the tool needs to know the table to access, the columns to return values from, the columns to compare against, and the comparator type to use in each comparison.

Using this, the tool can generate the necessary SQL SELECT statement to fetch the matching results, along with the necessary PHP to execute that statement and process the results.

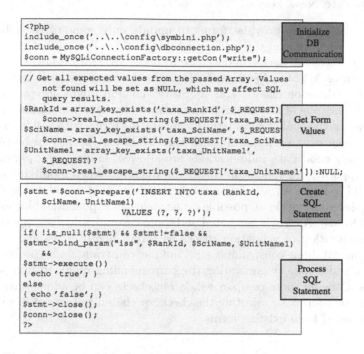

Fig. 5. Generated blocks of a DBAutoAwesome insert connector.

If values from more than one table are needed, more information is required. The tool needs all items listed in the previous paragraph, but for each table accessed it also needs the description of how to connect the tables. Currently, DBAutoAwesome only supports inner joins. For each join, the tool needs to know which two tables to perform the join on, and which columns to join on. The complete set of tables must form a single chain of joined tables. Provided with this extra information, the tool can generate a more complex SQL SELECT statement to fetch the matching results from the combined columns of all joined tables. A successful query will return the fetched results as JSON, while a failed query will return an error message.

The most complicated template to generate is the delete data from a table. Performing a delete operation on a single MySQL table is simple, but a table does not exist in a vacuum. A table may be referenced by other tables through foreign key constraints. To ensure the integrity of the data, a delete operation cannot be performed on any data that is currently referenced by a matching value in another table. In a sense, these restrictions pin the data so it cannot be deleted or modified, until all references are modified to no longer refer to those values. DBAutoAwesome chases the chain of foreign key constraints to ensure that all data is deleted in the correct order.

3.3   Generate New Forms

An application usually provides forms to update only some of the tables in a collection, or only some of the fields in a table. If there is no update form, users will directly access the back-end database to make necessary changes, *e.g.,* using phpmyadmin or MYSQL Workbench. But direct access methods lack application specific validation checks, *e.g.,* a "State" column might accept any string rather than only one of fifty possible state names. So form generation in DBAutoAwesome has the goal of automatically generating forms with validation checkers reused from existing forms. Ideally, the validation checks can be pipelined to ensure only good data modifications are allowed, unlike using phpmyadmin where an application's validation checks are bypassed when modifying data.

To build a form, an administrator first selects tables and fields the user interface (since generating all possible forms yields an exponential blow-up in the number of forms). A form is generated and some customization is supported such as the configuration of validation checks as shown in Fig. 6. Validation checks for common database constraints, *e.g.,* unique constraint, are checked in the application code, *e.g.,* by generating the corresponding query to find potential duplicates. Code for more complex validation checks can be added directly, and reused for other forms by selecting the check, or chosen from a list of validation checks harvested from existing forms.

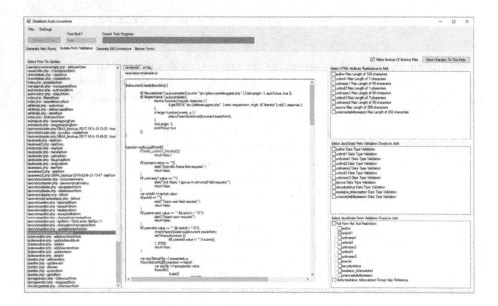

Fig. 6. Building a form, choosing validation checks.

Various types of information are fed into each portion of the form generation process, as shown in Fig. 7. By bringing this information into the process, DBAutoAwesome can generate completely new or enhanced ways of interacting with the DBApp with minimal guidance from the administrator.

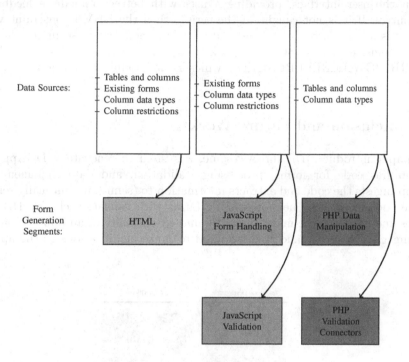

Fig. 7. Data sources that inform each portion of code generation

3.4 Regenerate Existing Forms

Going one step further, it is possible to *automatically regenerate forms* when a schema changes due to new functionality or improving schema design, *i.e.,* normalization. Forms and processing scripts currently "pin" schemas preventing schema changes because schemas are hard-coded into processing scripts. For instance, an INSERT INTO a table typically lists all of the fields in a table together with the values to insert. This prevents a table from being decomposed (common to normalization to improve design) into several tables. To decompose it would be necessary to rewrite the INSERT and processing script. It is better if an existing form and processing script could be regenerated from a schema as needed.

3.5 Checking Database Constraints in Scripts

A third enhancement is *adding code to check database constraints* in processing scripts. Database constraints such as foreign key and unique constraints can be checked in a script prior to performing a data modification. For instance, most of the Symbiota validation code duplicates constraints that are present in the database. We conjecture that this is common in many DBApps. The value of checking in a script is that a bad modification can be caught and handled in the user interface, providing a user with better, immediate feedback and control. If it is not caught in the script, then the DBMS constraint violation message is passed to a user, but such messages are terse in commonly used systems, *e.g.,* a MySQL foreign key violation reports "Error Code 256: HA_ERR_ROW_IS_REFERENCED", which is not useful information for most users.

4 Conclusion and Future Work

This paper introduces DBAutoAwesome, a system to renovate a DBApp. A DBApp has code for forms, processing, validation, and data management. DBApp ingests the code and extracts information to (semi-)automatically refactor the code, generating new or existing forms with validation checks. DBAutoAwesome improves the maintainability and extensibility of an application by reducing the knowledge and time required to make modifications to the application.

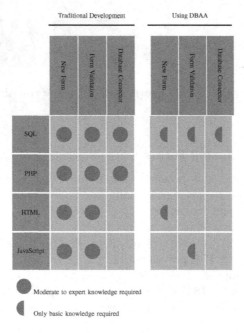

Fig. 8. Knowledge required to perform DBApp modifications in various areas with or without DBAutoAwesome

Figure 8 compares the knowledge required in traditional development with DBAutoAwesome. DBAutoAwesome removes the requirement to know PHP, the most used technology in a DBApp like Symbiota. It also reduces the SQL knowledge required to a basic understanding of how data is stored in tables and columns and of how comparators are used in SQL statements. A basic understanding of HTML will aid in formatting and organizing the forms being generated. Some understanding of JavaScript will aid in identifying desired form validation scripts when updating an existing form's validation. No other knowledge is required to operate DBAutoAwesome.

DBAutoAwesome does not completely remove the need for an understanding of software development technologies, but it significantly reduces that barrier when compared to traditional development.

We are working to refactor data modifications into modules, but have not completed this part of DBAutoAwesome. INSERT, DELETE, and UPDATE statements in a processing script can be refactored, placing them in modules. The module takes as input a "state" of processing, which consists of a global state (*e.g.*, user making the update) and local state (*e.g.*, values entered into a form). The data modification is performed with respect to the state. By modularizing these operations automatically they could be replaced with calls to other DBMSs, *e.g.*, MYSQL updates replaced with Postgres updates, or other kinds of data models, *e.g.*, substituting MYSQL operations with corresponding modifications in Cypher, a graph database language.

There are other areas where a DBApp could be automatically or semi-automatically enhanced: creating interfaces to other tools, content management system integration, and database mediation and migration scripts. Work in these areas could yield additional enhancements for reducing the skills required to build unique applications from an existing application.

References

1. PHPMetrics MS Windows NT kernel description. http://www.phpmetrics.org/. Accessed 30 Mar 2016
2. SQL Server Migration Assistant. https://msdn.microsoft.com/en-us/library/mt613434.aspx
3. An, Y., Khare, R., Song, I.-Y., Hu, X.: Automatically mapping and integrating multiple data entry forms into a database. In: Jeusfeld, M., Delcambre, L., Ling, T.-W. (eds.) ER 2011. LNCS, vol. 6998, pp. 261–274. Springer, Heidelberg (2011). https://doi.org/10.1007/978-3-642-24606-7_20
4. Cedrim, D.: Context-sensitive identification of refactoring opportunities. In: Proceedings of the International Conference on Software Engineering, ICSE, pp. 827–830 (2016)
5. Frakes, W.B., Terry, C.: Software reuse: metrics and models. ACM Comput. Surv. **28**(2), 415–435 (1996)
6. Goeminne, M., Decan, A., Mens, T.: Co-evolving code-related and database-related changes in a data-intensive software system. In: 2014 Software Evolution Week - IEEE Conference on Software Maintenance, Reengineering, and Reverse Engineering, CSMR-WCRE 2014, Antwerp, Belgium, 3–6 February 2014, pp. 353–357 (2014)

7. Gries, C., Gilbert, E., Franz, N.: Symbiota - a virtual platform for creating voucher-based biodiversity information communities. Biodivers. Data J. **2**, e1114 (2014)

8. Ilyas, I.F., Markl, V., Haas, P.J., Brown, P.G., Aboulnaga, A.: Automatic relationship discovery in self-managing database systems. In: 1st International Conference on Autonomic Computing (ICAC 2004), New York, NY, USA, 17–19 May 2004, pp. 340–341 (2004)

9. Jagadish, H.V., Chapman, A., Elkiss, A., Jayapandian, M., Li, Y., Nandi, A., Yu, C.: Making database systems usable. In: Proceedings of the ACM SIGMOD International Conference on Management of Data, Beijing, China, 12–14 June 2007, pp. 13–24 (2007)

10. Jayapandian, M., Jagadish, H.V.: Automated creation of a forms-based database query interface. PVLDB **1**(1), 695–709 (2008)

11. Nandi, A., Jagadish, H.V.: Assisted querying using instant-response interfaces. In: Proceedings of the ACM SIGMOD International Conference on Management of Data, Beijing, China, 12–14 June 2007, pp. 1156–1158 (2007)

12. Oh, J.S., Lee, S.H.: Resource selection for autonomic database tuning. In: Proceedings of the 21st International Conference on Data Engineering Workshops, ICDE 2005, 5–8 April 2005, Tokyo, Japan, p. 1218 (2005)

13. Sharma, T.: Identifying extract-method refactoring candidates automatically. In: Fifth Workshop on Refactoring Tools 2012, WRT 2012, Rapperswil, Switzerland, 1 June 2012, pp. 50–53 (2012)

14. Vial, G.: Database refactoring: lessons from the trenches. IEEE Softw. **32**(6), 71–79 (2015)

15. Voigt, H., Kissinger, T., Lehner, W.: SMIX: self-managing indexes for dynamic workloads. In: Conference on Scientific and Statistical Database Management, SSDBM 2013, Baltimore, MD, USA, 29–31 July 2013, pp. 24:1–24:12 (2013)

16. Wang, G., Jia, Z., Xue, M.: Data migration model and algorithm between heterogeneous databases based on web service. JNW **9**(11), 3127–3134 (2014)

17. Wolf, G., Kalavagattu, A., Khatri, H., Balakrishnan, R., Chokshi, B., Fan, J., Chen, Y., Kambhampati, S.: Query processing over incomplete autonomous databases: query rewriting using learned data dependencies. VLDB J. **18**(5), 1167–1190 (2009)

18. Xin, R., Dantressangle, P., Lightstone, S., McLaren, W., Schormann, S., Schwenger, M.: MEET DB2: automated database migration evaluation. PVLDB **3**(2), 1426–1434 (2010)

19. Zisman, A., Kramer, J.: Information discovery for interoperable autonomous database systems. Ph.D. thesis, Imperial College London, UK (1998)

Full Research Papers: Data Mining and Applications

Uncovering Attribute-Driven Active Intimate Communities

Md Musfique Anwar[1]([⊠]), Chengfei Liu[1], and Jianxin Li[2]

[1] Swinburne University of Technology, Melbourne, Australia
{manwar,cliu}@swin.edu.au
[2] University of Western Australia, Perth, Australia
jianxin.li@uwa.edu.au

Abstract. Most existing studies in community detection either focus on the common attributes of the nodes (users) or rely on only the topological links of the social network graph. However, the bulk of literature ignores the interaction strength among the users in the retrieved communities. As a result, many members of the detected communities do not interact frequently to each other. This inactivity will create problem for online advertisers as they require the community to be highly interactive to efficiently diffuse marketing information. In this paper, we study the problem of detecting attribute-driven active intimate community, that is, for a given input query consisting a set of attributes, we want to find densely-connected communities in which community members actively participate as well as have strong interaction (intimacy) with respect to the given query attributes. We design a novel attribute relevance intimacy score function for the detected communities and establish its desirable properties. To this end, we use an indexed based solution to efficiently discover active intimate communities. Extensive experiments on real data sets show the effectiveness and performance of our proposed method.

Keywords: Information diffusion · Intimacy score
Intimate community

1 Introduction

Recently, the availability of rich attribute data associated with objects in real-world information networks has given rise to attributed graphs, where every node is characterized by a number of attributes describing the properties of the nodes, and the edges correspond to a topological structure. The task of community detection in information networks refers to clustering nodes of attributed graphs into communities, where a community (or a cluster) means group of nodes (users) are closely connected to each other, interact with each other more frequently than with those outside the group, and may have interests on common topics.

Earlier works on community detection in online social networks (OSNs) mostly considered only the explicit structural social connections between users.

© Springer International Publishing AG, part of Springer Nature 2018
J. Wang et al. (Eds.): ADC 2018, LNCS 10837, pp. 109–122, 2018.
https://doi.org/10.1007/978-3-319-92013-9_9

As a result, the communities thus generated have very random distribution of node properties within the communities. Some recent approaches explore the content of the nodes in OSNs, e.g. [9,14], to detect meaningful communities by considering users' interests on common topics. However, these methods did not consider the intimacy or degree of interactions among the users. As a result, such communities contain weakly connected users since it is common that some users have very less interactions with others or even no communication. This inactivity creates a problem in targeted advertising and viral marketing, which require to identify the right target audience where users are well connected as well as interactive in order to facilitate the diffusion of marketing information.

A few recent works [3,8] proposed methods for identifying community members based on their frequency of communication with other users in the community. However, most of these approaches did not pay enough attention to users' activeness, which emphasizes their degree of interest, and interaction strength with others with respect to the common attributes. We observed that users' activeness as well as degree of interactions with others vary widely for different attributes. These observations motivated us to study the problem of discovering attribute-driven *active intimate* communities in OSNs, where the community members should have similar activeness as well as high degree of interactions among other members with regards to a given query consisting a set of attributes. Finding an active intimate community with common attributes is important in many applications. E.g., in coauthor network where authors who collaborate with each other may have different attributes, such as research topics, positions held, and prolific values; and one may want to find active research groups in a particular research category. Then the desirable communities should have members who have interest as well as actively collaborate with others in that particular research category.

In our proposed method, we quantified the interaction link (edge) by assigning edge weights according to the rate of interactions w.r.t. the given query attributes that better integrate and enhance the connections, hence, the quality of the communities. An active intimate community is depicted as a connected induced k-core subgraph in which each node has a degree of at least k meaning each user should have interaction with at-least k other users within the community. The parameter k measures the structure cohesiveness of the community. In summary, our contributions are as follows:

- We propose an approach to detect active communities where community members actively participate as well as frequently communicate with others about their common attributes;
- We model and quantify users' activeness and degree of interactions with others with regards to attributes of a given query;
- We design an intimacy score function for the discovered communities and use an indexed based approach to efficiently discover the communities;
- We conduct extensive experiments using real datasets to show the effectiveness of our proposed approach.

In the rest of the paper, we present the related works in Sect. 2, and formulate the problem of discovering active intimate communities in Sect. 3. Section 4 presents the indexed based algorithmic solution. Our experimental results are shown in Sect. 5, and finally, we conclude the paper in Sect. 6.

2 Related Work

Earlier methods focus only on the information regarding the linkage behavior (connection) for the purposes of community detection. Two approaches [4,13] identify clusters with high structure density, and other methods [1,6] detect communities using hierarchical clustering algorithms. However, these methods ignore node attributes. Nowadays, there is a growing body of literature addressing the issue of utilizing the rich contents available in OSNs to determine communities. Li et al. [14] considered outer influence of community, which is the capability to spread internal information of communities to external users, to investigate the problem of the most influential community search. Various influence-based approaches have been proposed to investigate the problem of the personalized influential topic search [10] and influence maximization in location-aware social networks [5]. Some works focused on data anonymisation for privacy protection [2,12] and outlier detection [7] in OSNs. However, none of these work considers the degree of interactions among the users.

Some recent approaches take into account the interactions strength between the users. Correa et al. [3] developed the *iTop* algorithm which constructs a weighted graph of user interactions and greedily maximizes the local modularity in order to detect topic-centric communities based on a set of seed users. Lim and Datta [8] proposed a method which uses frequency of direct messages between users to construct a network of weighted links in order to detect interactive connected communities. However, all these methods ignored attribute-wise users' activeness as well as interaction strength with others. We aim to find communities where users have similar activeness as well as high degree of intimacy with others w.r.t. attribute set in the given query.

3 Preliminary and Problem Definition

We define some basic concepts before formally introducing our problem.

Attributed Graph: An attributed graph is denoted as $G = (U, E, \mathcal{A})$, where U is the set of nodes (representing users), E is the set of links between the nodes, and $\mathcal{A} = \{a_1, \ldots, a_m\}$ is the set of attributes associated with nodes in U. Each attribute a_i usually represents a topic.

k-CORE: Given an integer $k(k \geq 0)$, the k-core of a graph G, denoted by C^k, is the maximal connected subgraph of G, such that $\forall u \in C^k, deg_{C^k}(u) \geq k$, where $deg_{C^k}(u)$ refers to the degree of a node u in C^k. A k-core component H_j^k is considered as a community from structural point of view.

Node Core Number: The core number of a node u in G is the maximum k for which u belongs in the k-core of G.

Activity: An activity refers to an action that a user performs at a time point. We consider two types of activities in this paper. The first one is the participation of the users to reflect their activeness (interest) towards one or more attributes. For example, a user u in Twitter posts a tweet (message) containing set of attributes (e.g. hashtags representing specific topic(s)) ψ_u, this activity is recorded as an activity tuple $\langle u, \psi_u \rangle$. Another type of activity is the direct interactions among the users. For example, a user u in Twitter replies a tweet posted by user v. This activity is recorded as an activity tuple $\langle u, v, \psi_{uv} \rangle$, where ψ_{uv} indicates the set of attributes exchanged between u and v.

Query: An input query $Q = \{a_1, \ldots, a_n\}$ consisting a set of query attributes. In finding communities w.r.t. Q over attributed graphs, we want to ensure that the nodes in the discovered communities actively participate as well as frequently interact with each other related to Q.

Active User: A user u is said to be active towards a given query Q if u has performed at least $\gamma (\geq 1)$ activities related to Q, i.e., $|\{\langle u, \psi_u \rangle\}| \geq \gamma$, where $\psi_u \in Q$. The set of such active users is denoted by U^Q.

Active Interaction Edge: We consider the edge e_{uv} between two active users u and v as active interaction edge if they have at-least $\beta (\geq 1)$ number of interactions related to Q. In order to measure the interaction strength between two users related to Q, we need to consider their individual activeness as well as interaction frequency towards Q. There are two factors related to the individual activeness of a user u. The first factor $f_1(u, \psi_u)$ is the likelihood that a user u performs an activity in Q.

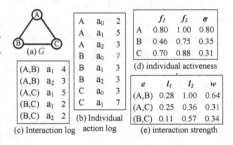

Fig. 1. A sample G with $Q = \{a_1, a_2\}$ and $\alpha = 0.5$

$$f_1(u, \psi_u) = \frac{|ACTS(u, \psi_u)|}{|ACTS(u, *)|} \tag{1}$$

where, $ACTS(u, \psi_u)$ indicates the set of activities containing the set of attributes $\psi_u \subseteq Q$ performed by u and $ACTS(u, *)$ denotes the set of all activities containing any attribute(s) performed by user u.

The second factor $f_2(u, \psi_u)$ is the participation of user u related to Q in comparison to the most active participant user related to Q in the network.

$$f_2(u, \psi_u) = \frac{|ACTS(u, \psi_u)|}{max_{z \in U^Q}|ACTS(z, \psi_z)|} \tag{2}$$

Then, the activeness (denoted as σ) of u related to Q is

$$\sigma_{(u,\psi_u)} = \frac{|\psi_u|}{|Q|} \times f_1(u,\psi_u) \times f_2(u,\psi_u) = \frac{|\psi_u|}{|Q|} \times \frac{|ACTS(u,\psi_u)|^2}{|ACTS(u,*)| \times max_{z \in U^Q}|ACTS(z,\psi_z)|}$$

(3)

A user's activeness should depend on the likelihood of her activities related to Q as well as the number of the query attributes that are covered by those activities. For this reason, we can see in Fig. 1 that the activeness (σ) of user C is lower compare with user B as C does not show her interest in all the query attributes, although C performs more activities (related to Q) than B.

Now, we want to measure the social link between two users u and v based on their individual activeness w.r.t. Q and it is denoted by the factor $l_1(u,v)$ as,

$$l_1(u,v) = \sigma_{(u,\psi_u)} \times \sigma_{(v,\psi_v)}$$

(4)

Next, we want to measure the social link related to Q between u and v in terms of their direct interactions. Factor $l_2(u,v)$ indicates their involvement in direct interactions compare with the most active pair of users in the network.

$$l_2(u,v) = \frac{|\psi_{uv}|}{|Q|} \times \frac{|ACTS(u,v,\psi_{uv})|}{max_{x,y \in U^Q}|ACTS(x,y,\psi_{xy})|}$$

(5)

where $ACTS(u,v,\psi_{uv})$ denotes the set of interaction activities between u and v containing $\psi_{u,v} \subseteq Q$. The interaction activeness between two users should depend on their interaction activities related to Q as well as the number of the query attributes that are covered by those activities. For this reason, we can see in Fig. 1 that although the users B and C have less number of activities between them related to Q compare to the users A and C, but the activities between the users B and C cover more query attributes and hence the factor $l_2(B,C)$ is better than $l_2(A,C)$.

Finally, by employing factors $l_1(u,v)$ and $l_2(u,v)$ together, we obtain a measure that considers both the participations of two users and the direct interactions between them related to Q to assess their overall interaction strength. The measure is formalized as follows.

$$w_{uv} = \alpha \times l_1(u,v) + (1-\alpha) \times l_2(u,v)$$

(6)

where $\alpha \in [0,1]$ is a weighting factor which adjusts the relative importance of the two factors.

Definition 1 (Active Intimate Community (AIC)). *Given an input query Q and an integer k, we generate an weighted graph $G^Q(U^Q, E^Q, W)$ from G, where U^Q is the set of active users, E^Q is the set of active edges between the active users, and W is the set of weights where $w_{uv}(w_{uv} \in [0,1])$ indicates the interaction strength of the edge e_{uv}. Then an active intimate community H_j^k is an induced subgraph that meets the following constraints.*

1. **Connectivity.** $H_j^k \subset G^Q$ is connected;
2. **Structure cohesiveness.** $\forall u \in H_j^k$ has interaction degree of at least k;
3. **Active intimacy.** $\forall e_{uv} \in H_j^k$, the interaction strength of e_{uv} is $w_{uv} \geq \theta$ and $\theta \in [0,1]$ is a threshold.

The key properties that a good active intimate community should have are:

1. Property 1: The more the average interaction strength among the members of H_j^k, the better the community.
2. Property 2: The more query attributes that are covered by the active edges, the better the community as it signifies homogeneity within the community w.r.t. shared query attributes.
3. Property 3: A good community should be structurally more cohesive.

Based on the above properties, we define an intimacy score function denoted as $\lambda(H_j^k, Q)$ for the detected communities that establishes a balance of attribute homogeneity and coverage, interaction strengths between the community members and the structure cohesiveness.

$$\lambda(H_k^j, Q) = \frac{\sum w_{uv}}{|E(H_k^j)|} \times \frac{\eta}{|Q|} \times \frac{|E(H_k^j)|}{|U(H_k^j)|} = \frac{\sum w_{uv} \times \eta}{|Q| \times |U(H_k^j)|}, \quad \text{and} \quad \eta = \sum_{a_i \in Q} \frac{|E_{a_i} \cap E(H_k^j)|}{|E(H_k^j)|} \quad (7)$$

where $E_{a_i} \in E(H_k^j)$ is an edge that overs query attribute $a_i \in Q$. In Eq. 7, η captures the popularity of each query attribute a_i inside the community H_j^k by calculating the fraction of edges of H_j^k that cover a_i. Finally, the factor $\frac{|E(H_j^k)|}{|U(H_j^k)|}$ is used to reward the communities that are structurally more cohesive.

Problem Definition. Given an attributed graph G, an input query Q, and parameters k and r, the problem is to find the top-r active intimate communities with the r highest intimacy scores.

Figure 2(a) shows a social graph G with the core number for each node, e.g., the nodes with 3-core are $\{A, B, C, D\}$. Figure 2(b) shows the active interaction edges for a given query $Q = \{a_1, a_2\}$.

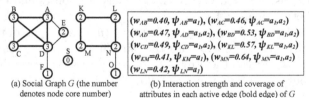

(a) Social Graph G (the number denotes node core number)   (b) Interaction strength and coverage of attributes in each active edge (bold edge) of G

Fig. 2. A graph G with active interaction edges

Suppose we want to find the active intimate communities for $k = 2$ and $\theta = 0.4$. We get $H_1^k = \{A, B, C, D\}$ and $H_2^k = \{K, L, M, N\}$. We see that the query attribute a_1 is covered by all the active edges in both H_1^k and H_2^k, while a_2 is covered by 4 active edges in H_1^k and 2 active edges in H_2^k. So the intimacy score of H_1^k is $\lambda(H_1^k, Q) = \frac{2.35}{5} \times \frac{(1+0.8)}{2} \times \frac{5}{4}$ $= 0.53$ and of H_2^k is $\lambda(H_2^k, Q) = \frac{2.04}{4} \times \frac{(1+0.5)}{2} \times \frac{4}{4} = 0.38$. Although the average interaction strength (0.47) of H_1^k is lower than the average interaction strength (0.51) of H_2^k, but H_1^k is structurally more cohesive and the query attributes are more popular than H_2^k, hence H_1^k has better intimacy score.

4   AIC Detection Algorithm

To efficiently discover AIC, we adjusted an indexing mechanism with slight modification called `CL-tree` (Core Label tree) [9], which organizes the k-cores into a tree structure.

4.1   Index Overview

The CL-tree index is built based on the observations that cores are nested, i.e., a $(k + 1)$ core must be contained in a k-core. A subgraph containing nodes with a minimum degree of $(k + 1)$ already satisfy the condition of a minimum degree of k. Therefore after computing the k-core of G, we assign each connected components induced by k-core as a child node of a tree. Each node in the tree contains four elements: (i) *coreNum:* the core number of the k-core, (ii) *nodeSet:* set of graph nodes, (iii) *invertedList:* a list of $<key, value>$ pairs, where the *key* is an attribute contained by the nodes in *nodeSet* and the *value* is the list of nodes in *nodeSet* containing *key*. In our proposed work, for each node, we add the number of activities related to *key*, and (iv) *childList:* a list of child nodes.

Using the tree structure, for a given k and input query Q, it is very efficient to find all the nodes having activeness related to Q and a core of at least k by traversing the CL-tree.

4.2   Index-Based Algorithm

In `AIC-Index` (shown in Algorithm 1), we first find the set of active nodes U^Q from G and then compute the induced graph G^Q formed by U^Q (lines 1–2). Next, we identify the maximal k-core of $C^k(G^Q)$ from the induced graph G^Q (line 3). Then, we iteratively invoke the following procedure to compute the connected active inti-

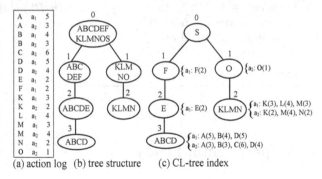

(a) action log   (b) tree structure   (c) CL-tree index

Fig. 3. CL-tree index for the graph in Fig. 2

mate k-core communities. We remove the inactive edges (whose $w_{uv} < \theta$) from each connected component H_j^k of $C_k(G)$ (lines 5–7). Removal of an edge e_{uv} decreases the degree of the end points (u and v) of e_{uv} by 1 which may result into violation of the cohesiveness constraint by either u or v or both. Removal of a node u requires to recursively delete all the nodes that violate the cohesiveness constraint using DFS procedure (lines 14–19). This is because the degree of u's neighbor nodes decrease by 1 due to the removal of the node u which may lead to the violation of structure cohesiveness constraint by some of u's neighbors.

Due to this, they cannot be included in the subsequent communities, and thereby we need to delete them. Similarly, we also need to verify the other hops (e.g., 2-hop, 3-hop, etc.) neighbors that they satisfy the cohesiveness constraint. Finally, it outputs the top-r active connected intimate communities from $C^k(G^Q)$ (line 13).

Algorithm 1. AIC-Index

Input: $G = (U, E, \mathcal{A}), Q, \alpha, \beta, \gamma, \theta, k, r$
Output: Top-r active intimate communities
1: Find the set of active users U^Q
2: compute the induced graph G^Q on U^Q
3: compute the k-core $C^k(G^Q)$ on G^Q
4: **for** each k-core component H_j^k from $C^K(G^Q)$ **do**
5:    **for** each edge $e_{uv} \in H_j^k$ **do**
6:       **if** $w_{uv} < \theta$ **then**
7:          remove edge e_{uv}
8:          **if** $deg_{H_j^k}(u) < k$ **then**
9:             DFS(u)
10:          **if** v exists and $deg_{H_j^k}(v) < k$ **then**
11:             DFS(v)
12:    Maintain H_j^k as k-core connected and compute $\lambda(H_j^k, Q)$
13: Output the top-r active connected components from $C^k(G^Q)$
14: **Procedure** DFS(u)
15: **for** each $v \in N(u, H_j^k)$ **do** $\triangleright$ $N(u, H_j^k)$ is the list of u's neighborhood
16:    remove edge e_{uv} from H_j^k
17:    **if** $deg_{H_j^k}(v) < k$ **then**
18:       DFS(v)
19: remove node u from H_j^k

---

5   Experimental Study

In this section, we evaluate the performance of our algorithm on three real graph datasets. All experiments are performed on an Intel(R) Core(TM) i7-4500U 2.4 GHz Windows 7 PC with 16 GB RAM.

5.1   Experimental Datasets

DBLP Dataset. We use the DBLP[1] Bibliography data which contains papers from data mining conferences like KDD, SDM, ICDM, WSDM and PKDD which we consider as node attributes. This dataset is a network of 6,282 authors with

---

[1] https://aminer.org/topic_paper_author.

22,862 co-author relationships between these authors. In DBLP, authors express their activeness by publishing research papers and the co-authored information is considered as interaction between the authors.

Twitter Datasets. We conduct our experiments on two Twitter datasets: a small dataset CRAWL [11] and a very large dataset SNAP[2]. We consider different topics as node attributes and choose different hashtags that represent those topics. CRAWL contains 9,468 users, 2.5 million follower links and 14.5 million tweets. In the CRAWL dataset, we choose the topics of *politics* (#Obama, #election2012 etc.), *entertainment* (#nowplaying, #itunes etc.), *social media* (#fb, #tcot etc.) and *business and marketing* (#tax, #budget etc.) for the experiments. In the SNAP dataset, we randomly choose 1,00,000 users who have 3,938,007 connections between them. We consider users' tweets from June 11, 2009 to July 12, 2009. We choose the topics of *election in Iran* (#Iranelection, #helpiranelection etc.), *Follow Friday*[3](#FollowFriday, #FFD etc.), the death of pop star *Michael Jackson* (#MichaelJackson, #thankyouMJ etc.), and *social media* in SNAP. A user in Twitter interacts with others in the form of replies, mentions and retweets.

5.2   Comparison Methods and Evaluation

We compare our AIC-Index algorithm with three other methods. We select Highly Interactive Community Detection (HICD) method [8] based on users' interaction frequencies with their following links of celebrities of particular interest category. We also select iTop [3] which detects topic-centric communities by first selecting a set of seed users who are identified based on a textual search of their Twitter user profile biography. Then it iterates two steps - (i) expanding the set of seed users by measuring the degree of interactions of each seed user with k other connected users in the network and then (ii) greedily maximize local modularity by filtering weak links from the previous step. Finally, we modified our proposed algorithm by considering only the users' activeness while forming the communities known as k-core *active* community (k-core-AC).

5.3   Efficiency

Figure 4 shows the running time at different values of k. Observe that iTop requires more time compare to the other methods as it needs to recursively perform several steps in order to maximize local modularity. HICD also takes more time as it requires to perform the Clique Percolation Method (CPM) on the network generated by the set of celebrities and their followers. The computation time for both HICD and iTop depend on the size of G as we see that they take more time for large SNAP dataset. A lower k renders more subgraphs, due to which it takes more computation time for all the methods. k-core-AC ignores

---

[2] http://snap.stanford.edu/data/twitter7.html.
[3] A tradition in which the users can recommend their followers to follow more people.

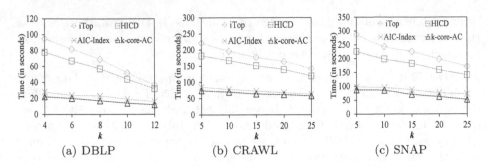

Fig. 4. Run-time for different values of k ($r = 5, \theta = 0.5, \alpha = 0.5, \gamma = 5, \beta = 5$)

interactions between the nodes, hence it requires less computation time compare with `AIC-Index`. But we will see later that the quality of the communities detected by `AIC-Index` method are better the ones in `k-core-AC`.

5.4   Community Quality Evaluation

We vary the length of the Q to $|Q| = 2, 3, 4$ and use three measures of density, entropy and average intimacy score to evaluate the quality of the top-r communities generated by different methods. The definition of density and entropy are as follows.

$$density(\{H_j^k\}_{j=1}^r) = \sum_{j}^{r} \frac{|\{(u,v)|u, v \in H_j^k, (u,v) \in E\}|}{|E|}$$

Density measures the compactness of the communities in structure.

$$entropy(\{H_j^k\}_{j=1}^r) = \sum_{j}^{r} \frac{|U(H_j^k)|}{|U|} entropy(H_j^k), \quad \text{where} \quad entropy(H_j^k) = -\sum_{i=1}^{n} p_{ij} log_2 p_{ij}$$

and p_{ij} is the percentage of nodes in community H_j^k which are active on the query attribute a_i. $entropy(\{H_j^k\}_{j=1}^r)$ measures the weighted entropy considering all the query attributes over top-r communities. Entropy indicates the randomness of attributes in communities. Generally, a good community should have high density, low entropy and high intimacy score.

Figure 5(a) shows the density comparison between the four methods on DBLP dataset. We set $k = 5$ for DBLP because it has many small-sized research groups. Both `AIC-Index` and `k-core-AC` have the same communities initially by considering only the users' activeness. But the size of the community decreases afterward in `AIC-Index` due to the removal of inactive edges, hence it has lower density value compare with `k-core-AC`. The increase rate of density value by `iTop` method is not as good as `AIC-Index` and `k-core-AC` because it does not focus on the interactions between the non-seed users. Similarly, `HICD` achieves poor density values because it requires connection between normal users to the

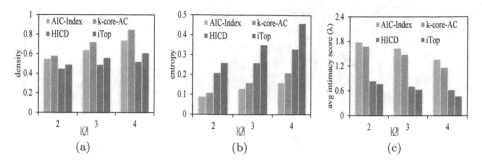

Fig. 5. Performance comparison on DBLP dataset: (a) density, (b) entropy, (c) avg. intimacy score ($k = 5, r = 5, \theta = 0.5, \alpha = 0.5, \gamma = 5, \beta = 5$)

celebrities, i.e., high profile researchers in this case. We find that not many authors have connections with high profile researchers which effect the performance of HICD method. We also see that the density values of all the methods are higher as $|Q|$ goes high. The reason is that the number of users having activeness in one or more query attributes increases as $|Q|$ increases, resulting large and more densely connected communities.

Figure 5(b) shows the entropy comparison between the four methods. Both AIC-Index and k-core-AC take into account the relevance (activeness) of the users w.r.t. the query attributes while forming a community. As a result, we see that both methods achieve better performance in the aspect of the entropy. As the size of the communities are smaller in AIC-Index compare with k-core-AC, so it has better percentage of users related to the query attributes resulting better entropy value. On the other hand, HICD achieves higher entropy value because many connected normal users do not have interest in all the common research topics. iTop also achieves higher entropy value because it does not focus on attribute wise interactions between the seed users and their followers.

AIC-Index method achieves better intimacy score compare with k-core-AC as shown in Fig. 5(c), because it has better interaction strength among the members as well as better coverage of the query attributes inside the communities due to the removal of inactive edges. The average intimacy score in iTop is lower even for higher values of $|Q|$ because most of the users within a community have no or very low interactions related to Q. The average intimacy score in HICD method is not remarkable because most of the normal users do not have strong interactions with each other and the popularity of the query attributes inside the communities are not as good as AIC-Index and k-core-AC.

Figure 6(a) shows the comparison of density value on CRAWL dataset. The network of CRAWL is very densely connected compare with the other datasets. As a result, the impact of removing inactive users/edges usually have not much effect in AIC-Index and in k-core-AC. So both methods have larger and denser collaboration structure among the members in the communities resulting better density values. For the same reason, as shown in Fig. 6(b), the entropy values by

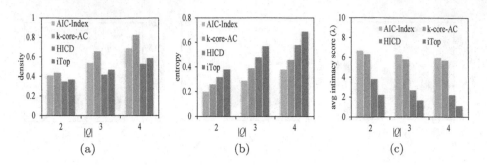

Fig. 6. Performance comparison on CRAWL dataset: (a) density, (b) entropy, (c) avg. intimacy score ($k = 15, r = 10, \theta = 0.5, \alpha = 0.5, \gamma = 40, \beta = 15$)

both methods are higher for higher values of $|Q|$ because not all the community members have active participation in all the query attributes. In case of `HICD` method, it is difficult to have large number of normal users having connection with all the high profile users. Furthermore, `HICD` merely focuses on users' association with the query attributes while forming a community. So there are many users in each community who have no interest towards the given query. This causes the entropy value by `HICD` to go high for higher values of $|Q|$. Again, the normal users have very weak interaction between them resulting poor intimacy score as shown in Fig. 6(c). The entropy and intimacy score of `iTop` are very poor due to the ignorance of attribute wise interactions. On the other hand, the community members in `AIC-Index` have very strong interactions with others as well as better coverage of the query attributes compare with `k-core-AC`, hence it has better intimacy score.

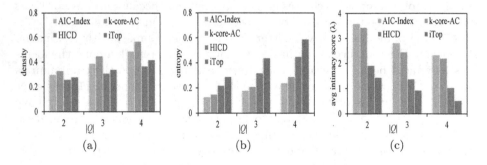

Fig. 7. Performance comparison on SNAP dataset: (a) density, (b) entropy, (c) avg. intimacy score ($k = 10, r = 10, \theta = 0.5, \alpha = 0.5, \gamma = 25, \beta = 10$)

In Fig. 7(a), we see that the density values by all the methods in SNAP dataset (our version) are lower compare with the other datasets as the network of SNAP is very sparse in structure. So presence of an inactive node/edge results a deletion of many nodes in `AIC-Index` and k-`core-AC`. As a result, the communities generated by both methods are not that much large and dense compare with the ones in CRAWL. For both `HICD` and `iTop` methods, there are no significant increases in the number of normal users for higher values of $|Q|$ resulting poor density values. We see in Fig. 7(b) that the entropy values by all the methods are better in SNAP compare with CRAWL because we have smaller communities which have better percentage of community members having association with the query attributes. As shown in Fig. 7(c), `AIC-Index` achieves better intimacy score since it takes into account the attribute similarity during the interactions between the community members. The intimacy score of `iTop` is very low as the users within the communities have poor attribute wise interactions. `HICD` method also has lower intimacy score because it has very weak interactions between the community members and also have low coverage of the query attributes.

5.5 Value of α for Different Networks

We vary α to tune our proposed method in different datasets to achieve higher intimacy scores for the detected communities, which in turn means good quality communities. For networks which have more one-to-one interactions within the community, the algorithm achieves better λ values for lower values of α. DBLP network (Fig. 8(a)) can be considered in this regard. Whereas, for sparse network like SNAP version in our experiment, the system achieves higher λ values for higher values of α (Fig. 8(c)). For network like CRAWL which has dense connections and also the users have balanced individual activities and interactions with others, we achieve the highest λ value when α is near 0.5 (Fig. 8(b)).

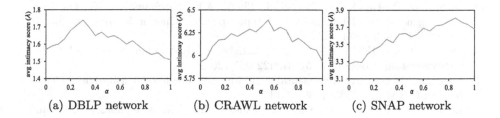

(a) DBLP network   (b) CRAWL network   (c) SNAP network

Fig. 8. α vs λ for different networks

6 Conclusion

In this paper, we studied the problem of discovering active intimate communities in OSNs. Our observation is that the users' individual activeness and interactions with others vary widely for different attributes. We designed an intimacy score function for the detected communities and developed an index-based method to discover the communities in an efficient manner. Extensive experiments on real data sets demonstrated the effectiveness of our proposed method.

Acknowledgment. This work is supported by the ARC Discovery Projects DP160102412 and DP170104747.

References

1. Weng, W., Zhu, S., Xu, H.: Hierarchical community detection algorithm based on local similarity. J. Digit. Inf. Manag. **12**(4), 274–280 (2014)
2. Sun, X., Wang, H., Li, J., Zhang, Y.: Injecting purpose and trust into data anonymisation. Comput. Secur. **30**(5), 332–345 (2011)
3. Correa, D., Sureka, A., Pundir, M.: iTop - interaction based topic centric community discovery on Twitter. In: PIKM, pp. 51–58 (2012)
4. Chen, J., Saad, Y.: Dense subgraph extraction with application to community detection. TKDE **24**(7), 1216–1230 (2012)
5. Li, J., Sellis, T., Culpepper, J.S., He, Z., Liu, C., Wang, J.: Geo-social influence spanning maximization. TKDE **29**(8), 1653–1666 (2017)
6. Dev, H., Ali, M.E., Hashem, T.: User interaction based community detection in online social networks. In: Bhowmick, S.S., Dyreson, C.E., Jensen, C.S., Lee, M.L., Muliantara, A., Thalheim, B. (eds.) DASFAA 2014. LNCS, vol. 8422, pp. 296–310. Springer, Cham (2014). https://doi.org/10.1007/978-3-319-05813-9_20
7. Zhang, J., Tao, X., Wang, H.: Outlier detection from large distributed databases. WWW **17**(4), 539–568 (2014)
8. Lim, K.H., Datta, A.: An interaction-based approach to detecting highly interactive Twitter communities using tweeting links. In: Web Intelligence, pp. 1–15 (2016)
9. Fang, Y., Cheng, R., Luo, S., Hu, J.: Effective community search for large attributed graphs. VLDB **9**, 1233–1244 (2016)
10. Li, J., Liu, C., Yu, J.X., Chen, Y., Sellis, T., Culpepper, J.S.: Personalized influential topic search via social network summarization. TKDE **28**(7), 1820–1834 (2016)
11. Bogdanov, P., Busch, M., Moehli, J., Singh, A.K., Szymanski, B.K.: The social media genome: modeling individual topic-specific behavior in social media. In: ASONAM, pp. 236–242 (2013)
12. Sun, X., Wang, H., Li, J., Zhang, Y.: Satisfying privacy requirements before data anonymization. Comput. J. **55**(4), 422–437 (2012)
13. Singh, S., Awekar, A.: Incremental shared nearest neighbor density-based clustering. In: CIKM, pp. 1533–1536 (2013)
14. Li, J., Wang, X., Deng, K., Yang, X., Sellis, T., Yu, J.X.: Most influential community search over large social networks. In: ICDE, pp. 871–882 (2017)

Customer Churn Prediction in Superannuation: A Sequential Pattern Mining Approach

Ben Culbert[1], Bin Fu[2], James Brownlow[2], Charles Chu[2], Qinxue Meng[2], and Guandong Xu[1(✉)]

[1] Advanced Analytics Institute, University of Technology, Sydney, Australia
Ben.Culbert@student.uts.edu.au, Guandong.Xu@uts.edu.au
[2] Colonial First State, Sydney, Australia
{Bin.Fu,James.Brownlow,Charles.Chu,
Qinxue.Meng}@cba.com.au

Abstract. The role of churn modelling is to maximize the value of marketing dollars spent and minimize the attrition of valuable customers. Though churn prediction is a common classification task, traditional approaches cannot be employed directly due to the unique issues inherent within the wealth management industry. Through this paper we address the issue of unseen churn in superannuation; whereby customer accounts become dormant following the discontinuation of compulsory employer contributions, and suggest solutions to the problem of scarce customer engagement data. To address these issues, this paper proposes a new approach for churn prediction and its application in the superannuation industry. We use the extreme gradient boosting algorithm coupled with contrast sequential pattern mining to extract behaviors preceding a churn event. The results demonstrate a significant lift in the performance of prediction models when pattern features are used in combination with demographic and account features.

Keywords: Churn prediction · Superannuation · Sequential patterns

1 Introduction

Churn modelling is one of the most common applications for machine learning in industry and forms a key component of any effective customer relationship management framework [4]. Due to intense competition and the high costs associated with new customer acquisition, many businesses are looking to machine learning to guide customer retention strategy [2, 5, 11]. While there is no commonly accepted definition for customer churn it is generally understood as the termination of a financial relationship between a customer and a business [2]. Churn prediction refers to the statistical and computational processes used to derive expectations from historical customer data about the state of a customer relationship at a specified time in the future. Churn prediction is an important part of customer relationship management since it allows businesses to prioritize relationships and marketing spend to entice the most risky customers to stay with their brand or service [3].

In the past, customer retention programs utilized by the superannuation industry have relied heavily on descriptive statistics and domain knowledge. Historical attrition

© Springer International Publishing AG, part of Springer Nature 2018
J. Wang et al. (Eds.): ADC 2018, LNCS 10837, pp. 123–134, 2018.
https://doi.org/10.1007/978-3-319-92013-9_10

rates are used to guide decision making with respect to customer campaigning and relationship management. Customer segment groups with higher than system attrition are identified as *at-risk* and subsequently engaged through customer campaigning. Prioritization of customer relationships is ineffective in driving positive return on investment for marketing spend and there is limited evidence to suggest that advanced approaches to data mining have been utilized effectively to drive business benefits.

The Australian superannuation industry represents a unique set of challenges and opportunities for customer churn prediction. Research indicates that few Australians have an adequate understanding of the basic principles of superannuation [15]. Despite this, the majority of the nation's current and retired workforce hold superannuation as their most valuable asset, second only to the family home. This paradigm, whereby participants in the system have a limited knowledge of how it works, has come about due to the obligatory participation in superannuation through compulsory employer contributions. As a result, legislation has evolved to allow apathetic customers to defer by default the decision making process for their superannuation up until retirement [16]. This means that customer engagement data is scarce, and represents a substantial challenge to super funds looking to understand their customers through customer engagement data.

The tendency for Australians to default to employer funds means that many accrue multiple super accounts during their working lives. This proliferation of apathy has seen the balance of lost super funds climb to $8.45bn and 496k accounts nationally [1]. The result is two-fold, while customer churn is high (as represented by Fig. 1) industry data indicates that a proportion of open accounts are dormant and will inevitably become *lost*. These accounts represent unseen churn and are not captured using conventional approaches.

Due to the heavily mandated nature of superannuation, employers are compelled to make compulsory super guarantee (SG) contributions on a regular basis. The regularity of SG contributions means that they are highly predictable, and follow strongly time dependent patterns. Figure 2 below depicts this time dependency and illustrates that spikes occur at 7, 14, 28 and 30 days, corresponding with weekly and monthly patterns.

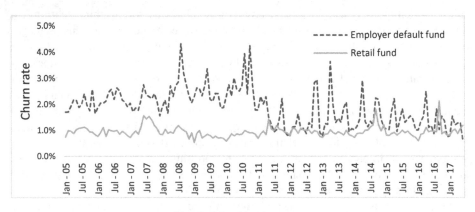

Fig. 1. Monthly churn rate

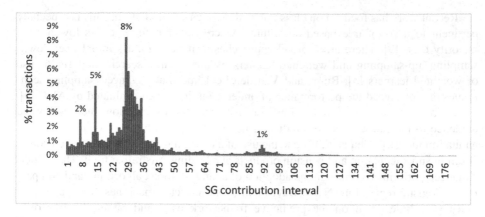

Fig. 2. Super guarantee contribution interval

Through this paper we find that the existing approach to customer retention and churn prediction in unable to appropriately address the challenges (scarce engagement data and unseen churn) and opportunities (predictable contribution patterns) for the superannuation industry. We propose a solution using machine learning which adopts a definition for customer churn which addresses the issue of unseen churn. We build intermediary features at scale to uncover previously hidden customer engagement data. Finally we use an advanced pattern mining technique to discover predictable contribution patterns. Through this research we demonstrate how churn prediction can be enhanced through the application of advanced pattern mining techniques.

The remainder of this paper is organized as follows. Section 2 reviews relevant and related work. Section 3 discusses the problem statement. In Sect. 4 we describe the predictive framework. Section 5 provides an overview and discussion of the results, and Sect. 6 concludes.

2 Related Work

2.1 Customer Churn Prediction

There is a substantial body of research for churn prediction. Examples of customer churn prediction are common in industries such as telecommunications [6, 10], multimedia [7, 8] and retail banking [2, 5]. Past research has focused primarily on issues and developments in the area of machine learning algorithms [2, 7–10], sampling techniques [9–11] and feature engineering [4, 5].

Research highlights a great diversity of machine learning algorithms for churn prediction. Among these, random forests, support vector machines, neural networks, logistic regression and decision trees feature most prominently [6, 11]. A long history of customer churn prediction has seen substantial advancement against classical approaches such as RFM indexes (recency, frequency, monetary value) [4]. While there is some disagreement around which machine learning algorithms are superior, recent work indicates that the random forest algorithm provides the best results [6, 8].

Recent work has focused on class imbalance for churn prediction. This is especially pertinent to users of tree based algorithms, where research finds a bias towards the majority class [9]. There are 3 broad approaches to handling class imbalance; downsampling, up-sampling and weighted learners. While recent research supports the use of weighted learners [6], Burez and Van den Poel find that advanced sampling techniques do not exceed the performance of under-sampling when evaluated by AUC [9].

Despite a diversity of applications for customer churn prediction, there is limited evidence to indicate that churn prediction has been used within the Australian superannuation industry. Chu et al. [3] cite the use of a random forest algorithm for customer churn in superannuation and pension products at a leading Australian fund. They report enhanced performance through the adoption of a random forest algorithm, and compare this to logistic regression, Naïve Bayes and support vector machines. The paper provides very little detail on the predictive framework used and rather, focuses on a business integration problem for predictive analytics. To our knowledge, this paper is the first to deeply articulate a predictive modelling framework for customer churn in the Australian superannuation industry.

2.2 Contrast Sequential Pattern Mining

Contrast sequential pattern mining is useful for predicting patterns in ordered events while contrasting against multiple classes [12]. While sequential pattern mining is shown to be effective for prediction it is unable to solve for a classification problem.

CSP is a variation of sequential pattern mining. Where sequential pattern mining builds evaluation metrics (support and confidence) against an itemset [13], CSP does so independently for positive and negative classes [12]. CSP is therefore complementary to classification problems.

3   Problem Statement

This paper presents a special case of churn prediction for a leading Australian superannuation fund.

For many Australians, superannuation exists solely as a vehicle for the accumulation of employer super guarantee contributions. While the cessation of super guarantee is often a precursor to a churn event, empirical evidence suggests that many accounts remain open and inactive for extended periods of time following a final employer contribution (Fig. 3 illustrates this point, where 49% of accounts remain open after 12 months of inactivity). Often, by the time there is sufficient evidence to predict a likely account closure the customer relationship has already ended. As a result, traditional churn prediction has limited effectiveness in making timely and actionable predictions for customer churn management.

To address this issue we build a prediction model for super guarantee attrition. In our approach we expose patterns in employer contributions and surface evidence for attrition through the behaviors of investors and their financial advisers. By predicting the cessation of an ongoing employer contribution stream we find that prediction outcomes are timely, relevant and actionable. The model presented in this paper

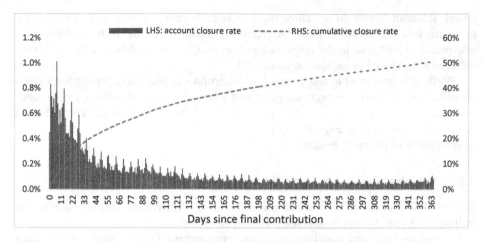

Fig. 3. Account churn by days since last contribution

recognizes contributions as they arrive and, based on a number of factors, predicts the likelihood that it will be the member's last contribution. If the evidence for super guarantee attrition is compelling, the business is able to take immediate action to retain the customer.

A binary label variable is built using a 6 months observation window. Where an account has not received a super guarantee contribution within the observation window it is deemed to have lapsed and the label variable is given a value of 1. Alternatively, super guarantee is ongoing and the label variable receives a value of 0.

4   Prediction Framework

Churn prediction models were developed using multiple algorithms and trained on 447 features and one binary label variable. The training data is built on 284,762 retail, employer default and employer retained superannuation accounts. Only accounts which have recently received (within 6 months) a super guarantee contribution are included in the final training data set. The prediction outcome provides a measure of probability for an account not receiving an SG contribution in the following 6 months.

4.1   Classifier

Multiple classification algorithms are used for comparison – a decision tree, random forest [17] and extreme gradient boosting (XGBoost) [20]. All models share their tree based structure however each has unique merits. A decision tree is a simple model and allows for the extraction of business rules. Decision trees are however at risk of overfitting without appropriate testing and pruning against a test dataset. Random forests on the other hand do generalize well as an outcome of the bagging function. Furthermore, the use of the random forest algorithm is supported by research [6, 18, 19] where it is demonstrated to perform marginally better by AUC than other classifiers tested. Random forests do not allow users to visually review the decision tree and are therefore less interpretable. Extreme gradient boosting also suffers from diminished interpretability relative to the decision tree however has been shown to perform very well for a variety of classification tasks [20].

While it is important to test a variety of algorithms to maximize results for a given classification problem research suggests that many common classifiers can achieve comparable performance, and that gains in predictive performance are achieved through superior feature engineering [6]. As a result, the focus of this research is the development of meaning features.

4.2 Designing Static and Sequential Features

In total, 447 demographic, financial, transactional and behavioral features are built for training and used for super guarantee churn prediction.

The aforementioned scarcity of customer engagement data represents a significant challenge to wealth management businesses looking to better understand their customers through engagement data. The highly intermediated nature of superannuation in Australia however represents a substantial opportunity to combat this shortage of customer data. Intermediaries, including financial advisers, licensees and employers, all play a role in managing customer accounts. The interactions these agents have with a super fund can be very insightful in understanding a customer. Once aggregated at the intermediary level, these features can expose trends in customer behavior and intermediary policy.

The following feature groups are representative of the training set

1. **Customer.** Customer features include demographic variables such as age, gender, race, marital status and socio-economic segment.
2. **Intermediary.** Intermediary variables include interactions data for agents and aggregated customer and account variables. These variables serve to provide insight into trends at the agent level and expose agent initiated churn.
3. **Account.** Account level features include variables around product, investment and asset class selection, valuation and insurance. Account features are enriched with data around additional financial holdings such as home loans, credit cards and savings accounts.
4. **Engagement.** Engagement data comes from multiple CRM systems and databases. Engagement features include information around contact center enquires and online banking activities.
5. **Financial.** Financial features include all transactional level variables. Examples of financial features include asset switching, withdrawals, contributions, fees, premiums and derived features from this data. Numerous features were created to expose contribution patterns within member accounts and generate flags where those patterns are violated.
6. **Sequential patterns.** Strings of sequential patterns bringing together financial and engagement data were created and captured all interactions for a 6 months period. Sequential pattern features include all active and passive customer and account events. We used an implementation of contrast sequential pattern mining as described by Zheng et al. [12] and applied a cut-off contrast rate of 2 (Fig. 4).

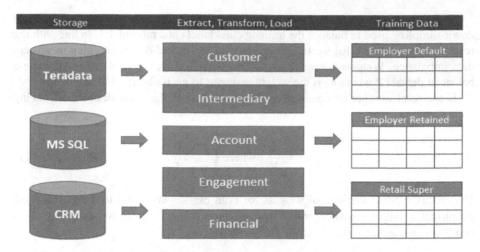

Fig. 4. Data processing flow

5 Results and Discussion

5.1 Data Collection

Final data cleansing and segmentation was carried out to improve model performance and avoid erroneous results.

Missing observations were imputed with appropriate values. For missing character variables a value of *NULL* replaced blank cells. Missing dates and timespans were given a date of *01/01/9999*. This ensures that the results for these observations are distinctly different while allowing derived variables to continue functioning. Missing numerical variables were given a value of *0*.

The imputed data table was split by product group; Employer Default, Employer Retained and Retail Super. Employer Default accounts are originated by a business who own an employer plan. They are the default option for employees who choose not to exercise super choice. Employer Retained accounts are those which have previously been associated with an employer default account and have since stopped working with the employer. When this relationship ends the members account is migrated to an employer retained account, and the employer no longer has administrative privileges over the account. The final product group, Retail Super, is open to the public and is commonly originated by a customer in consultation with a financial adviser. Since retail super accounts are most often opened as part of a financial advice strategy, they represent the lowest level of churn risk. The segmentation of data by product group is necessary to address a practical consideration for machine learning. Employer features are not applicable to the retail customer base and as such, it makes sense to separate datasets with distinctly different features. Further, due to the nature of the employer retained product, these members represent a distinctly different customer base and are modelled as such.

The resulting three datasets are partitioned at a ratio 80:20 training to test data and down-sampling used to balance the training class labels at a ratio of 1:1. In line with the results of Huang et al. [6] we tested weighted instance and down-sampling to address data imbalance. Weights for weighted instance method were calculated to generate a balanced dataset P where w_i is the weight assigned to each observation and $\sum w_i = 1$. N_i is the total number of observations by class, and is the class designation, taking values of 0 or 1.

$$w_i = \frac{1}{N_i}, \text{ where } \begin{cases} i = 0 \\ i = 1 \end{cases} \tag{1}$$

Under this method the sum of weights for both classes are equal to 1 and balanced. Empirical results showed improved performance when using down-sampling. As a result down-sampling was used for class imbalance.

5.2   Evaluation Metrics

Model performance is measured against evaluation metrics recall and AUC. Total recall at the top 20% is used to describe the lift the model generates and is useful in a business setting as it describes the allocative efficiency expected from a given intervention. The definition for recall is below, where R is recall and TP is the number of true positives, given a threshold t. We use $t = 20\%$.

$$R_t = \frac{\sum TP_t}{\sum TP} \tag{2}$$

Area Under the Curve (AUC) is also used to describe the overall performance of the model. AUC is a useful evaluation metric as it reports performance independent of a cut-off value for classification and is not influenced scaling of the class label [13]. AUC is therefore a less biased measure. AUC is defined below where i relates to all data points for m when the churn label is 1 and j relates to all data points for n with churn label 0. p_i and p_j are probabilities assigned to each class and **1** is an indicator function, which is true where the condition $p_i > p_j$ is satisfied.

$$AUC = \frac{1}{mn} \sum_{i=1}^{m} \sum_{j=1}^{n} \mathbf{1} p_i > p_j \tag{3}$$

For benchmarking, a logistic regression is included. In a business setting, interpretability of models is important and findings around the magnitude and direction of influence of features with respect to a label variable are an important input to the development of an effective customer relationship management solution. Improved performance against the logistic regression represents added value from the superior algorithm and is weighed against the cost of diminished interpretability. A decision tree, random forest and gradient boosting (XGBoost) algorithm are used for comparison.

5.3   Prediction Performance

The results (Table 1) show XGBoost performed strongly against all other methods and overall high predictive performance on the test dataset. Results show that XGBoost outperformed other algorithms by recall, and outperformed by AUC for the employer default and retail super models.

Recall at 20% for the three models; Employer Default, Employer Retained and Retail Super is 86.9%, 71.6% and 80.6% respectively. This indicates that 86.9%, 71.6% and 80.6% of all positive cases are captured within the top 20% of predictions. With recall we can calculate model lift, which represents the improved efficiency against random guess. Model lift for the three models 4.4, 3.6 and 4.0. This means that by selecting the top 20% of predictions we identify 4.4 times more churners than we would by random guess.

We find that the XGBoost algorithm consistently outperforms logistic regression and note limitations of the logistic regression. A logistic regression can only model linear relationships between dependent and independent variables. Tree based algorithms however can model more complex relationships and rules perpendicular to the solution space. As a result, it is evident that logistic regression cannot adequately model the complex relationships between churn and financial data. Furthermore, gradient boosting consistently outperforms decision tree and random forest models by recall in our experiment. Despite marginally higher performance by AUC for the random forest employer retained model we identify gradient boosting as the superior algorithm in all cases. From a practical perspective, recall is a more important statistic for our purposes. The ability to speak to more churners in a smaller sample equates to lower marketing costs and higher retention.

Table 1. Model performance

Model	Classifier	AUC	Gini	Recall@20%
Employer default	Logistic regression	0.9243	0.8486	81.30%
	Decision tree	0.9265	0.8529	81.73%
	Random forest	0.9393	0.8786	85.00%
	XGBoost	0.9473	0.8945	86.90%
Employer retained	Logistic regression	0.9143	0.8286	68.50%
	Decision tree	0.9163	0.8326	69.54%
	Random forest	0.9232	0.8464	70.10%
	XGBoost	0.9173	0.8345	71.60%
Retail super	Logistic regression	0.8874	0.7748	77.40%
	Decision tree	0.8931	0.7861	78.25%
	Random forest	0.9044	0.8088	80.50%
	XGBoost	0.9090	0.8180	80.60%

To objectively assess the impact of pattern features we retrain gradient boosting models with pattern features omitted and report AUC. Results for sequential pattern mining demonstrate the substantial impact pattern features have on model results. The results below (Table 2) show that Employer Default model experiences an absolute percentage change in AUC of −9.6% when pattern features are omitted. The Employer Retained model changes by −13.8% and the Retail Super model by −21.8%.

Table 2. Sequential pattern results

Model	Classifier	AUC	Gini	Recall@20%
Employer default	XGBoost ex. Pattern Features	0.914	0.828	78.53%
	XGBoost	0.947	0.895	86.90%
Employer retained	XGBoost ex. Pattern Features	0.869	0.739	61.69%
	XGBoost	0.917	0.835	71.60%
Retail super	XGBoost ex. Pattern Features	0.827	0.654	63.02%
	XGBoost	0.909	0.818	80.60%

Contrast sequential pattern mining provides several interesting customer insights. On average, we find that a lack of activity provides the most compelling evidence for SG churn. In rare cases however we find strings of events which are highly predictive for SG churn. Events such as customer contact center enquiries, adviser change, change of address, and logins to the secure online portal are highly indicative of SG churn.

5.4 Analysis of Feature Importance

Variable importance reports provide insight into the impact of model features. Table 3 below reports the top 10 features by Gini reduction and highlights the importance of features representing contribution timing, customer engagement, sequential patterns and intermediary.

Table 3. Variable importance by Gini reduction – top 10

	Employer default	Employer retained	Retail super
1	sg_last_interval	sg_flags	sg_total_amount
2	sg_flags	sg_last_interval	sg_last_interval
3	Age	sg_times	sg_flags
4	balance_change_ratio_6_month	call_flags	sg_median_interval
5	sg_max_interval	days_no_sg	open_days
6	days_no_sg	sg_median_interval	sg_times
7	employer_median_interval_last	balance_change_ratio_6_month	balance_change_ratio_6_month
8	sg_times	balance_change_6_month	balance_change_6_month
9	open_days	sg_total_amount	cba_wealth_band
10	sg_median_interval	call_times	balance

6   Conclusion

This paper presents a real world application of churn prediction in a leading Australian superannuation fund. With an understanding of the superannuation industry and its participants, we recognize several unique challenges to the industry. We identify issues related to unseen churn and scarce customer engagement data. To address the issue of unseen churn we focus on the underlying driver for account churn and design a label variable for this, super guarantee churn. To address the scarcity of customer engagement data, we build intermediary features to capture interactions from administrative agents of superannuation accounts. Through our modelling results we find the XG Boost algorithm with under-sampling is superior to other techniques tested. Variable importance reports indicate that intermediary, pattern and time dependent features make a significant contribution to the predictive performance of our models. Side by side models with and without pattern features objectively demonstrate the substantial impact these features have on model performance.

To our knowledge this is the first paper to comprehensively detail the implementation of a customer churn prediction framework for a leading Australian superannuation fund. Future work will focus on evaluating the effectiveness of super guarantee churn in delivering timely and relevant predictions in contrast to account churn prediction.

References

1. Australian Prudential Regulation Authority. In: Annual Superannuation Bulletin (2016)
2. Popović, D., Bašić, B.D.: Churn prediction model in retail banking using fuzzy C-means algorithm. Informatica 33(2) (2009)
3. Chu, C., Xu, G., Brownlow, J., Fu, B.: Deployment of churn prediction model in financial services industry. In: 2016 International Conference on Behavioral, Economic and Socio-Cultural Computing (BESC), pp. 1–2. IEEE (2016)
4. Ballings, M., Van den Poel, D.: Customer event history for churn prediction: how long is long enough? Expert Syst. Appl. 39(18), 13517–13522 (2012)
5. Ali, Ö.G., Arıtürk, U.: Dynamic churn prediction framework with more effective use of rare event data: the case of private banking. Expert Syst. Appl. 41(17), 7889–7903 (2014)
6. Huang, Y., Zhu, F., Yuan, M., Deng, K., Li, Y., Ni, B., Dai, W., Yang, Q., Zeng, J.: Telco churn prediction with big data. In: Proceedings of the 2015 ACM SIGMOD International Conference on Management of Data (2015)
7. Tsai, C.-F., Chen, M.-Y.: Variable selection by association rules for customer churn prediction of multimedia on demand. Expert Syst. Appl. 37(3) (2010)
8. Coussement, K., De Bock, K.W.: Customer churn prediction in the online gambling industry: the beneficial effect of ensemble learning. J. Bus. Res. 66(9), 1629–1636 (2013)
9. Burez, J., Van den Poel, D.: Handling class imbalance in customer churn prediction. Expert Syst. Appl. 36(3), 4626–4636 (2009)
10. Idris, A., Rizwan, M., Khan, A.: Churn prediction in telecom using random forest and PSO based data balancing in combination with various feature selection strategies. Comput. Electr. Eng. 38(6), 1808–1819 (2012)

11. Xie, Y., Li, X., Ngai, E.W.T., Ying, W.: Customer churn prediction using improved balanced random forests. Expert Syst. Appl. **36**(3), 5445–5449 (2009)
12. Zheng, Z., Wei, W., Liu, C., Cao, W., Cao, L., Bhatia, M.: An effective contrast sequential pattern mining approach to taxpayer behaviour analysis. World Wide Web **19**(4), 633–651 (2016)
13. Wright, A.P., Wright, A.T., McCoy, A.B., Sittig, D.F.: The use of sequential pattern mining to predict next prescribed medications. J. Biomed. Inform. **53**, 73–80 (2015)
14. Mooney, C.H., Roddick, J.F.: Sequential pattern mining–approaches and algorithms. ACM Comput. Surv. (CSUR) **45**(2) (2013)
15. Agnew, J.R., Bateman, H., Thorp, S.: Financial literacy and retirement planning in Australia. Numeracy: Adv. Educ. Quant. Lit. **6**(2) (2013)
16. Gallery, N., Newton, C., Palm, C.: Framework for assessing financial literacy and superannuation investment choice decisions. Australas. Account. Bus. Financ. J. **5**(2), 3 (2011)
17. Breiman, L.: Random forests. Mach. Learn. **45**(1), 5–42 (2001)
18. Phua, C., Cao, H., Gomes, J.B., Nguyen, M.N.: Predicting near-future churners and win-backs in the telecommunications industry. arXiv preprint arXiv:1210.6891 (2012)
19. Coussement, K., Van den Poel, D.: Churn prediction in subscription services: an application of support vector machines while comparing two parameter-selection techniques. Expert Syst. Appl. **34**(1), 313–327 (2008)
20. Chen, T., Guestrin, C.: XGBoost: a scalable tree boosting system. In: ACM SIGKDD International Conference on Knowledge Discovery and Data Mining, pp. 785–794. ACM (2016)

Automated Underwriting in Life Insurance: Predictions and Optimisation

Rhys Biddle[1], Shaowu Liu[1], Peter Tilocca[2], and Guandong Xu[1][✉]

[1] Advanced Analytics Institute, University of Technology Sydney, Sydney, Australia
rhys.biddle@student.uts.edu.au, {shaowu.liu,guandong.xu}@uts.edu.au
[2] OnePath Insurance, ANZ Wealth, Sydney, Australia
peter.tilocca@onepath.com.au

Abstract. Underwriting is an important stage in the life insurance process and is concerned with accepting individuals into an insurance fund and on what terms. It is a tedious and labour-intensive process for both the applicant and the underwriting team. An applicant must fill out a large survey containing thousands of questions about their life. The underwriting team must then process this application and assess the risks posed by the applicant and offer them insurance products as a result. Our work implements and evaluates classical data mining techniques to help automate some aspects of the process to ease the burden on the underwriting team as well as optimise the survey to improve the applicant experience. Logistic Regression, XGBoost and Recursive Feature Elimination are proposed as techniques for the prediction of underwriting outcomes. We conduct experiments on a dataset provided by a leading Australian life insurer and show that our early-stage results are promising and serve as a foundation for further work in this space.

1 Introduction

The concept of an insurance fund is to create a pool of wealth such that an unfortunate loss incurred by the few can be compensated by the wealth of the many [9]. It is clear that the success of this concept relies on accurately making the distinction between the few, those deemed to have a high chance of claiming, and the many, those deemed to have a low chance of claiming. The process of making such decisions is called underwriting.

The goal of underwriting from the perspective of the insurer is to accurately assess the risk posed by individual applicants, where risk in life insurance can be considered as the likelihood of an injury, sickness, disease, disability or mortality. A direct outcome of the underwriting process is the decision to accept or decline an individuals access into the insurance fund and what financial cost they should incur in exchange for access. Most individuals will incur a standard cost for access to the fund but some may incur a penalty, known as a *loading*, that should ideally reflect the level of risk they pose and their likelihood of claiming. In addition to a loading an individual may be granted special access to the fund but with certain claiming constraints attached, known as an *exclusion*. An exclusion is

J. Wang et al. (Eds.): ADC 2018, LNCS 10837, pp. 135–146, 2018.
https://doi.org/10.1007/978-3-319-92013-9_11

applied to prevent a specific individual claiming as a result of a particular event, back injury for example, but still allowing them access to the fund and rights to claim for other events they are not excluded from. Correctly identifying risks and applying the relevant loadings and exclusions during the underwriting process is fundamental to maintaining the wealth of a life insurance fund.

Underwriting is a tedious and labor intensive process on behalf of both the applicant and the underwriter. An applicant must fill out a highly personal questionnaire that delves into almost all aspects of their life which can be up to 100 pages long and consist of over 2 and a half thousand questions, an imposing amount of paperwork that can turn individuals off pursuing insurance cover [11]. The industry is well aware of the growing market group of millennials, forecast to reach 75% of the workforce by 2025, who prioritise fast and seamless digital user experiences [1]. Current underwriting processes do not allow for these kinds of digital experiences and insurers are aware that significant time and costs must be allocated to transforming current practices in order to capture the attention of this growing market [1]. In addition to being tedious on behalf of the user this questionnaire must be closely examined by a team of skilled underwriters who must follow guidelines mixed with intuition to arrive at a decision, resulting in a process that takes many weeks to complete. The mixture of guidelines and intuition is evident in the common phrase in the industry that underwriting is both an art and a science [3]. It has been reported in industry trend analysis that there is a need to improve the quantitative methods that make up the science aspect of the underwriting process in order to maintain the relevancy of the industry. Fortunately, with recent advances in machine learning and pattern recognition, it becomes possible to make significant improvements to the decision making process.

Existing research on automated underwriting in life insurance sector is lacking in broad and deep coverage. A combination of a neural network and fuzzy logic is presented without any experimental validation in [12], the strengths of the proposed approach is only informally justified with no proofs. The prototyping and implementation of a knowledge based system given requirements gathered from a survey of 23 individuals from Kenyan life insurance companies was proposed in [9], however, no experimental validation provided. We believe that this lack of depth and coverage is due to the difficulty in gaining access to real world life insurance datasets and the proprietary nature of any endeavor to implement such a system. There is also a noted distinction between life and non-life insurance industries in the literature due to the differing complexity and sensitivity of the information involved. It has been shown in [14], that classical data mining algorithms, specifically Support Vector Regression (SVR) and Kernel Logistic Regression (KLR), can successfully classify the risk and accurately predict insurance premiums in the automotive industry using real-world data. In this paper, we aim to propose a prediction framework based on state-of-the-art machine learning algorithms and evaluate on 9-years of life insurance data collected by a major insurance provider in Australia.

The rest of the paper is organized as follows. In Sect. 2, we introduce the basic concepts of automated underwriting followed by problem formulation. Section 3 is devoted to describing our methodology. Experiment results are presented in Sect. 4, and Sect. 5 concludes.

2 Preliminary

This section briefly summarises necessary background of automated underwriting and problem formulation that form the basis of this paper.

2.1 Automated Underwriting

Automation of the underwriting process can assist in a number of ways and benefit all parties involved. Timeliness of the underwriting process can be significantly improved, instances of human error can be reduced and misunderstandings or knowledge gaps in the underwriters can be filled. The current underwriting completion time frame of weeks can be reduced significantly with the assistance of automated decision making tools. Most applications go through the underwriting process with no exclusion or loading applied, underwriters spend a lot of time dealing with these cases that could be streamlined and allow that time to be spent focusing on the more complex cases. In some instances rule-based expert systems have been crafted to identify and process these simple applications but they are complex and cumbersome to update in light of new information [3]. The breadth and detail covered by the thousands of questions within the questionnaire requires a considerably deep and wide knowledge base to be able to deeply understand the answers and the implications for risk. In addition to gaining a thorough understanding of these numerous knowledge areas, an ambitious task alone, there is the added difficulty of being able to identify the complex relationships between the diverse knowledge areas and how they can be used to forecast risk. The use of machine learning and pattern recognition tools can assist the underwriter in increasing their knowledge base and identifying these complex relationships.

2.2 Underwriting Outcome

One of the most important underwriting outcomes is identifying *exclusions*. An exclusion inhibits an individual from making a specific claim due to information gathered from the applicants questionnaire. The reason for exclusions are numerous, in the thousands, and considerably specific. This specific nature of the exclusion is necessary when evaluating any claim made by an individual. If an applicant has a history of left knee medical issues and experiences frequent pain or limitations as a result of these issues than they may be excluded from making any claims that related to their left knee. As well as numerous exclusions targeting specific claims they may also have a temporal condition attached, such as a 90 days or 12 months exclusion from a particular claim. Exclusions allow an insurance fund to tailor products to each individual applicant by choosing what specific risks they are willing to accept and provide cover for and those which they are not.

2.3   Exclusions Prediction Problem

The prediction of an exclusion can be approached as a supervised binary classification problem. We have a dataset $D = \{(\mathbf{x}_1, y_1), (\mathbf{x}_2, y_2), \ldots, (\mathbf{x}_n, y_n)\}$ where $\mathbf{x}_i$ is a feature vector for applicant i and y_i is a binary label indicating the presence of a particular exclusion for applicant i. The feature vector $\mathbf{x}_i$ consists of the responses to all binary questions filled out by applicant i, some continuous features such as age and sum insured amounts. The questionnaire covers a large range of information about each applicant including family and medical history, occupation details, finances as well as leisure activities. In the current process of underwriting a team experts comes up with y_i for each exclusion. We propose to learn a function f that can accurately predict y_i given $\mathbf{x}_i$ using the labels provided by the expert underwriters to evaluate the performance of f. There are a few properties of this problem that make it an interesting supervised classification problem. Firstly the questionnaire has been designed and refined over the years to catch as many risky applicants as possible yet make it streamlined for the applicant. This results in a questionnaire that contains conditional-branching, which is the creation of unique pathways through the questionnaire depending on responses to particular questions. A result of this conditional branching is that the responses to the questionnaire are considerably sparse because only a small subset of the questions need to be answered by all applicants, i.e., the majority of $x_i^j = 0$ for some questions j. Questions are designed to catch exclusions so for any exclusion we expect a small subset of feature vector $\mathbf{x}_i$ to be very strong features for the predictive task and the large majority to be redundant. In addition to this sparsity we have the added issue of class imbalance due to the specificity and rarity of exclusions. As mentioned previously exclusions must be detailed enough so that the insurer can cover themselves at claim time resulting in thousands of different and highly specific exclusion types.

3   Methodology

We propose to address the problems identified in the underwriting process and the gaps in the existing research by implementing and evaluating two learning models to the problem of exclusion prediction on a real-world dataset. There are two key goals of this work, the prediction of exclusions and providing recommendations for questionnaire optimisation. In building our methodology both predictive accuracy and high interpretability of results are equally important. This limits our choice of data preparation methods and learning algorithm as addressed in the following sections.

3.1   Feature Selection

Reducing the size of the feature space is an important first step in learning problems and provides many benefits. A reduction in the size of feature vectors decreases the learning time, can improve accuracy and avoid overfitting [8]. A decrease in learning time is due to the smaller size of the training data after the reduction of the feature space. Overfitting is a well known pitfall and occurs when a model learns the training data so well that the predictive capabilities on new unseen data begins to suffer [15]. A large feature space with numerous redundant features can lead to overfitting and a reduction of these redundant features is a strategy to combat this pitfall [15]. In addition to this a model trained on a large feature space is complex and can be difficult to interpret.

There are two main approaches to feature space reduction, transformation-based and selection-based methods. Transformation-based methods perform a transformation of the initial input feature space to a smaller space [7,13] where as selection-based methods look to find an optimal subset of the original feature space [15].

Transformation-based methods are unsuitable for our work because they would destroy the one-to-one relationship of feature to question response. Preservation of this one-to-one relationship is key for us to assess the impact of individual questions and the respective response provided by an applicant.

There are numerous approaches that can be taken for feature selection methods. Filter methods involve ranking features under a chosen criterion and specifying a threshold at which to remove features from the feature space for training. Wrapper methods use the prediction results of a learning algorithm to identify and select features that are deemed important by the learning algorithm. In Embedded methods the feature selection process is part of the learning algorithm and it is difficult to separate the two processes. We have chosen to implement a wrapper method in our learning pipeline.

For the wrapper method we have chosen Recursive Feature Elimination (RFE) [6,8]. RFE is an iterative wrapper method that consists of training a classifier on numerous feature subsets and provides feature rankings for each subset. The three steps for RFE are: (i) train a classifier using feature set $\mathbf{f}$; (ii) get feature importances from trained classifier, rank them; (iii) remove a of subset the worst performing features for $\mathbf{f}$. There are two main parameters to be set for RFE, the size of the desired feature subset at the end of the algorithm and the number of features to remove at each iteration. The size of the desired feature subset can be found via cross-validation. RFE can be fit across all training folds in the cross-validation loop and the feature subset that gives the best averaged results across all testing folds can be selected as the optimal feature subset.

3.2   Prediction Models

Logistic Regression and Regularisation. Logistic regression was chosen as a baseline method because linear models are a favored tool in the insurance sector because of the simple implementation, interperatability and their connection with traditional statistics [10]. Logistic Regression is a popular statistical method used for modeling binary classification problems by prescribing a weight to all input features to perform a linear separation of the two classes. There is no feature selection inherent in the construction of Logistic Regression model however the addition of l_1 regularisation addresses this. Logistic Regression with the addition of l_1 as penalty term is referred to as Lasso Regression. The addition of this penalty term in Lasso Regression performs feature selection because it shrinks the weights of unimportant features to zero.

Gradient Boosting Trees. Gradient Boosting methods [2,5] are tree-based ensemble methods for supervised learning that are founded on the hypothesis that numerous weak learners provide more accurate predictions than a single learner [10]. A weak learner in this context is a simple model that can be considered to be only slightly better than random guessing. The simplest approach to combining all the predictions from the individual learners to arrive at a single prediction is via a voting procedure. A prediction by each weak learner is considered a vote and all of these are tallied up and the label predict by most weak learners is chosen as the final prediction. A motivation for using tree-based ensemble methods in insurance is that the decision making process is made up a large number of simple conditional rules, if applicant ticks "yes" to question A but "no" to question B then accept, which can be learnt by the numerous different weak learners in the ensemble [10]. Interpretability of Gradient Boosting methods in comparison to other learning techniques of similar power and complexity, such as Neural Networks and Support Vector Machines, is another motivation for using it in our work. Gradient Boosting methods provide clear and intuitive metrics for each input feature that indicate their importance in the resulting prediction, this aligns with our goal for providing recommendations for questionnaire optimisation. The nature of tree construction in gradient boosting means that all variables are candidates for splitting the tree and are evaluated. A direct result of this is that feature selection is inherent within the ensemble construction and is capable of dealing with redundant features. In this work, the XGBoost [2] implementation is employed.

3.3   Proposed Pipelines

We propose to use four separate feature selection and classification pipelines for implementation and evaluation. Firstly a pipeline of RFE with a standard Logistic Regression model as the learning algorithm for the RFE process. Cross-validation will be used to select the ideal number of features and the Logistic Regression model will be fit on the reduced subset produced by the RFE procedure. Our second pipeline will consist of Lasso Regression with the cross-validation used to select the ideal strength of the l_1 penalty term. Another pipeline will be XGBoost with cross-validation to select the ideal number of weak estimators and the learning rate. Lastly a pipeline of RFE with XGBoost as learning algorithm.

4   Experiment

In this section, we introduce the experimental settings and a large-scale data collection from Australian insurer, followed by experiment results and discussions.

4.1   Dataset Preparation

We have been given access to data from a leading insurer in the Australian life insurance sector dating from 2009 to 2017. As with any real-world dataset a considerable amount of effort was needed to prepare the data for modelling. There were several key issues that needed to be addressed before modeling could be performed on the entire dataset. Firstly the questionnaire data and the underwriting data had been stored and maintained by separate entities due to privacy concerns. In addition to this the data had changed hands several times across this time period due to organizational takeovers and vendor changes. Questionnaire data was most impacted by these changes and underwent four major changes in this time period. There were numerous changes that were made to the applicant data in how it was stored, such as different attributes and data types with no master data dictionary available to resolve these changes. In this time period the questionnaire itself had also changed with the addition, removal and modification of the questions contained within. These issues are currently being resolved and as a result the latest version of the questionnaire data, 2014–2017, has been used for modeling.

A straightforward match between the questionnaire data and underwriting data was not possible for privacy reasons and as a result we had to come up with a process to merge the separate data stores. We used three attributes relating to the applicant found in both application and underwriting data. These were related to the suburb, age and gender of the applicant. In such a large dataset we found numerous applicants sharing these traits so we used the date in which each applicant was entered into the two separate systems to resolve any ambiguous cases. Through this process we were able to identify approximately 60 thousand individuals from the 2014–2017 period.

As can be seen in Fig. 1 the response rates to questions are considerably low, the majority of applicants fill out less than 10% of the entire questionnaire, due to the conditional-branching structure of the questionnaire. This results in sparse feature vectors for the majority of applicants. As well as the sparse feature vectors the data exhibits sparsity in relation to the application of exclusions resulting in extreme class imbalances when predicting the binary problem of exclusion application. There are over 1 thousand different exclusions applied in the data set. Many of these exclusions are extremely rare occurring far too infrequently, single digit frequency counts, and thus not included in experiments. The most frequently applied exclusion is applied to only 1.5% of all applications, see Fig. 2.

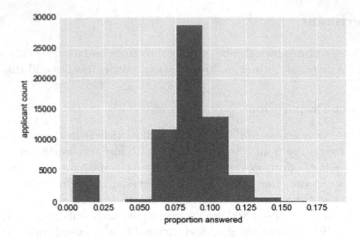

Fig. 1. Histogram of response proportion on questionnaire

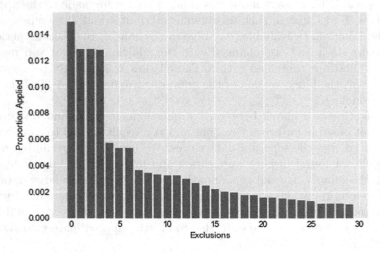

Fig. 2. Histogram of application rate for the 30 most common exclusion codes in descending order

4.2   Experimental Settings

We ran our proposed pipeline on the 20 most frequent exclusion codes. Our experiments were conducted using the scikit learn library for the python programming language. For the two pipelines that utilised RFE as feature transformation the following was implemented. Nested cross validation (CV) loop containing RFE with CV as the outer loop and Grid Search with CV as the inner loop to optimise the hyper-parameters of the learning algorithm. The embedded feature selection approaches required no such nested loop as there was no need for the transformation before prediction. CV was set to 5 stratified folds for all experiments, seed was kept the same for all experiments to ensure of the same dataset splits. For all learning algorithms the sampling procedure was weighted to account for the class imbalance.

4.3   Evaluation Metrics

We used area under the Receiver Operating Curve (ROC) [4] to evaluate the performance of our approach. An ROC curve is a plot of the rate of true positive predictions, correctly predict an positive example, against the rate of false positive predictions, predict a positive label when in fact negative. This is plotted across all thresholds for the prediction score of the model. The area under the ROC curve (AUC) is a single metric that can be interpreted as the ability of a model to correctly rank a positive example as more likely to be positive than a negative example. AUC is a common tool for comparing models in supervised binary classification problems.

4.4   Results and Discussions

Predictions. The prediction results vary considerably between exclusion codes, see Fig. 3. The worst average AUC across all models is 0.83, while the best average AUC is 0.96. In all but five of the top 20 exclusions setting a strong l_1 regularization penalty on Logistic Regression provides greater or equal predictive accuracy when compared to using RFE with CV as a feature selection phase before Logistic Regression with no l_1 penalty as shown in Fig. 3. However the mean difference in AUC between Logistic Regression with l_1 and RFE and Logistic

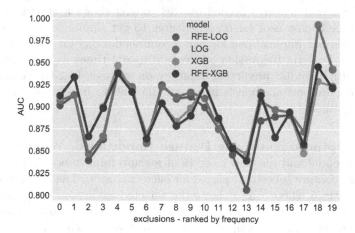

Fig. 3. Prediction results on the 20 most common exclusion codes, ranked in descending order. The results from four pipelines in this figure (i) RFE-LOG: Recursive Feature Elimination with Logistic Regression (ii) LOG: Logisitic Regression with l_1 regularisation (iii) XGB: Extreme Gradient Boosting, (iv) RFE-XGB: Recursive Feature Elimination with Extreme Gradient Boosting

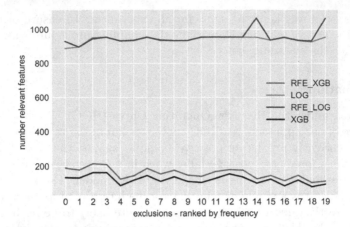

Fig. 4. Number of features used by the four modelling pipelines (i) RFE-LOG: Recursive Feature Elimination with Logistic Regression (ii) LOG: Logisitic Regression with l_1 regularisation (iii) XGB: Extreme Gradient Boosting, (iv) RFE-XGB: Recursive Feature Elimination with Extreme Gradient Boosting

Regression with no penalty is −0.006 which is insignificant. The mean difference in AUC between XGBoost and RFE with XGBoost is even more insignificant at only −0.0006. XGBoost and Logistic Regression with l_1 regularisation deal adequately with the feature selection process requiring no need for the prior feature selection step. Logistic Regression with l_1 is the best performing model with an average AUC 0.0035 units greater than XGBoost the next best model. There is little to separate these models in terms of predictive performance. The number of relevant features needed by each model shows a clear gap between the models. XGBoost uses far fewer features to get similar accuracy as shown in Fig. 4. This has implications for our recommendations for the questionnaire optimisation. Logistic Regression on average uses 4 times as many features as XGBoost with a similar prediction accuracy on average. Our recommendations for questionnaire optimisation is based on the feature importance as given bu the XGBoost model.

Question Optimisation Using Feature Importance. We further explore the trained model and discover insights of feature importance, i.e., the importance of each feature (question) played for each exclusion. The result is shown as heatmap in Fig. 5 where x-axis shows the selected exclusions and y-axis shows the features. Note that the actual question names and exclusion names have been removed and dummy names are shown in place. Each cell is colored from blue to red where red indicating the feature is high relevant to deciding the corresponding exclusion. The heatmap is interactive allowing for ranking by either exclusion or question. For example, when configured to rank questions by their import to "exc_1", the heatmap shows that the question "q_906" is the most important for deciding to apply exclusion "exc_1". It can also be seen that this question relevant for very few other exclusions, the numerous blues cells for the row corresponding to "q_906". In addition to red cells the blue cells are helpful for questionnaire optimisation. For example, the rows for "q_25" and "q_24" are filled entirely by blues cells, showing no relevance to any of the exclusions, which suggests this is a potential redundant question. Note that due to the large number of questions and exclusions, only a small fragment of the full interactive heatmap is shown here. Also from this heat map we can identify relationships between exclusion codes, such as exclusions "exc_1" and "exc_2" sharing the same three questions "q_906", "q_615", "q_611" as the three most important for determining the application of each exclusion respectively.

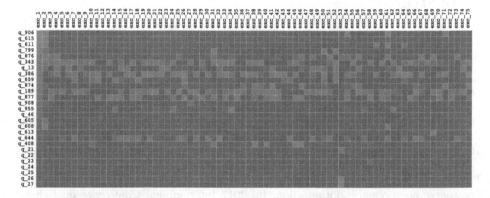

Fig. 5. Feature importance as heatmap. X-axis showing exclusions, Y-axis showing questions. Dummy labels provided for both exclusions and questions. (Color figure online)

5 Conclusions

In this paper, we implemented and evaluated a number of different machine learning algorithms and feature selection methods to predict the application of exclusions in life insurance applications. The results show that this simple approach performs well and can add value to the insurer. XGBoost is the most ideal model due to the need for the significantly smaller number of features needed to produce similar accuracy. For future work we would like to look into implementing a cost-sensitive approach to the prediction of exclusions. Data from claims made by applicants along with the current data would be needed to completely understand the cost of the underwriting decisions. We currently have not processed enough of the dataset to utilize the claims data making this approach unfeasible at the moment. Given that we only have last 3 years worth of usable data at present moment the number of claims for this period is too small to be of any use. Another direction for future work is the incorporation of the free text responses provided by the applicants into the feature set.

References

1. Howlette, B., Rajan, M., Chieng, S.P.: Future of life insurance in Australia. Technical report, PricewaterhouseCoopers (2017)
2. Chen, T., Guestrin, C.: XGBoost: a scalable tree boosting system. In: Proceedings of the 22nd ACM SIGKDD International Conference on Knowledge Discovery and Data Mining, pp. 785–794. ACM (2016)
3. Gandhi, D., Kaul, R.: Life and health - future of life underwriting. Asia Insur. Rev. **52**, 76–77 (2016)
4. Fawcett, T.: An introduction to ROC analysis. Pattern Recogn. Lett. **27**(8), 861–874 (2006)
5. Friedman, J.H.: Stochastic gradient boosting. Comput. Stat. Data Anal. **38**(4), 367–378 (2002)
6. Granitto, P.M., Furlanello, C., Biasioli, F., Gasperi, F.: Recursive feature elimination with random forest for PTR-MS analysis of agroindustrial products. Chemometr. Intell. Lab. Syst. **83**(2), 83–90 (2006)
7. Hu, Q., Liu, J., Daren, Y.: Mixed feature selection based on granulation and approximation. Knowl.-Based Syst. **21**(4), 294–304 (2008)
8. Guyon, I., Weston, J., Barnhill, S., Vapnik, V.: Gene selection for cancer classification using support vector machines. Mach. Learn. **46**, 389–422 (2002)
9. Joram, M.K., Harrison, B.K., Joseph, K.N.: A knowledge-based system for life insurance underwriting. Int. J. Inf. Technol. Comput. Sci. **9**, 40–49 (2017)
10. Guelman, L.: Gradient boosting trees for auto insurance loss cost modeling and prediction. Expert Syst. Appl. **39**, 3659–3667 (2012)
11. Liu, S., Xu, G., Zhu, X., Zhou, Z.: Towards simplified insurance application via sparse questionnaire optimization. In: 2017 International Conference on Behavioral, Economic, Socio-Cultural Computing (BESC), pp. 1–2, October 2017
12. Arora, N., Vij, S.: A hybrid neuro-fuzzy network for underwriting of life insurance. Int. J. Adv. Res. Comput. Sci. **3**, 231–236 (2012)
13. Jensen, R., Shen, Q.: Semantics-preserving dimensionality reduction: rough and fuzzy-rough-based approaches. IEEE Trans. Knowl. Data Eng. **16**, 1457–1471 (2004)
14. Kacelan, V., Kacelan, L., Buric, M.N.: A nonparametric data mining approach for risk prediction in car insurance: a case study from the montenegrin market. Econ. Res.-Ekonomska Istraivanja **29**, 545–558 (2017)
15. Rodriguez-Galiano, V.F., Luque-Espinar, J.A., Chica-Olmo, M., Mendes, M.P.: Feature selection approaches for predictive modelling of groundwater nitrate pollution: an evaluation of filters, embedded and wrapper methods. Sci. Total Environ. **624**, 661–672 (2018)

Maintaining Boolean Top-K Spatial Temporal Results in Publish-Subscribe Systems

Maryam Ghafouri[1]([✉]), Xiang Wang[1], Long Yuan[1], Ying Zhang[1,2], and Xuemin Lin[1]

[1] The University of New South Wales, Sydney, Australia
{mghafouri,xiangw,longyuan,yingz,lxue}@cse.unsw.edu.au
[2] The University of Technology, Sydney, Australia

Abstract. Nowadays many devices and applications in social networks and location-based services are producing, storing and using description, location and occurrence time of objects. Given a massive number of boolean top-k spatial-temporal queries and the spatial-textual message streams, in this paper we study the problem of continuously updating top-k messages with the highest ranks, each of which contains all the requested keywords when rank of a message is calculated by its location and freshness. Decreasing the ranks of existing top-k results over time and producing new incoming messages, cause continuously computing and maintaining the best results. To the best of our knowledge, there is no prior work that can exactly solve this problem. We propose two indexing and matching methods, then conduct an experimental evaluation to show the impact of parameters and analyse the models.

1 Introduction

We use location-aware publish/subscribe systems, such as eBay, Groupon, Twitter or Facebook to be informed about news and events, obtain reviews and comments, sell or buy. Subscribers submit their interested keywords to receive the nearest and newest relevant messages. Then with arriving a new message, the system finds and notifies related subscriptions. Matching keywords, computing ranks and comparing large number of messages in milliseconds, have made the performance of these systems very challenging.

We consider every message with its location, textual containments and arrival time and every query with its location, requested keywords and specified k as a limit for the number of receiving messages. Given a massive number of queries and large number of continuous incoming messages, in this paper, we evaluate the importance of a message with these three criteria: *(1) superset containment keywords matching (2) distance and (3) time freshness*. Answering boolean expressions queries and returning just top-k messages, allow users to specify their interests with boolean expressions and then customize their needs with retrieving top-k results.

© Springer International Publishing AG, part of Springer Nature 2018
J. Wang et al. (Eds.): ADC 2018, LNCS 10837, pp. 147–160, 2018.
https://doi.org/10.1007/978-3-319-92013-9_12

Table 1. Messages

m	Terms	m.t
m_1	a, b, f	2
m_2	a, b, c	2
m_3	a, b, c, d	2
m_4	b, c, f	1
m_5	a, c, d	2

Table 2. Subscribers at $t = 2$

S	Terms	k	Top-k results
s_1	a, b	2	$m_1(0.96)$, $m_2(0.93)$
s_2	a, b, c	2	$m_2(0.98)$, $m_3(0.94)$
s_3	b, c	1	$m_4 (0.85)$
s_4	a, d	1	$m_5 (0.96)$
s_5	a	1	$m_5 (0.96)$

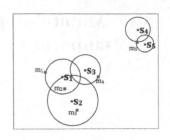

Fig. 1. Subscribers at $t = 2$

Example 1. Figure 1 illustrates a snapshot of our example while five subscriptions s_1, s_2, s_3, s_4, s_5 are registered with their locations and favourite keywords, intending to be updated about the most relevant new published messages. A message m will be delivered to a subscription s if m has all the requested keywords and the spatial-temporal score of m against s is higher than at least one of its top-k results. Table 1 shows messages m_1, m_2, m_3, m_4, m_5 arrived at timestamps 1 or 2 and Table 2 demonstrates subscriptions with their desired keywords and requested number of results as k. The most recent top-k results of any query at time-stamp of 2 are calculated and shown in Table 2. For every subscription, we draw a circle with the subscription in centre and maximum acceptable distance at time t, as radius, where maximum acceptable distance is calculated by using rank of kth result of the query. Obviously, any new message outside of this circle could not be a new result since their ranks are less than any current top-k results. Note that the ranking score of each object in the top-k results declines over time and we need to re-compute them each time when a new object arrives. As long as no new message is inserted to the top-k results, the ranks of messages decrease by time and maximum acceptable distances continually grow.

We aim at maintaining the up-to-date top-k results for a large number of subscriptions, over a stream of messages. Continuous monitoring of spatial textual queries necessitates several long-running queries at the same time to compute the scores and keep the results up to date. In a *naive* approach, for each new message m, we check keywords to cover the query keywords and compute its ranking score w.r.t. each subscription s; If the score is larger than the ranking score of the current k^{th} result of s, m becomes a result and is used to update the current top-k results for s. This approach is computationally expensive when the number of subscriptions is large or the messages arrive at a high rate. While, handling millions of matching processes is a challenging problem and needs considerable attention, the matching process must guarantee the high efficiency of the extreme event arrival rate.

Challenges. We evaluate messages for any queries according to these three criteria: (1) superset containment keywords matching (2) distance and (3) time freshness score. Processing and matching new messages are huge challenges as scores of top-k results are constantly decreasing by time. Thus, our method should consider age of the latest top-k results and re-computing scores. Therefore, it is desirable to reduce the number of matching calculations through grouping queries and messages by effective pruning and filtering techniques. Based on these observations, we propose a pruning technique which matches keywords by a trie and group queries by their locations. Then, we further organize queries with our **S**patial-**T**extual Temporal **In**dexing and matching method, namely **SATIN**, which smoothly indexes queries considering the rank of kth result. It is worth mentioning that a similar problem studied in [2], considers the text similarity ranking and their techniques cannot be applied to the problem studied in this paper.

Contributions

- We formally define the problem of continuously updating boolean top-k spatial temporal results for queries in publish-subscribe systems. Results should contain all the requested keywords and have the highest ranks where the rank of a message calculates by its occurrence time and its distance to the query. To the best of our knowledge, there is no prior work that can exactly solve this problem.
- We propose an indexing technique for each individual message, namely QOOKET. QOOKET follows the filtering-and-refinement paradigm and integrates the superset containment keyword indexing and spatial indexing techniques to facilitate the filtering process and then refines using the rank score.
- We further enhance the performance by introducing a new algorithm, namely SATIN, which reduces the computation via clustering the messages by the rank of their k^{th} result. This facilitates us to find maximum acceptable distance for each group of queries, to wisely prune the search space by considering only groups of candidate messages within this distance.
- Experimental evaluation validates that SATIN is up to 12 times better than naive algorithm and nearly 4 times faster than QOOKET.

2   Related Work

Most of existing spatial textual indexes that support top-k or kNN spatial keyword queries do not consider the age of messages. Maintaining up-to-date results for a large number of subscriptions, over a stream of messages, needs re-evaluating top-k results from scratch for the affected subscriptions, which is very costly and infeasible. Chen et al. [2] considered the problem of maintaining up-to-date results for a large number of spatial textual queries, based on the concept of conditional influence region. They proposed temporal spatial-keyword top-k publish/subscribe (Task) as a model that defines a textual bound for every subscription and subsequently it applies document-at-a-time traversing in inverted file for each spatial node. Although, this is the most similar study to our paper, they used scoring function to calculate the textual relevancy score between queries and messages, while our problem is a superset containment matching from textual perspective.

SKYPE [11] uses a sliding window model over streaming geo-textual data to provide the most recent information under control. SKYPE proposed a novel cost-based k-skyband method, which determines the size of k-skyband buffer, based on a cost model carefully. However, their paper is about spatial textual relevance score and using sliding window, notwithstanding, our work is different in case of boolean textual matching and ranking top-k results by scoring time and distance.

Chen et al. [3] divided proposed geo-textual indices according to structure of the spatial index into R-tree, grid and space filling curve. According to the text indexes they are divided into inverted file based and signature file based. Although, there are several studies about efficient mixing of texts and spatial properties of queries, most of them combine a R-tree family index or space-filling curve with an inverted list and also focus on spatial part of indexing more than textual processing. BEQ-Tree [7] integrates Quadtree with Boolean expressions to support matching of spatial Boolean expression and construction of the safe region, in the dynamic environment. IQ-tree [1] belongs to spatial-first indexing method which textual filtering techniques are based on inverted indexes and using a Quadtree for spatial indexing.

Guided by a cost model, AP-Tree [12] can be built adaptively by choosing keyword or spatial partitions. STARI (Spatio-Textual Adaptive Ranking- based Index) [9] which uses an in-memory grid-based compact spatial index of R-tree family combined with an inverted list. Yu et al. [13] proposed MBRTrie and PT-Quadtree to address the problem of instant message filtering in pub/sub system. Choudhury et al. [4] proposed a method for batch processing of queries with respect to the spatial proximity of multiple queries and improved the performance of processing groups of queries when the results of the queries have large overlaps with beneficent of using time slot. While these studies are not adjustable to our problem, to the best of our knowledge, there is no prior work that can exactly solve this problem.

3   Preliminary

In publication/subscription systems, subscribers submit long lasting queries under the form of keyword-based subscriptions. Given a set of spatial-textual messages, here a top-k spatial-textual result returns k messages, where the similarity rank considers both spatial distance and freshness of messages and a match occurs if all of the keywords of a subscription also exist in a message. Table 3 summarizes the notations frequently used throughout the paper.

Definition 1 (Temporal Spatial Textual Message). *Formally, a temporal spatial textual message m is modelled as* $m = (\psi, \rho, t)$, *where* $m.\psi$ *denotes a set of distinct terms (keywords) from a vocabulary set V,* $m.\rho$ *represents a geo-location and* $m.t$ *is creation time of the message.*

Table 3. The summary of notations

Notation	Definition
ψ	A set of distinct keywords
ρ	Location of message or subscriber
t	Creation time of the message
k	The desire number of top-k results
$\mathcal{R}$	Top-k result for subscriber s, sorted by score
t_{cur}	Current time
$dist_{max}$	Maximal possible distance in spatial area
θ	Threshold for spatial index
μ_{cur}	The lowest score of top-k result in t_{cur}

Definition 2 (Spatial Textual Subscription). *Any subscription defined as* $s = (\psi,\ \rho,\ k)$, *where s.ψ denotes a set of distinct keywords from a vocabulary set V/, s.ρ represents a geo-location and s.k is the desire number of results. The set of subscriptions is indicated by S.*

Definition 3 (Textual Matching). *In case of textual property, a spatial-textual message matches a spatial-keyword query if it covers all the requested keywords by the subscriber.*

Definition 4 (Temporal Spatial Score). *Temporal spatial score of a message m at current time t_{cur} for subscription s is defined as follows:*

$$SIM(s, m, t_{cur}) = SS(s, m) . TS(t_{cur}, m.t) \qquad (1)$$

where SS(s, m) computes the spatial relevance between m and s and TS(t_{cur}, m.t) computes the message recency score. Following previous works such as [2] the spatial relevance SS(s, m) between m and s is calculated by the normalized Euclidean distance:

$$SS(s, m) = 1 - (dist(m.\rho, s.\rho)/dist_{max}) \qquad (2)$$

where dist(m.ρ, s.ρ) is the Euclidean distance between m and s, and $dist_{max}$ is the maximal possible distance in the spatial area. The recency of message m which is denoted by TS(t_{cur}, m.t), is calculated by the exponential decay function:

$$TS(t_{cur}, m.t) = B^{(t_{cur} - m.t)/\tau} \qquad (3)$$

where B is base number that determines the rate of the recency decay and τ is used to smooth and scale the results. t_{cur} indicates the current time, and m.t refers to the creation time of message m. Efron and Golovchinsky [6] showed effectiveness of this function in blending the recency and text relevancy of objects while score of a message is monotonically decreasing by $(t_{cur} - m.t)/\tau$.

Problem Statement. Given a massive number of spatial-textual queries and spatial-textual messages streams, in this paper, we study the problem of continuously updating boolean top-k spatial temporal results for queries in Publish-subscribe systems. Each result should contain all the requested keywords and have the highest ranks where the rank of a message is calculated by its occurrence time and distance to the query. With arrival of a new messages stream, we aim to quickly identify which subscribers may be affected and should be updated to continuously maintain their top-k results.

Example 2 In Fig. 2, we showed 3 subscribers from Example 1 at time $= 3$. As mentioned before, the score of any message in regards to any subscriber drops by time and consequently the score of kth result of the subscriber decreases. So, maximum distance that a new arriving message can affect top-k results increases. In Fig. 2, solid line circles show the maximum acceptable distances in $t = 2$ and dashed line in $t = 3$. Message 6 with m.$\psi = $ b, c, d is located in acceptable distance of subscriber 2 and 3, but it can only affect top-k result of s_3 as all the textual, spatial, and temporal information are important in retrieving top-k results.

4   Framework

Even in a typical geo web page, there are at least tens of words where there is only one single spatial property. It is mentioned in several papers such as [5] that focusing on spatial structure prior to textual indexing, decreases the performance significantly. However, our main reason to put textual indexing first is because it is a part of indexing which is not changing frequently (Fig. 3).

Textual Filtering. Textual matching with naive approach is checking if all the terms of subscription are contained in the incoming message. Obviously, this solution does not scale to millions of subscriptions while the nature of the problem is superset containment match. Almost all the current existing methods for textual filtering are based on inverted indexes and are suitable for subset containment queries. But even count-based or ranked-key inverted list [8], may enormously increase query throughput by increasing the keyword size.

Using ordered keyword trie structure and following [8] each node corresponds to a keyword. Since there is an order for keywords, each query can be found

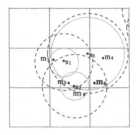

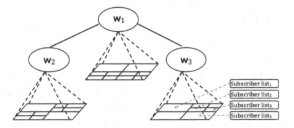

Fig. 2. Snap shot at $t = 3$ **Fig. 3.** Quadtree Over Ordered Trie (QOOKET)

Algorithm 1. *Textual_Indexing*(m, sorted_keywords , N)

Input: *sorted_keywords* : all or part of sorted message keywords
     N: current node,

1 **if** *N contains subscriptions* **then**   // Adding m to current node N
2 | $\mathcal{L} := messages\_list\,of\,N$;
3 | $\mathcal{L} := \mathcal{L} \cup$ m;

4 *sorted_keywords* $\leftarrow$ *sorted_keywords*\ keyword(N);
5 **for** *each keyword $w_i \in$ sorted_keyword* **do**
6 | childNode $\leftarrow$ get child for term w_i ;
7 | **if** *childNode* $\neq \emptyset$ **then**
8 | | *Textual_Indexing*(m, sorted_keywords $- w_i$, childNode);

---

through a distinct path following its ordered keywords. Algorithm 1 gives the process of grouping textual matching results in the node of trie. Every message adds to every visited node in traversing the trie by message keywords.

Spatial Filtering. Quadtree [10] as a grid based indices, is used to divide a two-dimensional space by recursively subdividing it into four regions. Chen et al. [2] specified that compared to R-tree based indexes, Quadtree is more suitable in application with massive updating, while R-tree suffers from additional cost for maintaining the MBRs in new queries arrival.

4.1 Temporal Spatial Textual Indexing and Matching by Quadtree Over Ordered Keyword Trie (QOOKET)

We assume our subscriptions have current top-k results. In a naive approach, for each new message m which passes the textual filtering, we compute its ranking score w.r.t. each subscription s. If the score is at least larger than the score of the current kth result of s, m becomes a result and is used to update the current top-k results for s. The scores of messages continually decrease by time and we need to re-compute them continuously. However, ranking of two different messages w.r.t. a query is consistent over time, which means if SIM(s, m_i, t) $\geq$ SIM(s, m_j, t), then SIM(s, m_i, t $+ \Delta$t) $\geq$ SIM(s, m_j, t $+ \Delta$t). Since spatial similarity scores are unchanging, this property is only associated with the recency scores and we do not need to re-rank top-k results. We state the message with the least score as kth result and its score in current time as μ_{cur}.

Huge number of queries and incoming messages necessitate efficient indexing technique which reduces the number of refinement by filter out a large number of unpromising messages at a cheap cost. We group queries and messages in leaf nodes of Quadtrees by their textual and spatial properties. Then we only consider cells that can have messages with scores higher than μ_{cur}. It is obvious that every spatial point in the cell c and its children are far more than minDist(s, c) which is the shortest distance between c and s.

Definition 5 (Maximum Acceptable Distance). *The shortest distance between any new message m and query s, caused a score higher than μ_{cur}.*

$$MAD(s, t_{cur}) = (1 - \mu_{cur}) * dist_{max} \tag{4}$$

This is different to the radius of circular influence region from [2] which is the distance from the query location to its kth result. If $minDist(s, c) > MAD(s, t_{cur})$, there is not any message in c that can have higher score than μ_{cur}. Thus we can use minDist for defining a lower bound for distance from q to any objects in the cell. For every query s, the value of μ_{cur} is calculated. If the node has a Quadtree which means there are more than θ messages in the node, then messages are processed according to the distance between their cells and queries (line 8). Clearly, we do not need to further explore a cell c and its children if it is farther than calculated $MAD(s, t_{cur})$. Otherwise, the messages in the cell add to candidate list. The candidate messages are refined and evaluated by μ_{cur} in line 17 and only messages with temporal spatial score higher than μ_{cur} should be considered. Finally they cause updating top-k list of the query (line 22).

As we will discuss in experimental section, the major cost of Algorithm 2 is lines 17–22 for the refinement cost, which have to calculate the similarity of any query with each candidate message and compare it with μ_{cur}. To address the problem, pruning more candidate messages is desirable.

4.2   Spatial-Textual Temporal Indexing and Matching Method - Share Computation by Qrouping Queries in Quadtree cells and Ordered Keyword Trie (SATIN)

SATIN groups all the queries with their textual and spatial properties. Since the major cost in Algorithm 2 is for the refinement and calculating the similarity score of a query with any candidate message and comparing with μ_{cur}, our idea is to group queries of any Quadtree cell by their μ_{cur} and prunes more messages by using the score of groups and Quadtree cells. Figure 4 shows this idea and Algorithm 3 explains the indexing.

Definition 6 (k^{th} Time). k^{th} *Time is defined as the occurrence time of the message with lowest score in the top-k results of the subscription.*

By using k^{th} Time, queries divide into f time_interval_groups (TIG_i) and the maximum possible distances for every group are calculated. To facilitate this idea, the upper and lower time values for f TIG_is are calculated once and used to group queries. Since recency similarity between a message and a query is a number between 0 and 1, if $f = 10$, we consider recency scores groups should be $(0 - 0.1), (0.1 - 0.2) \ldots (0.9 - 1)$. The upper bound distance for TIG_is are calculated as below:

$$b_i = dist_{max} * (f - i)/f; \tag{5}$$

Algorithm 2. *Matching_with_Quadtree_Over_Ordered_Trie($\mathcal{O}$)*

Input : $\mathcal{O}$: a set of objects organized by Ordered Trie,
Output: Updated top-k results of $\mathcal{S}$

1 $\mathcal{C} := \emptyset;\ \mathcal{R} := \emptyset;$
2 $\mathcal{Q} \leftarrow$ push root of $\mathcal{O};$
3 **while** $\mathcal{Q} \neq \emptyset$ **do**
4   N := element popped from $\mathcal{Q};$
5      $\mathcal{S} :=$ queries popped from N;
6   **for** *each query $s \in \mathcal{S}$* **do**
7   Derive μ_{cur};
8   **if** *N is indexed by Quadtree $\mathcal{QT}$* **then**   // $\mathcal{M} \geq \theta$
9   Derive $MAD(s, t_{cur})$ from equation 4;
10   **for** *each leaf cell $c \in \mathcal{QT}$* **do**
11   **if** *$minDist(s, c) \leq MAD(s, t_{cur})$* **then**
12                     $\mathcal{M} :=$ candidate messages popped from c;
13                     $\mathcal{C} := \mathcal{C} \cup \mathcal{M}$

14   **else**
15             $\mathcal{M} :=$ candidate messages popped from N;
16             $\mathcal{C} := \mathcal{C} \cup \mathcal{M}$

17   **for** *each candidate message $m \in \mathcal{C}$* **do**
18   Derive $SIM(s, m, t_{cur})$ from equation 1 ;
19   **if** *$SIM(s, m, t_{cur}) \leq \mu_{cur}$* **then**   // prune
20                 $\mathcal{C} := \mathcal{C} \setminus m;$

21   **for** *each message m in $\mathcal{C}$* **do**   // validate
22             $\mathcal{R}$ of s is verified and updated by $\mathcal{C}$;

23   **if** *N is an intermediate entry* **then**   // refinement
24   Push child entries of N into $\mathcal{Q}$;

25 **return** $\mathcal{S}$;

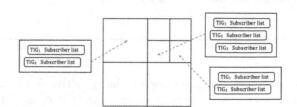

Fig. 4. Indexes for Quadtree cells

For every group we can calculate the occurrence time of kth messages that cause those scores with below formula:

$$time_i = t_{cur} + (log(i/f) * \tau/log(B));\qquad (6)$$

Algorithm 3. *Grouping_Subscribers_in_SATIN* $(\mathcal{N})$

Input: $\mathcal{N}$: SATIN Node

       f: number of time intervals;

       $time_i$ calculated by equation 6;

       b_i calculated by equation 5;

1 $\mathcal{S}_n :=$ queries popped from $\mathcal{N}$;

2 $\mathcal{QT} :=$ Quadtree of $\mathcal{N}$;

3   **for** *each query* $s \in \mathcal{S}_n$ **do**

4 $\lfloor$ push s into $\mathcal{QT}$;

5 $\mathcal{S}_n := \emptyset$;

6   **for** *each Quadtree_node* $qtn \in \mathcal{QT}$ **do**

7 $\mathcal{S}_q :=$ queries popped from qtn;

8   **for** *each query* $s \in \mathcal{S}_q$ **do**

9   Drive the TIG_i of s by its k^{th}Time, $time_i$, b_i;

10   push s to its TIG_i;

Algorithm 4. *Finding_Candidate_Messages* $(TIG_i, b_i, \mathcal{C}, qtc)$

Input   : TIG_i: the group of queries

        b_i :maximum possible distance;

        $\mathcal{C}$: $candidate messages for TIG_i$;

        c_s : Quadtree cell contains TIG_i;

        qtc: current Quadtree cell;

Output: $\mathcal{C}$: Updated candidate messages for TIG_i

1   **if** *qtc is leaf* **then**

2 $\mathcal{M} :=$ candidate messages popped from qtc;

3 $\mathcal{C} \cup \mathcal{M}$;

4   **else**

5   **for** *each child node ch of node qtc* **do**

6   **if** $minDist(c_s, ch) \leq b_i$ **then**

7 $\lfloor$ Finding_Candidate_Messages $(TIG_i, b_i, \mathcal{C}, ch)$;

8   **return** $\mathcal{C}$;

We calculate minimum distance between the Quadtree cell c_s and any other cell contains messages c_m in the Quadtree as $minDist(c_s, c_m)$, then compare with b_i of every time_interval_groups. If $minDist(c_s, c_m) > b_i$, there is not any message in c_m and its children that can be a new top-k result for any queries of time_interval_groups. Subscriptions of returned cells are tested for removing false positive results. Grouping similar subscriptions improves the efficiency by simultaneously processing a group against new messages.

Algorithm 5. *Maintaining_Top-k($\mathcal{N}$)*

Input : $\mathcal{N}$: SATIN Node

1 **for** *each leaf cell $c_s \in \mathcal{QT}$* **do**
2   **for** *each $TIG_i \in c_s$* **do**
3   Drive b_i from equation 5;
4      $\mathcal{C}$: find candidateMessages for TIG_i from Algorithm 4

5   **for** *each query s in TIG_i* **do**
6   Derive $MAD(s, t_{cur})$ from equation 4;
7   **for** *each candidate message $m \in \mathcal{C}$* **do**
8   Derive $SIM(s, m, t_{cur})$ from equation 1;
9   **if** $\mu_{cur} \leq SIM(s, m, t_{cur})$ **then**   // prune
10          $\mathcal{C}_2 := \mathcal{C}_2 \cup m$;

11   **for** *each message m in $\mathcal{C}_2$* **do**   // validate
12        $\mathcal{R}$ of s is verified and updated by $\mathcal{C}_2$;

---

5 Experiment

In this section, to evaluate the effectiveness and efficiency of our proposed techniques we present results of our performance study. All experiments are implemented in JAVA and conducted on a computer with 2.7 GHz Intel Core i5 processor, 8 GB 1867 MHz DDR3 of memory. We assume the indexes are fit in the main memory to support real-time response, which is the typical setting of Pub/Sub systems. For evaluating and comparing the performances of the algorithms, average time for matching and index construction is used. Keywords are ordered by their frequencies in subscriptions.

- **Naive:** A simple top-k temporal textual spatial matching with comparing every message with every query.
- **QOOKET:** The top-k textual spatial matching techniques proposed in Sect. 4.1 as Quadtree Over Ordered Keyword Trie.
- **SATIN:** The algorithm proposed in Sect. 4.2 as SATIN for spatial-Textual Temporal indexing and matching method.

Datasets. TWEETS dataset is collected for experimental evaluations from a real-life dataset collected from Twitter, containing 12 million tweets with geo-locations from May 2012 to August 2012.

Subscription Workload. We generate subscription workloads from above dataset. Spatial-textual messages are randomly chosen from corresponding dataset. For each sampled message, we randomly pick i terms as subscription keywords where i is a random number between 1 and 5 and k is selected from 5, 10 or 15.

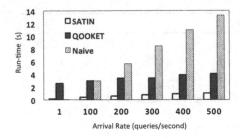
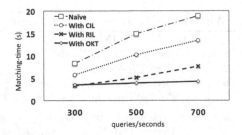

Fig. 5. Effect of arrival rate   **Fig. 6.** Different textual techniques

5.1   Performance Evaluation

Effect of Arrival Rate. Figure 5 shows effect of different amount of incoming messages on matching time for 1 million of queries. The performance of both Naive and QOOKET for a stream of 100 messages are more than a second and are getting worse for more messages. Our experiments show that SATIN can handle up to 500 messages in a second which is 12 times better than naive algorithm and nearly 4 times better than QOOKET.

Textual Matching. Following [8] we used and compared different textual indexing methods to find the best and most suitable one for SATIN. The average matching time for different message streams are shown in Fig. 6. The performance of Ordered Keyword Trie (OKT) outperforms Naive, Count-Based Inverted List (CIL) and Ranked-key Inverted List (RIL), thanks to group queries and messages at the same place and prune a lot of undesired messages at the beginning of the algorithm.

5.2   Experimental Tuning

In this part, we tune the parameters in the SATIN to achieve its best performance. The tweets arrival rate is 300 messages in a second for 1 million of queries.

Effect of f. The idea of dividing queries into $f\ TIG_i$, helps us to calculate maximum possible distance for every group. While a small f means less numbers of group and faster indexing, it means more time for matching. A small f can cause a further distance for pruning and more false positive messages for refinement. However a large f causes more accurate maximum acceptable distance but more indexing time while groups are sparser. We vary f to find the best value and show the results for indexing and matching in Fig. 7(a).

Effect of τ. The recency of message is calculated by the exponential decay function. While the function is monotonically decreasing with $(t_{cur}\text{-m.t})/\tau$, τ is used to smooth and scale the scores. Depending on the importance of freshness we select a proper rate for τ. Figure 8(a) depicts the effects of selecting different τ on the rate of decreasing temporal score of a message during a month and

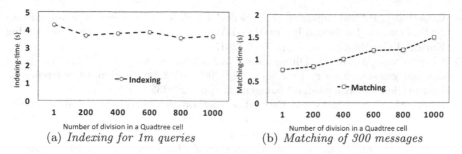

(a) *Indexing for 1m queries*   (b) *Matching of 300 messages*

Fig. 7. Effect of different *f*

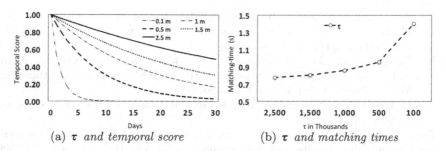

(a) *τ and temporal score*   (b) *τ and matching times*

Fig. 8. Effect of different *τ*

Fig. 8(b) shows matching time caused by different *τ*. According to Fig. 8(a) a smaller *τ* causes faster reaching to zero score for k^{th} result, further maximum acceptable distance and consequently more filtering and refinement for matching time.

6   Conclusion

In this paper, we introduce Maintaining Top-K Spatial Textual Results In Publish-Subscribe Systems. Our methods integrate textual and spatial aspects of subscriptions and messages. SATIN groups subscriptions by their current k^{th} result. Extensive experimental evaluation validates that SATIN is up to 12 times better than naive algorithm and nearly 4 times faster than QOOKET.

References

1. Chen, L., Cong, G., Cao, X.: An efficient query indexing mechanism for filtering geo-textual data. In: Proceedings of the 2013 ACM SIGMOD International Conference on Management of Data, pp. 749–760 (2013)
2. Chen, L., Cong, G., Cao, X., Tan, K.L.: Temporal spatial-keyword top-k publish/subscribe. In: Proceedings - International Conference on Data Engineering, pp. 255–266 (2015)
3. Chen, L., Cong, G., Jensen, C., Wu, D.: Spatial keyword query processing: an experimental evaluation. PVLDB **6**(3), 217–228 (2013)

4. Choudhury, F.M., Culpepper, J.S., Sellis, T.: Batch processing of top-k spatial-textual queries. In: Second International ACM Workshop on Managing and Mining Enriched Geo-Spatial Data, pp. 7–12 (2015)
5. Christoforaki, M., He, J., Dimopoulos, C., Markowetz, A., Suel, T.: Text vs. space: efficient geo-search query processing. In: 20th ACM International Conference on Information and Knowledge Management, pp. 423–432 (2011)
6. Efron, M., Golovchinsky, G.: Estimation methods for ranking recent information. In: Proceedings of the 34th International ACM SIGIR Conference on Research and Development in Information Retrieval, pp. 495–504. ACM (2011)
7. Guo, L., Zhang, D., Li, G., Tan, K.-L., Bao, Z.: Location-aware pub/sub system: when continuous moving queries meet dynamic event streams. In: SIGMOD, pp. 843–857 (2015)
8. Hmedeh, Z., Kourdounakis, H., Christophides, V., du Mouza, C., Scholl, M., Travers, N.: Content-based publish/subscribe system for web syndication. J. Comput. Sci. Technol. 31(2), 359–380 (2016)
9. Ray, S., Nickerson, B.G.: Dynamically ranked top-k spatial keyword search. In: Proceedings of the Third International ACM SIGMOD Workshop on Managing and Mining Enriched Geo-Spatial Data (2016)
10. Samet, H.: The quadtree and related hierarchical data structures. ACM Comput. Surv. 16(2), 187–260 (1984)
11. Wang, X., Zhang, Y., Zhang, W., Lin, X., Huang, Z.: SKYPE: top-k spatial-keyword publish/subscribe over sliding window. Proc. VLDB Endow. 9(7), 588–599 (2016)
12. Wang, X., Zhang, Y., Zhang, W., Lin, X., Wang, W.: AP-tree: efficiently support continuous spatial-keyword queries over stream. In: 31st International Conference on Data Engineering, pp. 1107–1118. IEEE (2015)
13. Yu, M.: A cost-based method for location-aware publish/subscribe services. CIKM 1, 693–702 (2015)

Interdependent Model for Point-of-Interest Recommendation via Social Networks

Jake Hashim-Jones[✉], Can Wang, Md. Saiful Islam, and Bela Stantic

School of Information and Communication Technology, Griffith University,
Brisbane, Australia
jake.hashim-jones@griffithuni.edu.au,
{can.wang,saiful.islam,b.stantic}@griffith.edu.au

Abstract. Point-of-Interest (POI) recommendation is an important way to help people discover attractive places. POI recommendation approaches are usually based on collaborative filtering methods, whose performances are largely limited by the extreme scarcity of POI check-ins and a lack of rich contexts, and also by assuming the independence of locations. Recent strategies have been proposed to capture the relationship between locations based on statistical analysis, thereby estimating the similarity between locations purely based on the visiting frequencies of multiple users. However, implicit interactions with other link locations are overlooked, which leads to the discovery of incomplete information. This paper proposes a interdependent item-based model for POI recommender systems, which considers both the intra-similarity (i.e. co-occurrence of locations) and inter-similarity (i.e. dependency of locations via links) between locations, based on the TF-IDF conversion of check-in times. Geographic information, such as the longitude and latitude of locations, are incorporated into the interdependent model. Substantial experiments on three social network data sets verify the POI recommendation built with our proposed interdependent model achieves a significant performance improvement compared to the state-of-the-art techniques.

1 Introduction

Location-based social networks have become increasingly popular in the past few years. Popular networks such as Foursquare, WhatsApp, FaceBook, Snapchat and even Instagram all include check-in functionality, allowing users to share their location-based information with their friends. In 2016, the social network Foursquare had over 50 million users and 8 billion POI check-ins [1]. A point of interest (POI) is essentially a locational hotspot, such as a restaurant, shopping center or public park. With the emergence of location-based social networks, POI recommender systems have been developed to recommend locations for visit [1].

Compared with traditional recommendation problems (e.g. product and movie), there are a number of key performance-limiting challenges that current POI recommender systems face. One of the prominent issues is the scarcity

© Springer International Publishing AG, part of Springer Nature 2018
J. Wang et al. (Eds.): ADC 2018, LNCS 10837, pp. 161–173, 2018.
https://doi.org/10.1007/978-3-319-92013-9_13

of available data. Recommender systems generally work by analyzing a user's activities with respect to items (which in this case is POIs) [2]. A key issue with POI data in particular, is the high scarcity. A set of POIs can be extensive, however users only tend to visit a limited number of them [1]. As a result, there is a limited amount of POI visitation data available that a recommender system can use to model a user's preferences and behavior. Another challenging issue with POI recommender systems is that generally, they are incapable of dealing with rich contexts (e.g. geographical and social data), and base their predictions solely on the visiting frequencies [2]. As visiting frequency tends to be scarce, it is important that the influence of additional rich contexts on user behavior is considered.

Three popular methods used to power recommender systems are: item-based and user-based collaborative filtering, and matrix factorization techniques. The item-based models consider the similarity between locations based on common users that have visited them [3]. User-based models involve generating user predictions based on similarities between users who have visited similar locations [3]. Matrix factorization works by decomposing user visitation data into various latent factors of users and locations [4]. These methods tend to be subject to the same issues that all POI recommender systems face: data scarcity and a lack of rich contextual awareness. Another factor that is not usually considered is the coupled relationship between locations. Some research work [1] has analyzed the explicit statistical relationship for locations based on check-ins. However, they do not address the underlying implicit relationship, thus failing to capture the complete semantic relationship between locations.

This study aims to address the challenge of capturing the coupled relationship between locations, and implementing them in a POI recommender system. The purpose is to address the data scarcity problem by introducing more information, as well as taking more rich context into account by geographical data. In this work, we propose a novel approach to measure the relationship between locations by capturing both the intra-similarity and inter-similarity, using the co-occurrence and link between them, respectively. The interdependent model is based on statistical analysis of location occurrence patterns to determine how similar locations are (intra-similarity), based on check-ins. We also attempt to capture the relationship between locations that are not visited by the same users (inter-similarity), via implicit links. Throughout this paper, we use interdependent and coupled interchangeably. The key contributions are as follows:

- **Interdependent Similarity of Locations:** We capture the coupled relationship between multiple locations with respect to both intra-similarity and inter-similarity, via modelling the co-occurrences and links of locations.
- **Geographical Information:** We also integrate explicit rich context data in the form of geographical distance using longitude and latitude, whilst capturing the implicit coupled relationship between locations. This results in a successful implementation of the interdependent item-based model.
- **Excellent Performance on Real-Life Social Networks:** We run our model on the real-life data, including the world-wide Gowalla data, Australia

Gowalla data, and a closer case-study in Gold Coast via Twitter. We observe major performance increases in terms of accuracy and error reduction. In some instances, the increase exceeds 32-fold (3118%). It verifies the effectiveness of applying the coupled similarity and geographic information.

2   Related Work

Content-based filtering (CBF) and collaborative filtering (CF) techniques are two popular approaches for recommender systems. CBF [2] approaches produce recommendations for users by analyzing the content of items and user profiles. CF [2] methods produce recommendations or predictions relying solely on the past activities of users. CF can be classified into two classes: memory-based and model-based algorithms. Memory-based algorithms are further divided into user-based and item-based methods under different hypothesis [3]. User-based approaches assume that similar users have similar tastes and make recommendations based on the opinion of users' most similar neighbors [3]. On the other hand, item-based methods assume that users are interested in similar items [3]. Unlike memory-based approaches, which use the entire user-item matrix to make recommendations, the model-based approaches [4] learn a predictive model from training data to predict. Some of the most successful realizations of model-based algorithms are built upon matrix factorization [3], due to their good scalability and predictive accuracy. Matrix factorization techniques assume that users' preferences and items' characteristics are described by latent factors [4].

A few more recent and advanced methods include the Poisson factor models [1], deep learning models [5], and probabilistic models [6], and etc. However, none of them consider the coupling relationship between locations in the POI recommendation. In our proposed interdependent model, the basic item-based method is used to incorporate the coupling relationship to determine if it produces an improved prediction. We may consider to apply the interdependent model to integrate with the sophisticated approaches as the future work, since our proposed interdependent similarity is capable to be widely fit to different model settings as required.

3   Problem Statement

A large number of users with multiple locations can be represented by the user-location frequency graph, which is a weighted undirected bipartite graph $G_{ul}^f = (U, L, E_{ul}, W_{ul}^f)$, where U is a set of vertices that represent users, L is a collection of nodes that represent locations, E_{ul} is a set of edges to denote visits, and the edge weights W_{ul}^f specify the number of visits to a location by a user. Given m users $U = \{u_1, \cdots, u_m\}$ and n locations $L = \{l_1, \cdots, l_n\}$, we then can define an adjacency matrix $M_{ul}^f = [x_{si}] \in \mathbb{R}^{m \times n}$ for the frequency graph G_{ul}^f. Each entry x_{si} in M_{ul}^f quantifies how many times the user u_s visits each location l_i. For example, Fig. 1a represents a tabular form of an adjacency matrix, referred to as a "user-location frequency matrix", in which m users are each represented by rows, and n locations are denoted by columns. The entry for a user u_s and a location l_i reflects the frequency that the user has visited the location, i.e. f_{u_s,l_i}.

The POI recommendation problem is to predict the top-K ranking locations for the user u_s with the estimated check-in entries (prediction scores) p_{u_s,l_i}, which is predicted via analyzing the historical visiting locations. For example, Fig. 1b shows a tabularized matrix which now contains prediction scores (p_{u_s,l_i}) for each user (u_s) for visiting each location (l_i) (the ideal output of a system addressing the POI recommendation problem). In this example, u_3 shows a series of numbers (prediction scores) for each location. A higher prediction score indicates that the system predicts the user more likely to visit that location. Hence, in this example, if $K = 2$, the top-2 locations would be l_3 and l_5.

	l_1	l_2	l_3	...	l_n
u_1	f_{u_1,l_1}	f_{u_1,l_2}	f_{u_1,l_3}	...	f_{u_1,l_n}
u_2	f_{u_2,l_1}	f_{u_2,l_2}	f_{u_2,l_3}	...	f_{u_2,l_n}
u_3	f_{u_3,l_1}	f_{u_3,l_2}	f_{u_3,l_3}	...	f_{u_3,l_n}
...	...	...	...	...	...
u_m	f_{u_n,l_1}	f_{u_n,l_2}	f_{u_m,l_3}	...	f_{u_m,l_n}

(a) User-Location Frequency Matrix

	l_1	l_2	l_3	l_4	l_5
u_1	p_{u_1,l_1}	p_{u_1,l_2}	p_{u_1,l_3}	p_{u_1,l_4}	p_{u_1,l_5}
u_2	p_{u_2,l_1}	p_{u_2,l_2}	p_{u_2,l_3}	p_{u_2,l_4}	p_{u_2,l_5}
u_3	0.3	1.2	4.7	1.8	3.6
...	...	...	...	...	...
u_m	p_{u_n,l_1}	p_{u_n,l_2}	p_{u_m,l_3}	p_{u_m,l_4}	p_{u_m,l_5}

(b) User-Location Prediction Matrix

Fig. 1. Example user-location matrices represented in tabular form.

4   Interdependent Item-Based Model

4.1   Baseline Model

The basic model of the recommender system used is a classic example of item-based collaborative filtering [3], in which the items are POIs in the POI recommendation settings. In this model, a similarity matrix is calculated, representing the similarity between different POI locations. This matrix is based on cosine similarity between different location pairs [3]. The cosine similarity can then be used to calculate predicted frequency values based on Eq. (1) [7]. In this equation, the predicted frequency $(f_{s,i})$ of a user (u_s) for a location (l_i) is equivalent to the ratio of the sum of the similarities between l_i and all other locations multiplied by the frequency of visits for u_s at each location, and the sum of the absolute similarities between l_i and all other locations, as outlined below:

$$\hat{f}_{s,i} = \frac{\sum_{l_j} S_l^{cos}(l_i, l_j)(f_{s,j})}{\sum_{l_j} |S_l^{cos}(l_i, l_j)|}, \tag{1}$$

where $\hat{f}_{s,i}$ is the prediction score for user u_s at location l_i, and $S_l^{cos}(l_i, l_j)$ is the cosine similarity between l_i and l_j. Equation (1) is used to yield a matrix of predictions between each user and each location. Upon running data through the above processes, it is possible to obtain a prediction score for each user-location pair. It can then be added to a prediction matrix, as in Fig. 1(b). The baseline model only considers the explicit relationship between locations via check-ins.

4.2   Interdependent Model

The interdependent model addresses the coupling relationship among locations based on the user-location TF-IDF matrix, as well as geographic information.

User-Location TF-IDF Matrix. The user-location TF-IDF matrix (M_{ul}^{ti}) is derived from the user-location frequency matrix, by following an idea from text mining [8], where each document is regarded as a user, each term is regarded as a location, and the frequency of the word in an document is regarded as the frequency of location visits by a user. So in such a matrix, each row represents a user, while each column represents a location. The elements of the matrix are the TF-IDF values of each user-location pairing. As a result, the values along the matrix diagonal will always be 0. The TF in M_{ul}^{ti} can be calculated as the ratio of the location visit frequency (f_{l_i,u_s}) of a user and the total number of locations visited by the user ($\sum_{l_i' \in u_s} f_{l_i,u_s}$). The IDF in M_{ul}^{ti} can be calculated as the natural logarithm (for scaling purposes) of the ratio between the total number of users and the number of users that have visited a specific location ($|u \in U : l_i \in u|$). TF-IDF value is the product of TF and IDF, formalized as:

$$tf \cdot idf = \frac{f_{l_i,u_s}}{\sum_{l_i' \in u_s} f_{l_i,u_s}} \cdot \ln \frac{|U|}{|u \in U : l_i \in u|}. \tag{2}$$

The Location-Location Transition Matrix. For the geographical information, we include a location-location transition matrix in our proposed model. The rows and columns represent a set of POIs. Thus, every element of the matrix represents the geographical distance between a pair of POIs (l_i and l_j) taken from the set. This data can be calculated as the numerical form of Euclidean distance from geographical co-ordinates, by using longitude and latitude. We use such geographic information to define the coupled relationship among locations.

Based on the user-location TF-IDF matrix and the geographic information in the form of location-location transition matrix, we are ready to propose the coupled similarity between locations via intra-similarity and inter-similarity.

Intra-similarity of Locations. The first step in measuring the semantic relatedness between locations is to explore the explicit semantic relationship between them, referred to as the intra-similarity of locations.

The intra-similarity between locations is based on the statistical analysis of location occurrence patterns [1]. It supposes that locations are relational if they are visited by the same user, and the intra-similarity between locations can be estimated by calculating their co-occurrence frequency across all users.

In most of the previous approaches, the relationship between locations is simply estimated by the inner product of their distribution across the entire user set. Here, we adapt the popular co-occurrence measure Jaccard [9] to capture the intra-similarity between locations according to their association in the user sets. We capture the intra-relationship between locations for a single user, and then extended it to compute the intra-coupling across the whole user set.

The intra-similarity of locations matrix (δ^{Ia}) is derived from the user-location TF-IDF matrix. Both the rows and columns of this matrix represent locations of the data set and each element represents the intra-similarity of the respective location pair. At a user-level, intra-similarity is calculated for user u_s as follows.

$$\delta^{Ia}(l_i, l_j | u_s) = (x'_{si} \cdot x'_{sj}) / (x'_{si} + x'_{sj}), \tag{3}$$

where x'_{si} and x'_{sj} represent TF-IDF values for a specific user at l_i and l_j, respectively. To move intra-similarity of locations to the corpus level, the average intra-similarity is taken for the set of users that have visited either location. However, only the users that have visited both locations contribute to this total calculation (other-wise their contribution to the sum is 0), as defined below.

$$\delta^{Ia}(l_i, l_j | U) = \frac{1}{|S|} \sum_{u_s \in S'} \delta^{Ia}(l_i, l_j | u_s), \tag{4}$$

where $S = \{u_s | (x'_{si} \neq 0) \vee (x'_{sj} \neq 0)\}$ (the set of users visiting either location) and $S' = \{u_s | (x'_{si} \neq 0) \wedge (x'_{sj} \neq 0)\}$ (the set of users visiting both locations).

When constructing the final matrix, if l_i and l_j are the same, then their intra-similarity will always be 1, otherwise, the remaining intra-similarities are normalized via feature scaling. This process is shown in Eq. (5).

$$\delta^{Ia}(l_i, l_j) = \begin{cases} 1 & \text{if } i = j, \\ \dfrac{\delta^{Ia}(l_i,l_j|U) - \min\limits_{1 \leq i,j \leq n}\{\delta^{Ia}(l_i,l_j|U)\}}{\max\limits_{1 \leq i,j \leq n}\{\delta^{Ia}(l_i,l_j|U)\} - \min\limits_{1 \leq i,j \leq n}\{\delta^{Ia}(l_i,l_j|U)\}} & \text{if } i \neq j, \end{cases} \tag{5}$$

where $\delta^{Ia}(l_i, l_j)$ is the intra-similarity between l_i and l_j, $\delta^{Ia}(l_i, l_j | U)$ represents the corpus-level intra-similarity between those locations before normalization.

Inter-Similarity of Locations. The above intra-similarity only captures the relationship between locations based on their co-occurrence frequency. However, some locations are related to each other even though they do not happen to be visited by the same user. As the absence of this underlying relationship, the semantic information in the original locations cannot be completely captured, which brings difficulties into the recommender system. Hence, we propose to define the inter-similarity of locations to capture this underlying relationship.

We have captured the intra-similarity $\delta^{Ia}(l_i, l_k)$ between locations l_i and l_k, and $\delta^{Ia}(l_k, l_j)$ between locations l_k and l_j. The $\delta^{Ia}(l_i, l_k)$ indicates the possibility of visiting both locations l_i and l_k. Similarly, the $\delta^{Ia}(l_k, l_j)$ captures the possibility of visiting both locations l_k when l_j. Intuitively, it is easy to see that, $\delta^{Ia}(l_i, l_k)$ and $\delta^{Ia}(l_k, l_j)$ should imply the possibility to visit both locations l_i and l_j, thus the possibility can be determined using them.

The inter-similarity of locations matrix (δ^{Ie+geo}) compares the closeness of locations even when they have not been visited by the same users. Equation (6) is used to calculate the inter-similarity between locations. This matrix is derived based on the values of the intra-similarity of locations matrix. The process also involves taking geographic similarity into account, hence the information from the location-location transition matrix is used to build the weights for locations.

$$\delta^{Ie+geo}(l_i, l_j) = \max_{l_k \in L - \{l_i, l_j\}} \{\min \{g_{ik} \cdot \delta^{Ia}(l_i, l_k), g_{kj} \cdot \delta^{Ia}(l_k, l_j)\}\}, \qquad (6)$$

where δ^{Ia} is the intra-similarity between locations defined in Eq. (5). g_{ik} is the geographic similarity between locations l_i and l_k, and g_{ik} is obtained via transforming the normalized max-min distance $\hat{y}_{kj}$ to similarity, by applying $g_{ik} = 1/(1 + \hat{y}_{ik})$. The value of $\hat{y}_{ik}$ is calculated as in Eq. (7):

$$\hat{y}_{ik} = [y_{ik} - \min_{1 \leq i,k \leq n} \{y_{ik}\}]/[\max_{1 \leq i,k \leq n} \{y_{ik}\} - \min_{1 \leq i,k \leq n} \{y_{ik}\}], \qquad (7)$$

where y_{ik} is the (i, k) entry in the location-location transition matrix based on Euclidean distance. The same calculation process applies to g_{kj} as well. For $i = j$, we set $\delta^{Ie+geo}(l_i, l_j) = 1$. Otherwise, $\delta^{Ie+geo}(l_i, l_j)$ is used.

Interdependent Similarity of Locations. The intra-similarity discovers the explicit relationship between locations using their co-occurrences, and the inter-similarity discovers the implicit relationship by their interaction with other locations. Hence, to capture the complete semantic relationship between locations to build a high-quality recommender system, we couple the intra-similarity and inter-similarity together to measure the semantic relatedness between locations.

The final matrix is the interdependent location similarity matrix (δ^C), which is representative a graph derived from the inter-similarity of locations matrix and intra-similarity of locations matrix. This matrix is reflective of both the inter-similarity and intra-similarity between locations. During the coupling, the balance between intra-similarity and inter-similarity is controlled by the parameter α. α is between 0 and 1, with higher values giving more precedence to inter-similarity and lower values giving more precedence to intra-similarity. The equation used to calculate the interdependent similarity of locations is outlined as below.

$$\delta^C(l_i, l_j) = \begin{cases} 1 & \text{if } i = j, \\ (1 - \alpha) \cdot \delta^{Ia}(l_i, l_j) + \alpha \cdot \delta^{Ie}(l_i, l_j) & \text{if } i \neq j, \end{cases} \qquad (8)$$

where $\delta^C(l_i, l_j)$ represents the interdependent location similarity between l_i and l_j. If l_i and l_j are the same, $\delta^C(l_i, l_j)$ is set to 1. The value of $\delta^C(l_i, l_j)$ falls within

[0, 1], in which 0 indicates that two locations are completely unrelated, while 1 indicates that they have the highest relatedness. Hence, the higher the coupled score, the more similar the two locations. In our proposed interdependent model, we replace the cosine similarity from Eq. (1) with coupled similarity, to calculate the recommendation score.

5   Empirical Study

5.1   Data Sets

In this study, a total of three data sets were used. Two of these were derived from the public Gowalla data set. This data set included world-wide check-in data from February 2009 to October 2010. This data set was sourced from Liu et al. [1], who also filtered out users with fewer than 15 unique location check-ins and POIs with fewer than 10 visitors.

- **Gowalla:** The Gowalla data set used in this study is sometimes referred to as "Gowalla (0.1)". This is a version of the public Gowalla data set (mentioned above) that has been scaled down to only include the first 10% of users and first 10% of locations. This scaled version of the data set contains 1873 users, 3250 locations and 51330 check-ins. The data set has a sparsity of 99.16%.
- **Gowalla Australia:** This is referred to as the "Gowalla (Aus)" data set. It is filtered from the original public Gowalla data set obtained by [1], which again contains world-wide check-in data from February 2009 to October 2010. The filtered version of this data set contains check-ins to locations only within Australia. The data is also further filtered to remove users with less than 10 check-ins and locations with less than 10 visitors. The remaining data set consists of 7,717 check-ins from 866 users at 1,118 locations. The sparsity of this data set is 99.20%.
- **Gold Coast Twitter:** This data set (referred to as "GC Twitter") is obtained by cross-referencing a set of all tweets made in the Gold Coast with a set of known POIs obtained by crawling Foursquare. This is done by matching the geo-locations of tweets to the geo-locations of Foursquare POIs. The tweets were made between 1 January 2017 and 31 December 2017. The final data set is further filtered down to remove users with less than 5 tweet locations and locations with less than 5 users making tweets. The final GC twitter data set contains 31730 check-ins of 1529 different users at 786 Gold Coast POI locations. The sparsity of this data set is 99.30%.

The geographical bounding boxes of the Gowalla (Aus) and GC Twitter data sets are shown in Fig. 2. Training and testing data sets are obtained by randomly partitioning the frequencies in User-POI check-in matrix. 80% of the data is used to train the models and the remaining 20% is used to evaluate.

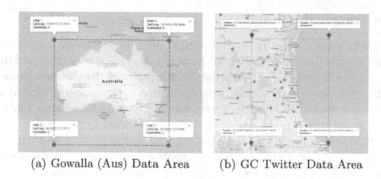

(a) Gowalla (Aus) Data Area   (b) GC Twitter Data Area

Fig. 2. The geographical areas for (a) Gowalla (Aus) and (b) GC Twitter data sets.

5.2 Performance Metrics and Experimental Settings

Mean Error. Two mean error metrics are used to evaluate the models. MAE and RMSE are both metrics that are used for evaluating absolute error [10]. For the existing methods, we use the user-location matrix as truth. For the interdependent model however, in order to address scaling issues, a TF-IDF matrix is applied as truth. The smaller the MAE and RMSE error scores, the better the recommendation quality.

Precision and Recall. Precision (Pre@K) and recall (Rec@K) are used to further evaluate the models. This involves calculating precision and recall in the top-K most recommended POIs. In this evaluation, precision is the ratio of positive predictions and the number of predicted recommendations [1]. Recall is the ratio of positive predictions and the number of POIs actually visited [1]. Since precision and recall are expected to display different behaviors with different values of K, the F1-score [11] is also used as a means of coupling precision and recall into a single metric. The larger the precision, recall, and F1 scores, the better the recommendation quality.

Experimental Settings. For comparative purposes, all three data sets are also run through three basic models: item-based collaborative filtering [3], user-based collaborative filtering [3], and matrix factorization (MF) using singular value decomposition [4]. There are no relevant parameters for the basic models. For the interdependent model, the value of α is set to 0.5 (giving equal weighting to both intra-similarity and inter-similarity when determining interdependent location similarity). Each figure in the following section represents the proposed interdependent model (the "Item-Based Coupled" model) using the red bar. All experiments are run on the *Griffith University Gowonda HPC Cluster* using Intel Xeon CPU X5650 processors @2.67 GHz.

5.3   Experimental Results

With respect to mean error (in both metrics) all values between all of the basic models are similar (as shown in Fig. 3). However, there is a very clear and distinctive drop in MAE and RMSE with the interdependent model when comparing it with the basic models. The most prominent drop occurs in the Gowalla (0.1) data set (which overall also has the lowest mean error for all models). The change (between the interdependent model and the basic model) in MAE is approximately -8.30-fold (an 87.95% decrease) and in RMSE, -5.58-fold (an 82.09% decrease). The second greatest drop in mean error occurs with the Gowalla (Aus) data set. For this data set, the change (between the interdependent item-based model and the basic item-based model) in MAE is approximately -2.24-fold (a 55.34% decrease) and the change in RMSE is approximately -1.86-fold (a 46.19% decrease). For the GC Twitter data set, the fold change (between the interdependent item-based model and the basic item-based model) in MAE is approximately -1.40 (a drop of 28.82%) whilst the change in RMSE is approximately -1.19 fold (a drop of 15.80%). This is the lowest drop in mean error. In terms of mean error, the interdependent model is thus considered a tremendous success as it reduces error significantly across all data sets.

The precision and recall data also shows a prominent increase in performance for both metrics with the interdependent model on the all data sets. There is a remarkable increase in precision, recall and F1-scores which usually supersedes all other models significantly. On all data sets, the basic item-based model tends to perform worse than all other models, however, the interdependent item-based model usually supersedes all other models. The most prominent changes in precision/recall metrics are observed when analyzing the Gowalla (0.1) data set (Fig. 4). Across all values of K, the average precision increase (between the interdependent item-based model and the basic item-based model) is approximately 31.68-fold (a 3068.68% increase). The average increase in recall is 31.06-fold (a 3005.86% increase) and similarly, the average increase in the F1-scores is 32.18-fold (a 3118.38% increase). The changes are also significant in the Gowalla (Aus) data set (Fig. 5). Again, across all values of K, the average precision increase

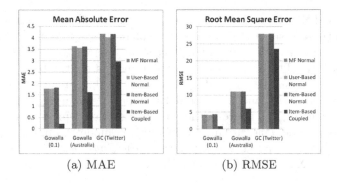

(a) MAE   (b) RMSE

Fig. 3. Mean error in all data sets.

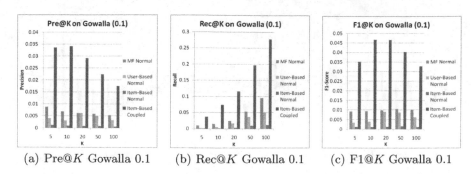

(a) Pre@K Gowalla 0.1   (b) Rec@K Gowalla 0.1   (c) F1@K Gowalla 0.1

Fig. 4. Precision, recall and F1-scores on the Gowalla (0.1) data set.

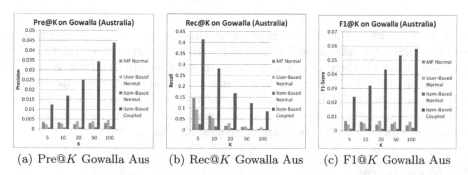

(a) Pre@K Gowalla Aus   (b) Rec@K Gowalla Aus   (c) F1@K Gowalla Aus

Fig. 5. Precision, recall and F1-scores on the Gowalla (Aus) data set.

(between the interdependent item-based model and the basic item-based model) is approximately 27.31-fold (a 2631.41% increase). Recall and F1-scores, respectively, experience approximate 19.90-fold and 25.74-fold increases. This is equivalent to increases of 1890.33% and 2473.89%.

The poorest precision and recall scores are observed with the GC Twitter data set (Fig. 6), across all values of K, the average precision increase (between the interdependent model and the basic model) is approximately 1.64-fold (a 43.078% increase). Similarly, the average increase in recall is approximately 1.70-fold (a 40.70% increase). When coupled as an F1-score, the average precision-recall increase is approximately 1.64-fold (a 38.55% increase). At some values of k (K10, K50 and K100) the interdependent model outperforms the matrix factorization model whereas at others (K5 and K20) the matrix model outperforms the interdependent model. On average however, the interdependent model still performs best (a 4.36% increase in precision compared to the matrix model, a 13.46% increase in recall and a 5.28% increase in F1-scores). It is also noted that the improvement of our interdependent model on the GC Twitter data is not as substantial as it is on the other two data sets. This is most likely due to the fact that the GC Twitter data set is not based on explicit check-in data, but rather, is implicitly derived under the assumption that a user is visiting a POI when they make a tweet nearby.

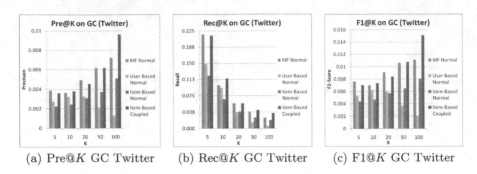

(a) Pre@K GC Twitter   (b) Rec@K GC Twitter   (c) F1@K GC Twitter

Fig. 6. Precision, recall and F1-scores on the GC Twitter data set.

Therefore, when considering model performance in terms of precision and recall accuracy, the interdependent model is considered very successful. In every data set analyzed, there is a significant increase observed. Whilst it is not as substantial with the GC Twitter data (when compared to the other data sets), it is still considered significant as a 5.28% increase in F1-scores. Such an excellent performance improvement is due to considering the coupling relationship between locations, and the inclusion of geographic information.

6   Conclusion

There are many limitations of traditional collaborative filtering models, mainly due to their poor performance on scarce POI data and lack of considering rich context information. A basic item-based collaborative filtering model is used to incorporate the interdependent location similarity to determine whether or not including this relationship improves prediction outcomes. In doing so, this study proposes a interdependent item-based model which successfully addresses the data scarcity and rich context issues by capturing the implicit relationship between the locations in terms of intra-similarity and inter-similarity. The interdependent item-based model also considers geographical data. The interdependent model displays excellent performance when used to analyze social network data sets. We observe excellent performance increases (up to 32-fold precision/recall increases and an 89% RMSE decrease) on a world-wide POI data set. Excellent performance is also observed when focusing on Australia and the Gold Coast social network data. The significant improvement verifies the great effectiveness of including the coupling relationship between locations, as well as the geographic information into the POI recommendation model.

The future directions of this research include optimizing the value of α with different data sets, considering what data characteristics may influence the coupled relationship between locations, and incorporating the coupled relationship into the advanced approaches for POI recommendation, e.g. deep learning model.

Acknowledgements. This work was supported by a Summer Scholarship project as well as two Griffith University's 2018 New Researcher Grants, with Dr. Can Wang and Dr. Md Saiful Islam being Chief Investigators, respectively.

References

1. Liu, Y., Pham, T.A.N., Cong, G., Yuan, Q.: An experimental evaluation of point-of-interest recommendation in location-based social networks. Proc. VLDB Endow. **10**(10), 1010–1021 (2017)
2. Lu, Z., Dou, Z., Lian, J., Xie, X., Yang, Q.: Content-based collaborative filtering for news topic recommendation. In: 2015 AAAI, pp. 217–223 (2015)
3. Ghazarian, S., Nematbakhsh, M.A.: Enhancing memory-based collaborative filtering for group recommender systems. Expert Syst. Appl. **42**(7), 3801–3812 (2015)
4. Koren, Y., Bell, R., Volinsky, C.: Matrix factorization techniques for recommender systems. Computer **42**(8), 42–49 (2009). http://base.sjtu.edu.cn/~bjshen/2.pdf
5. Yin, H., Wang, W., Wang, H., Chen, L., Zhou, X.: Spatial-aware hierarchical collaborative deep learning for POI recommendation. IEEE TKDE **29**(11), 2537–2551 (2017)
6. Yin, H., Zhou, X., Cui, B., Wang, H., Zheng, K., Nguyen, Q.V.H.: Adapting to user interest drift for POI recommendation. IEEE TKDE **28**(10), 2566–2581 (2016)
7. Liu, N.N., Yang, Q.: EigenRank: a ranking-oriented approach to collaborative filtering. In: 2008 ACM SIGIR, pp. 83–90 (2008)
8. Zhong, N., Li, Y., Wu, S.T.: Effective pattern discovery for text mining. IEEE TKDE **24**(1), 30–44 (2012)
9. Thomas, A., Sindhu, L.: A survey on content based semantic relations in tweets. Int. J. Comput. Appl. **132**(11), 14–18 (2015)
10. Sattari, M., Manguoglu, M., Toroslu, I.H., Symeonidis, P., Senkul, P., Manolopoulos, Y.: Geo-activity recommendations by using improved feature combination. In: 2012 Ubicomp, pp. 996–1003 (2012)
11. Vinyals, O., Kaiser, Ł., Koo, T., Petrov, S., Sutskever, I., Hinton, G.: Grammar as a foreign language. In: 2015 NIPS, pp. 2773–2781 (2015)

Child Abuse and Domestic Abuse: Content and Feature Analysis from Social Media Disclosures

Sudha Subramani[1]([✉]), Hua Wang[1], Md Rafiqul Islam[1], Anwaar Ulhaq[1], and Manjula O'Connor[2]

[1] College of Engineering and Science, Victoria University, Melbourne, Australia
sudha.subramani1@live.vu.edu.au
[2] Department of Psychiatry, The University of Melbourne, Melbourne, Australia

Abstract. Due to increase in popularity of social media, people have started discussing their thoughts and opinions in the form of textual posts. Currently, the people tend to disclose even the socially tabooed topics such as Child Abuse (CA), and Domestic Abuse (DA) to receive the desired response and social support in turn. The increasing volume of abuse related posts being shared on social media is of great interest for public health sectors and family welfare organizations to monitor the public health and promote support services. However, due to the large volume, high velocity and huge variety of context and content of user generated data, it is difficult to mine the different kinds of abuse (CA and DA) related posts from other general posts, that flood over the web. Hence, this paper aims to discover and differentiate the characteristics of CA and DA posts from the massive user generated posts, with the underlying context. Various features such as psycholinguistic, textual and sentimental features are analyzed and Machine Learning techniques are trained to analyze the predictive power of extracted features. Hence, the resulting model achieves more predictive power with high accuracy in classifying possible cases of abuse related posts from diverse user posts.

Keywords: Child Abuse · Domestic Abuse · Social media
Text mining · Machine learning

1 Introduction

The massive amount of data generated over social media is witnessing a foremost development in the last few centuries. Social media encourages the users for their freedom of thoughts and provides a platform to share their expressions, opinions, hopes and mental states. Social media has changed our lives tremendously with the increased social communication. Networking and interpersonal communication are the integral parts on social media.

Domestic Abuse (DA) [1] is one of the most prevailing forms of abuse (physical, sexual, verbal, emotional) in an intimate relationship. According to the

© Springer International Publishing AG, part of Springer Nature 2018
J. Wang et al. (Eds.): ADC 2018, LNCS 10837, pp. 174–185, 2018.
https://doi.org/10.1007/978-3-319-92013-9_14

World Health Organization, DA has serious impacts on the mental health of victims such as depression, sleep disturbances, anxiety, flashbacks, hyper-arousal, emotional distress and so on [2]. Another epidemic issue is Child Abuse (CA) [3], includes sexual abuse and neglect that pose serious health impacts such as depression, anxiety, feelings of isolation and stigma, poor self-esteem and so on [4]. Hence, both social issues are considered as the global health issues and pose the most important public health challenge.

Due to the alarming rate of global social issues and consequent health impacts, people increasingly share their opinions and thoughts on social media to promote awareness, express empathy or share their personal experiences. Hence, identifying the posts related to DA and CA would possibly provide unprecedentedly valuable information to the public health sectors. Nevertheless, the problem of identifying the abuse related posts on social media remain a challenging issue. (1) Considering the social media such as Twitter, user tweets are restricted in length. (2) Informal language structure that contains local slangs, misspellings, grammatical errors, acronyms and hashtags. (3) It is time consuming to generate ground truth or labeled data, that addressing the two most common social issues at a single step.

Considering the above-mentioned limitations, in addition to the unique characteristics of large streams of social media such as immense scale of volume, higher velocity and diverse variety of posts. This paper proposes a framework that automatically identifies the posts related to two prevailing social issues such as DA and CA. This is of great interest to public health sectors to provide actionable knowledge by monitoring and analyzing continuous and rich user generated content. Hence, our task is to identify the different kinds of abuse related posts on social media from the standard posts. Some of the example posts shared on social media, on the most global concerning issues and the general themes are explained in Table 1.

Table 1. Examples posts and the corresponding labels

ID	Social media posts	Context	Label
P_1	"I was a victim of Domestic Abuse, physically, emotionally and financially. I couldn't work due to mental health problems, anxiety, PTSD"	Domestic Abuse	Abuse
P_2	"Toddler Sara died after deliberate and protracted physical and sexual assault. Her mother has now broken her silence. "	Child Abuse	Abuse
P_3	"Editors' picks: our favorite things from this week. What caught your eye?"	Movie	General
P_4	"Best commentary ever!!!! someone call someone lol "	Sports	General

Though, identifying general posts for commercial and marketing purposes [5,6] are already addressed in the literature, our task of identifying global social impacts from social media are the first of its kind. To this end, this paper focuses on the global social and mental health issue in the context of public health monitoring via social media. Thus, the key contributions of our proposed work are as follows:

- Constructing and analyzing the feature sets based on psycholinguistic, textual and sentimental features to characterize and differentiate between abuse related posts and general posts.
- Training the various machine learning classifiers and evaluate their performance to examine the usefulness of the extracted features.

The structure of the paper is organized as follows. Section 2 explains about the influence of social media in conversing the various socially tabooed topics and mental health issues. Section 3 provides the solution to the problem, by means of methodology. Section 4 discusses about performance evaluation and finally, the conclusion is discussed in Sect. 5 with the advantage of using various features and the future work.

2   Background

Social media is emerged as a potential tool for discussing range of topics from socially tabooed topics (DA, CA) [1,3] to entertainment topics (sports, movies, technological advancements, fashion and politics) and so on. DA and CA are the most prevalent forms of abuse worldwide. Thus, 1 in 3 (35%) of women worldwide have experienced either physical or sexual abuse [2], and approximately 5 children die every day because of child abuse[1]. Considering this alarming statistic of social issues and subsequent health impacts, people increasingly share their opinions and thoughts on social media to promote awareness, and to leverage various dimensions of social support like emotional, instrumental, and informational support. Social support has been demonstrated to trigger many predominant positive outcomes such as wellbeing and life satisfaction [7].

With the increasing popularity of social media, several research studies focused on social media to analyze and predict real world activities like user sentiment analysis, opinion mining on political campaigns [8], natural disasters [9], epidemic surveillance [10], and so on. But, the recent studies focused on analyzing the socially tabooed topics and various mental illness, as follows. Reavley et al. [11] categorized the users' tweets related to depression and schizophrenia into various themes such as personal experience, awareness promotion and various categories to measure the attitude towards mental illness. Another study [12] classified the Facebook groups into support groups, self-help groups, advocacy and awareness groups, and fund raising groups based on their purposes and functionalities. They stated that individuals utilize online social networks to obtain

---

[1] https://www.dosomething.org/us/facts/11-facts-about-child-abuse.

information, raise awareness, and access support. Recent research [13] analyzed the Instagram posts and find that people use Instagram to engage in social network and explaining their personal story about difficult times. The sheer overwhelm of social media data makes it to be the one of Big Data's most significant sources [14,15] and some studies dealt with security and privacy issues [16–20], as the increasing sophistication of social media data is posing substantial threats to users privacy.

Schrading et al. [21] analyzed the Twitter corpus to seek insights into the reasons, victims give for staying in vs. leaving abusive relationships. Amrit et al. [22] identified and predicted child abuse cases in the public health institutions using text mining techniques. Another study states that, support seeking in stigmatized context of sexual abuse on Reddit and investigated the use of throw away accounts in the aspects of support seeking, anonymity and first-time disclosures [23]. Some studies have predicted mental health conditions by analyzing textual features [24]and Linguistic Inquiry and Word Count (LIWC) [25] to capture language characteristics and considered as the influential predictors of depression-related disorders and mental health.

Problem Formulation. Given the corpus of input posts, our task is to predict the associated class of each post based on the constructed feature sets. Let $B = \{p_i | 1 \leqslant i \leqslant n\}$ denote the corpus of n posts, where p_i is defined as $<p_1, p_2, p_3 \ldots p_n>$ of n posts, such that each post is associated with the class either as abuse-related or general, where $L = \{L_j | j = <abuse>, <general>\}$

For each post $p_i \epsilon B$ predict the class value L, based on psycholinguistic, textual and sentimental features f_j extracted from post: $F^{(p_i)} = [\ldots, f_j^{(p_i)} \ldots \ldots |1 \leqslant j \leqslant r]$. Then the machine learning classifiers are trained over the extracted features, by treating our task as binary text classification problem and the classifier predicts the class value for each post during testing.

3 Methodology

Our proposed framework for identification of posts related to different kinds of abuse (Fig. 1), are explained in the following sections.

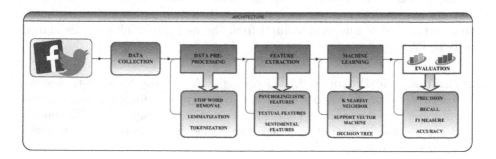

Fig. 1. Architecture of our proposed model

3.1   Data Collection and Preprocessing

Our framework is designed for identifying socially stigmatized topics, from the online posts of social media platforms (e.g. Facebook, Twitter, Reddit). Our chosen platform for this study is Facebook, as it allows lengthy submission and therefore, standard English is common. Thus, we extract the posts on Facebook using its Application Programming Interface, Graph API[2] from pages discussing about these social issues and other general themes. We extracted more than 10k posts and 25k comments. We excluded the posts and comments, that contain word length of less than 3, as it will not contain any meaningful information and the posts that contain only hyper-links. Thus, we finally considered 1821 abuse related posts and 2418 general posts. The posts are labeled according to their key search term.

All the captured data are publicly available and we abide by the terms, conditions and privacy policies of the Facebook, as the captured posts used in this research are public and not from personal accounts or Facebook Timeline. Due to the sensitive topic of the data analysed, we need to respect the users' privacy and reduce the risk of data being resurfaced through Google searches or in Facebook pages. So, we fabricated quotes slightly and used paraphrasing of posters' data, a common method in ethical social computing work. This is similar to what Markham says "fabrication as ethical practice", when using social media content in the paper [26].

In the next step, we performed text preprocessing techniques such as stop word removal, tokenization, and lemmatization. High quality information is extracted for effective feature analysis. We removed the stop words contain common English words like articles, prepositions, conjunctions, pronouns, etc., Few examples are the, a, an, the, in, and at. Next, we performed lemmatization, as it is used to reduce more inflectional forms of words into a more limited form of canonical forms. This helps to standardize terms appearance and to reduce data sparseness. However, data preprocessing is not performed, when analyzing the psycholinguistic features, as the pronouns, articles, prepositions are also considered as feature sets to discriminate the abuse related posts from others.

3.2   Feature Extraction

To characterize and differentiate diverse posts related underlying context, we construct and analyze the various feature sets based on psycholinguistic dimensions, textual and sentimental features from the user posts. They are explained briefly as follows:

Psycholinguistic Features. LIWC package [25] is a psycholinguistic lexicon created to recognize the various emotional, cognitive, and linguistic components lies on users' verbal or written communication. For each input in the corpus, it returns more than 70 output variables with higher level hierarchy of psycholinguistic features such as:

---

[2] https://developers.facebook.com/docs/graph-api.

- linguistic dimensions, other grammar, informal language
- temporal, affective, social processes
- cognitive, biological, perceptual processes
- personal concerns, drives, relativity.

These higher-level categories are further specialized in subcategories such as in

- biological processes - body, sexual, health and ingestion.
- affective processes - positive emotion, negative emotion
- and negative emotion further sub-classified as anger, anxiety, and sadness.
- drives - affiliation, achievement, power, regard, and risk.

For our task, we converted all the posts into mathematical vectors based on psycholinguistic features. The word in the posts could fit some categories and not fit into some categories. Hence, we could consider the classification of posts based on psycholinguistic dimensions, to which category it belongs. Table 2 shows the mean values of these LIWC psycholinguistic processes for the abuse related posts and general posts.

From the highlighted values of Table 2, it is inferred that the posts related to DA and CA have higher mean values for the features such as "negative emotions, anxiety, anger, sadness", because they usually explain some abusive experience and carry lot of negative emotions in it. On the contrast, the general posts have higher values of positive emotion. Also, the posts related to abusive content have higher values of "sexual, health, death" features and general posts scored higher values for "money, and leisure" features.

Textual Features. We extracted the textual features to find the most frequent words in the underlying posts between two classes. The reason for predicting the textual features from the user posts is to analyze the most frequent words, that underlies in the textual content and how it varies depends on the context. For instance, when predicting the abuse related posts, we can find the terms such as "abuse, violence, child, kids, family" are the most frequent. Whereas the entertainment terms, such as "watch, story, great, play" are more prevalent in the general posts.

The Bag of Words (BoW) model is the general way of extracting textual features. This is very simple and flexible model, and this algorithm counts the number of occurrence of words in the corpus. In our context, it can be represented as a binary word presence representation that indicates, if a word is present in each post. Each distinct word in the corpus corresponds to a feature in the representation. This provides list of words with their word counts per post. Table 3 illustrates the uni-grams belongs to each class and the visualization of the frequent vocabulary items are represented in the form of wordcloud (Fig. 2).

Sentimental Analysis. Sentiment analysis is the way toward deciding if a bit of writing is positive, negative or neutral. Its otherwise called sentiment mining, inferring the assessment or disposition of a speaker. A typical utilize case for this innovation is to find how individuals feels about a specific subject. In addition

Table 2. Mean sores of psycholinguistic features for abuse related and general posts

Category	Example	DA posts	CA posts	General posts
Total pronouns	I, Them	18.31	13.49	13.17
Personal pronouns	I, Her	13.76	7.34	7.63
1st person singular	I, Me	**6.48**	2.10	3.71
1st person plural	We, Us	0.72	0.55	0.73
2nd person	You, Your	1.28	1.86	1.78
3rd person singular	He, She	**4.69**	1.46	1.07
3rd person plural	They, Their	0.55	**1.34**	0.34
Impersonal pronouns	It, Those	4.55	**6.15**	5.52
Articles	A, The	5.08	5.39	5.57
Prepositions	For, Of	12.29	9.66	7.50
Auxiliary verbs	Do, Will	8.40	8.96	7.98
Adverb	Very, Really	4.11	4.78	5.00
Conjunctions	And, Whereas	6.24	5.66	3.47
Verb	Go, Big	16.49	14.95	14.83
Adjectives	Nice, Awesome	3.59	7.47	5.66
Positive emotions	Happy, Love	3.98	1.81	**15.64**
Negative emotions	Loser, Hurt	**4.42**	**17.63**	1.26
Anxiety	Worried, Fearful	**0.54**	**0.90**	0.08
Anger	Hate, Kill	**2.02**	**7.23**	0.50
Sadness	Crying, Sad	**0.60**	**3.21**	0.22
Family	Daughter, Husband	**1.67**	**1.00**	0.36
Friends	Buddy, Friends	0.61	0.20	0.43
Female	Girl	**3.31**	**1.14**	0.47
Male	Boy	**3.35**	1.33	1.35
See	View, Seen	0.80	0.58	**2.21**
Hear	Listen	0.62	0.58	**0.75**
Feel	Feels, Touch	0.56	**0.83**	0.44
Body	Hands, Head	**0.80**	**0.83**	0.46
Health	Clinic, Pill	**1.08**	**1.90**	0.15
Sexual	Sex, Incest	0.21	**1.16**	0.18
Ingestion	Eat, Pizza	0.17	0.16	**0.50**
Past tense	Ago, Did	5.09	2.23	2.94
Present tense	Today, Now	9.84	10.86	10.30
Future tense	Shall, Soon	1.08	0.98	1.44
Work	Job, Majors	1.22	1.10	0.99
Leisure	Cook, Chat	0.76	0.47	**2.10**
Money	Cash, Audit	0.60	0.69	**0.72**
Death	Kill, Bury	**0.52**	**0.84**	0.11

Table 3. Vocabulary analysis of user generated posts

Class	Sample words
DA posts	Abuse, violence, domestic, life, back, home, children, husband, story, police, leave, relationship, court, abuser, year
CA posts	Child, abuse, old, year, sad, sick, sexual, neglect, life, rape, stop, baby, mother, murder, girl
General posts	Well, pretty, best, watch, love, see, great, play, happy, game, movie, amazing, funny, trailer, imdb

(a) DA posts   (b) CA posts

Fig. 2. Wordcloud of unigrams generated from the user posts

Table 4. Analysis of various sentimental features

Category	Text	Pol.	Agr.	Subj.	Conf.	Irony
DA posts	Verbal and emotional abuse is just as damaging as physical abuse	Neg+	Agree	Yes	100	No
CA posts	Neglecting your child is abuse. Love all children unconditionally and with all your heart	Neg	Disagree	Yes	94	No
General posts	Thank god i'm not playing this year, might've been very expensive	Pos	Agree	Yes	90	Yes
General posts	I hope it doesn't have too much advertising	Pos	Agree	Yes	90	Yes

to the psychological and textual features, in this section, we also performed the sentimental analysis of user posts and comments to mine the opinion. These features reveal, the true emotions and opinions from the user posts, because of its immediacy and naturalness. This section analyze the polarity, agreement, subjectivity, confidence and irony of a sentence structure by using the meaning cloud API[3]. Table 4 shows the different examples of sentiment analysis.

---

[3] https://www.meaningcloud.com/products/sentiment-analysis.

3.3   Classification Model

This stage constructs prediction model for recognition of DA and CA posts, by considering the psycholinguistic and textual features as input. Consider our training corpus $B = p_1, p_2, ..., p_n$ of n posts, such that each post p_i is labeled with the class either as abuse-related or general, where $L = l_1|l_2$. The task of a classifier f is to find the corresponding label for each post.

$$f : B \epsilon L \quad f(p) = l \tag{1}$$

- *Support Vector Machines (SVM):* a non-probabilistic linear binary classifier, that maps an input feature vector into a higher dimensional space and find a hyperplane that separates the data into two classes with the maximal margin between the closest samples in each class [27].
- *Decision Tree (DT):* an interpretable classifier [28], creates the hierarchical tree of the training instances, in which a condition on the feature value is used to divide the data hierarchically. For the classification of text documents, the conditions on decision tree nodes are commonly defined in terms and a node may be subdivided to its children based on the presence or absence of a term in the document.
- *k-Nearest Neighbor (kNN):* a proximity-based classifier [29] use distance-based measures i.e., the documents which belong to the same class are more likely similar or close to each other based on the similarity measures.

3.4   Performance Evaluation

The final step is to evaluate the performance of the classifiers using various evaluation metrics [14] such as *Precision, Recall, F-Measure,* and *Accuracy* to evaluate the classification performance. They are defined as follows:

$$Precision\,(P) = \frac{TP}{TP + FP} \tag{2}$$

$$Recall\,(R) = \frac{TP}{TP + FN} \tag{3}$$

$$F - Measure = 2\frac{PR}{P + R} \tag{4}$$

$$Accuracy = \frac{TP + TN}{TP + TN + FP + FN} \tag{5}$$

where TP and TN stand for True Positive and True Negative, which measures and FP and FN stand for False Positive and False Negative.

4   Results and Discussion

We evaluated the performance of the classifiers on top of the constructed feature sets such as psycholinguistic dimensions, textual and sentimental features using 10 fold cross validation approach. We use default parameters settings in Matlab to evaluate the classifiers. The Table 5 shows that SVM and DT classifiers achieved higher accuracy of above 90% with respect to the LIWC and BoW features. Considering the psycholinguistic features, the abuse related posts have higher proportions for features such as "anxiety, anger, sadness, sexual, health and death". When the textual features are considered, the words such as "abuse, violence, domestic, child, family, rape, sexual, assault" are predominant in the user posts. Finally, when the sentimental features are considered, the abuse related posts carry lot of negative emotions in it. Thus, our selected features provide discriminative performance in prediction of various kinds of abuse related posts from general posts.

Table 5. Performance metrics of machine learning classifiers based on constructed feature sets

Method	Precision	Recall	F_1 value	Accuracy
SVM + Psycholinguistic features	0.94	0.93	0.93	0.94
KNN + Psycholinguistic features	0.82	0.94	0.88	0.88
DT + Psycholinguistic features	0.94	0.94	0.94	0.95
SVM + Textual features	0.92	0.93	0.92	0.92
KNN + Textual features	0.95	0.64	0.79	0.75
DT + Textual features	0.92	0.92	0.92	0.91
SVM + Sentimental features	0.83	0.88	0.85	0.87
KNN + Sentimental features	0.54	0.97	0.75	0.64
DT + Sentimental features	0.80	0.96	0.88	0.88

5   Conclusion

In this paper, we presented a framework for identification of various kinds of abuse related posts from diverse user generated posts. The results of this study demonstrated that the various features that extracted have the potential to discriminate the user posts and have higher classification accuracy in the prediction of posts. Therefore, by interpreting the use of proposed framework in this paper, public health organizations can quickly identify the posts related to various abuses and the appropriate support can be provided. There are many ways, this work can be extended further. Future Work can focus on (1) Extending the framework to find the most critical posts within the case of DA and CA. (2) Including more data from other social media platforms such as Twitter and Reddit.

References

1. World Health Organization: understanding and addressing violence against women: sexual violence (2012)
2. World Health Organization: global and regional estimates of violence against women: prevalence and health effects of intimate partner violence and non-partner sexual violence. World Health Organization (2013)
3. Van der Kolk, B.A.: This issue: child abuse & victimization. Psychiatr. Ann. **35**(5), 374–378 (2017)
4. Browne, A., Finkelhor, D.: Impact of child sexual abuse: a review of the research. Psychol. bull. **99**(1), 66 (1986)
5. Wang, J., Cong, G., Zhao, W.X., Li, X.: Mining user intents in Twitter: a semi-supervised approach to inferring intent categories for tweets. In: AAAI, pp. 318–324 (2015)
6. Gupta, V., Varshney, D., Jhamtani, H., Kedia, D., Karwa, S.: Identifying purchase intent from social posts. In: ICWSM (2014)
7. Turner, R.J., Brown, R.L.: Social support and mental health. In: A Handbook for the Study of Mental Health: Social Contexts, Theories, and Systems, vol. 2, pp. 200–212 (2010)
8. O'Connor, B., Balasubramanyan, R., Routledge, B.R., Smith, N.A., et al.: From tweets to polls: Linking text sentiment to public opinion time series. In: ICWSM, vol. 11, pp. 122–129 (2010)
9. Sakaki, T., Okazaki, M., Matsuo, Y.: Earthquake shakes Twitter users: real-time event detection by social sensors. In: Proceedings of the 19th International Conference on World Wide Web, pp. 851–860. ACM (2010)
10. Chunara, R., Andrews, J.R., Brownstein, J.S.: Social and news media enable estimation of epidemiological patterns early in the 2010 Haitian cholera outbreak. Am. J. Trop. Med. Hyg. **86**(1), 39–45 (2012)
11. Reavley, N.J., Pilkington, P.D.: Use of Twitter to monitor attitudes toward depression and schizophrenia: an exploratory study. PeerJ **2**, e647 (2014)
12. Martínez-Pérez, B., de la Torre-Díez, I., Bargiela-Flórez, B., López-Coronado, M., Rodrigues, J.J.: Content analysis of neurodegenerative and mental diseases social groups. Health Inform. J. **21**(4), 267–283 (2015)
13. Andalibi, N., Öztürk, P., Forte, A.: Sensitive self-disclosures, responses, and social support on Instagram: the case of# depression. In: CSCW, pp. 1485–1500 (2017)
14. Wang, H., Jiang, X., Kambourakis, G.: Special issue on security, privacy and trust in network-based big data. Inf. Sci. Int. J. **318**(C), 48–50 (2015)
15. Qin, Y., Sheng, Q.Z., Falkner, N.J., Dustdar, S., Wang, H., Vasilakos, A.V.: When things matter: a survey on data-centric internet of things. J. Netw. Comput. Appl. **64**, 137–153 (2016)
16. Wang, H., Zhang, Z., Taleb, T.: Special issue on security and privacy of IoT. World Wide Web **21**(1), 1–6 (2017)
17. Sun, X., Wang, H., Li, J., Zhang, Y.: Satisfying privacy requirements before data anonymization. Comput. J. **55**(4), 422–437 (2012)
18. Li, J., Wang, H., Jin, H., Yong, J.: Current developments of k-anonymous data releasing. Electron. J. Health Inform. **3**(1), 6 (2008)
19. Wang, H., Cao, J., Zhang, Y.: A flexible payment scheme and its role-based access control. IEEE Trans. Knowl. Data Eng. **17**(3), 425–436 (2005)
20. Wang, H., Sun, L.: Trust-involved access control in collaborative open social networks. In: 2010 4th International Conference on Network and System Security (NSS), pp. 239–246. IEEE (2010)

21. Schrading, N., Alm, C.O., Ptucha, R., Homan, C.: # WhyiStayed, # WhyiLeft: microblogging to make sense of domestic abuse. In: Proceedings of the 2015 Conference of the North American Chapter of the Association for Computational Linguistics, pp. 1281–1286. Human Language Technologies (2015)
22. Amrit, C., Paauw, T., Aly, R., Lavric, M.: Identifying child abuse through text mining and machine learning. Expert Syst. Appl. **88**, 402–418 (2017)
23. Andalibi, N., Haimson, O.L., De Choudhury, M., Forte, A.: Understanding social media disclosures of sexual abuse through the lenses of support seeking and anonymity. In: Proceedings of the 2016 CHI Conference on Human Factors in Computing Systems, pp. 3906–3918. ACM (2016)
24. Nguyen, T., Phung, D., Dao, B., Venkatesh, S., Berk, M.: Affective and content analysis of online depression communities. IEEE Trans. Affect. Comput. **5**(3), 217–226 (2014)
25. Pennebaker, J.W., Boyd, R.L., Jordan, K., Blackburn, K.: The development and psychometric properties of liwc2015. Technical report (2015)
26. Markham, A.: Fabrication as ethical practice: qualitative inquiry in ambiguous internet contexts. Inf. Commun. Soc. **15**(3), 334–353 (2012)
27. Cortes, C., Vapnik, V.: Support-vector networks. Mach. Learn. **20**(3), 273–297 (1995)
28. Quinlan, J.R.: Induction of decision trees. Mach. Learn. **1**(1), 81–106 (1986)
29. Han, E.-H.S., Karypis, G., Kumar, V.: Text categorization using weight adjusted k-nearest neighbor classification. In: Cheung, D., Williams, G.J., Li, Q. (eds.) PAKDD 2001. LNCS (LNAI), vol. 2035, pp. 53–65. Springer, Heidelberg (2001). https://doi.org/10.1007/3-540-45357-1_9

30 min-Ahead Gridded Solar Irradiance Forecasting Using Satellite Data

Todd Taomae[1], Lipyeow Lim[1]([✉]), Duane Stevens[1], and Dora Nakafuji[2]

[1] University of Hawai'i at Mānoa, Honolulu, HI, USA
lipyeow@hawaii.edu
[2] Hawaiian Electric Company, Honolulu, HI, USA

Abstract. Solar irradiance forecasting is critical to balancing solar energy production and energy consumption in the electric grid; however, solar irradiance forecasting is dependent on meteorological conditions and, in particular, cloud cover, which are captured in satellite imagery. In this paper we present a method for short-term solar irradiance forecasting using gridded global horizontal irradiance (GHI) data estimated from satellite images. We use this data to first create a simple linear regression model with a single predictor variable. We then discuss various methods to extend and improve the model. We found that adding predictor variables and partitioning the data to create multiple models both reduced prediction errors under certain circumstances. However, both these techniques were outperformed by applying a data transformation before training the linear regression model.

1 Introduction

One of the key problems faced by electric grid operators when integrating solar energy sources is the uncertainty in the production of solar energy. Most electric grid have very limited energy buffering capabilities, hence grid operators have to carefully match energy production to energy consumption. Energy consumption, also known as load, is relatively well understood to follow certain diurnal and seasonal patterns. In contrast to traditional oil-based energy generation, solar energy production is less well characterized and is dependent on atmospheric conditions, in particular, cloud cover.

In this paper, we study the problem of short term solar irradiance prediction using time series satellite imagery data over a 72 km by 58 km region covering the island of O'ahu in the state of Hawai'i. Short term is defined to be 30 to 90 min lead time. The satellite imagery data is collected via geostationary satellites and converted to gridded Global Horizontal Irradiance (GHI) data using the Perez method [20] (we will still call these gridded GHI data "images"). GHI is the total solar radiation received by a surface horizontal to the ground and is measured in watts per square meter (W/m^2). The computational problem can be described as: given a time series of GHI images, predict or forecast the next GHI image. In this paper, we investigate linear regression-based models for

© Springer International Publishing AG, part of Springer Nature 2018
J. Wang et al. (Eds.): ADC 2018, LNCS 10837, pp. 186–198, 2018.
https://doi.org/10.1007/978-3-319-92013-9_15

this computational prediction task where each pixel in the predicted images is dependent on surrounding pixels in the images of several previous time steps. This model is inspired by the atmospheric phenomenon known as persistence which essentially captures the locality of weather phenomena both spatially and temporally. We further investigate how different ways of partitioning the data and transforming the data can improve the performance of the prediction.

We tested our models on two years worth of satellite imagery data (2014-2014) using 2013's data as training and 2014's data as a testing data set. Our experiments show that the linear regression models perform surprisingly well. The best prediction error in terms of mean absolute error is 80.21 W/m^2 - the maximum solar irradiance during the sunniest part of the day is approximately 1600 W/m^2.

The rest of this paper is organized as follows. Section 2 describes related work. Section 3 describes satellite imagery data set used in this study. Section 4 details the various linear regression-based models used for predicting the GHI images. Section 5 presents the results of our investigation. Section 6 concludes the paper.

2   Related Work

There is a large body of work which has investigated solar irradiance forecasting with forecast horizons ranging from 5 min to 15 days. These methods can generally be broadly grouped into one of three different categories [6]. The first category consists of statistical models which are based on historical solar irradiance data. Another set of methods are based around cloud motion determined either from satellite images or from ground-based sky images. The last type of solar forecasting is based on a technique known as numerical weather prediction which uses observed weather variables as input into computer models which try to forecast the future state of the weather. A fourth category of hybrid models also exists.

Each of these categories of methods tend to perform better for different timescales. Statistical models and cloud motion based methods are typically used for forecasts up to 6 h, while numerical weather prediction models perform better beyond the 6 h range. These methods also operate at different spatial resolution. While numerical weather prediction can provide more accurate forecasts at larger timescales, it comes at the cost of much lower spatial resolution. Rather than operating at resolutions of 1 km or less, numerical weather prediction is limited to resolutions on the order of 10 to 100 km.

Statistical models can be further divided into linear and non-linear models. The simplest linear model is known as the persistence model or naïve predictor model and simply assumes that the solar irradiance at time t is equal to the irradiance at $t - n$. This method is sometimes used as a baseline for comparison to other methods. Other examples of linear models are autoregressive moving average (ARMA), autoregressive integrated moving average (ARIMA) [1,13], and coupled autoregressive and dymical system (CARDS) [14]. Non-linear methods include artificial neural networks [9,12,17] and wavelet neural networks [3,19].

Besides daily and annual irradiance patterns, which are deterministic based on the rotation and revolution of the earth, cloud cover is the main influence on solar irradiance at the surface. This is the basis for cloud motion based methods. These methods use either satellite images [10,11,16] or ground-based sky images [5] to extrapolate cloud motion based on recordings at previous time steps. Ground-based images can provide a much higher temporal and spatial resolution, but at the cost of much lower coverage.

Numerical weather prediction models attempt to model the state and evolution of the atmosphere using partial differential equations based on the laws of physics. Examples of numerical weather prediction models include the Global Forecast System (GFS) [8], the Integrated Forecast System (IFS) [18], and the Weather Research and Forecasting (WRF) Model [7].

The GFS and IFS models are both global models while WRF is a higher resolution, *mesoscale* model. IFS is also an example of an ensemble model which runs multiple simulations using slightly different initial conditions. This is used to help account for the uncertainty of initial observations and the chaotic nature and sensitivity to initial conditions of weather systems.

Hybrid models are used in an attempt to overcome limitations of methods using individual models. Examples of hybrid models include combining ARMA or ARIMA with neural networks [15,21], combining neural networks and fuzzy logic [3], and combining neural networks with wavelet analysis [2,4].

3 Satellite-Derived Global Horizontal Irradiance Data Set

The data set used in our experiments consists of Global Horizontal Irradiance (GHI) data estimated from satellite images using the Perez method [20] for a region surrounding Hawaii for the years 2013 and 2014. The data was provided by AWS Truepower.

The data set contains GHI information for a grid of 1,120 by 1,040 points at a 2 km resolution, centered over Hawaii. However, for this paper we will focus on a 36 by 29 grid over Oahu, which is shown in Fig. 1.

While the data set contains data for most of the day, we will focus on only the subset between 8AM and 5PM Hawaii Standard Time (HST). The reason for this choice is that we are guaranteed to have non-zero GHI throughout the entire year during this time interval. Most of the data is provided at 15 min intervals; however, there are some gaps of 30 min intervals. Figure 3 shows the times at which GHI data is available, within the window in which we are interested. The rows identify the hour in HST and the columns identify the minute within the hour. There is also some data missing throughout both years resulting occasional gaps greater than 30 min and up to several hours.

We will use the following notation to represent the GHI at the grid coordinate (x, y) at time t.

$$S(x, y, t)$$

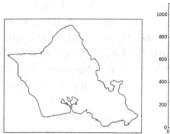

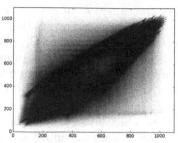

	00	15	30	45
08	x		x	x
09	x	x	x	x
10	x	x		x
11	x		x	x
12	x	x	x	x
13	x	x	x	x
14	x		x	
15	x	x	x	x
16	x	x	x	x

Fig. 1. GHI map   **Fig. 2.** $S(x,y,t)$ vs. $S(x,y, t-60)$ **Fig. 3.** Times available for GHI data

While specific values are not of interest to us, this notation allows us to easily discuss relative times and location. For example, $S(x+1, y-1, t-60)$ refers to the GHI at the grid point one unit to the east and one unit to the south of (x,y) at the time 60 min before t.

4   1-Hour Ahead Solar Forecasting via Linear Regression

In this section we describe a method for making approximately 1-h ahead predictions of the solar irradiance at a given location. We will call the time for which we wish to predict the GHI, time t. We will use information available to us at time $t-n$, where n is the number of minutes prior to t at which we are making the prediction. Intuitively, one might expect that the solar irradiance at $t-n$ at the same location would be a good predictor for our target. This is the basis on which we build linear regression models for forecasting GHI.

Linear regression is a method for modeling the relationship between a dependent variable and one or more predictor variables. In our case, the dependent variable is $S(x,y,t)$ and, in the simplest example, the predictor variable is $S(x,y,t-n)$. In this example with a single predictor variable, we wish to create a model as shown in Eq. 1 with constants c_1 and c_0 that will minimize the sum of the squared residuals, by way of ordinary least squares. The residual is the difference between the observed $S(x,y,t)$ and the value estimated by the linear regression model. This model will be based on all possible $S(x,y,t)$ and $S(x,y,t-n)$ for the region surrounding Oahu (shown in Fig. 1) during 2013.

$$S(x,y,t) = c_1 S(x,y,t-n) + c_0 \tag{1}$$

This can also described visually. Figure 2 is a scatter plot of the GHI for a given point at time t versus the GHI at that same point at $t-60$ for a portion of the data set. The residual is the vertical distance between a point and the line given by Eq. 1. So the goal of a linear regression is to choose c_1 and c_0 such that we minimize the sum of the squared vertical distances.

The model described above relies on a few assumptions. We are assuming that the GHI patterns are the same for all points on the grid, for all times of the day, and for all days of the year. However, this is obviously not true. For example, during the mornings GHI will generally trend upward while in the afternoons it will trend downward. While these assumptions allowed us to make a simple model, we will show later that it results in relatively poor performance. Throughout the remainder of this section, we will discuss various techniques to potentially increase the accuracy of our model. These techniques all work independently of each other and can be used individually or in combination with each other. First we will discuss including additional predictor variables, followed by partitioning the data and creating separate models for each partition of data, and lastly we will discuss a technique where we transform the data and use the transformed data to create the models.

4.1   Adding Predictor Variables

When using the simple model described above, there may be important information that is not captured by using only a single predictor variable. We can add predictor variables by either expanding temporally or spatially.

If we expand temporally, we would include more past data. Instead of using only data at $t - n$, we can, for example, use $[t - n_0, t - n_1, \ldots, t - n_m]$. Since we are including additional predictor variable, obviously our original model will no longer work. Instead, we will have a model that looks like Eq. 2 which uses data from k past times and will have constants c_k and c_0.

$$S(x, y, t) = \left(\sum_{k=1}^{m} c_k S(x, y, t - n_k) \right) + c_0 \tag{2}$$

If we expand spatially, we include data from neighboring grid points. We define r as the "radius" of the surrounding region, which will be centered on (x, y). The model is now defined by Eq. 3. Constants are not indexed by i and j.

$$S(x, y, t) = \left(\sum_{i=-r}^{r} \sum_{j=-r}^{r} c_{i,j} S(x + i, y + j, t - n) \right) + c_0 \tag{3}$$

We can also combine both of these techniques and expand both temporally and spatially. The resulting model is given by Eq. 4. We now index constants by i, j, and k.

$$S(x, y, t) = \left(\sum_{i=-r}^{r} \sum_{j=-r}^{r} \sum_{k=1}^{m} c_{i,j,k} S(x + i, y + j, t - n_k) \right) + c_0 \tag{4}$$

Figure 4 shows an example which uses both of these techniques. The red square in Fig. 4c represents $S(x, y, t)$ and the red boxes in Figs. 4a and b are our predictor variables.

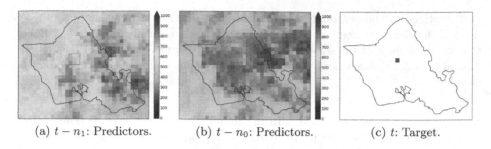

(a) $t - n_1$: Predictors.   (b) $t - n_0$: Predictors.   (c) t: Target.

Fig. 4. Predictors and target (Color figure online)

4.2 Partitioning Data

In the original model, we made several assumptions which led to a single model
for all data. However, it is unlikely that GHI patterns will be the same for all
points on the grid, for all times of the day, and for all days of the year. In order to
account for such differences, we can partition the data based on these differences
and create separate models for each partition. This partitioning can be either
temporal or spatial.

Temporal Partitioning. There are two main ways that we might partition
the data temporally. We can partition on either a daily or yearly scale. On a
daily scale, we might, for example, want to create a different model for each hour
of the day, while on a yearly scale, we might create a different model for each
month of the year. It is also possible to combine both of these which would leave
us with a different model for each hour of each month.

While partitioning the data at this granularity could potentially provide more
accurate models, it also means that we will have less data to train each model
and we will have many more models. If we were to combine both hourly and
monthly partitioning, we would end up with 108 different models, each with
approximately 108 times less data (9 h between 8AM and 5PM; 12 months in a
year).

Rather than partitioning by each hour, a more reasonable approach might
be to simply partition the data into morning and afternoon. This also has some
intuitive justification since there is a clear distinction in general GHI patterns
in the morning and afternoon. In the morning, we expect the GHI to generally
be increasing, while in the afternoon it will tend to decrease. The hope is that
these patterns can be more accurately captured by the linear regression models
if they separated.

On the yearly scale, it is less obvious how to partition the data. Seasonal
partitioning might be a good candidate. However, since the seasonal patterns
are not as distinct in Hawaii as many other places we will focus on a bi-annual
partition. We will refer to the combination of winter and spring as "winter" and
the combination of summer and autumn as "summer." While using equinoxes

and solstices as the seasonal boundaries might provide slightly more accurate models, for convenience, we will divide seasons on monthly boundaries. Each season will consist of three months, starting with winter consisting of December, January, and February and the rest of the seasons following in three month chunks.

Spatial and Elevation Partitioning. In addition to partitioning temporally, we can also perform spatial partitioning. On a global scale, it makes sense that, for example, the GHI patterns in Hawaii will be very different from those in Alaska. However, since we are only considering Oahu, it is less obvious how we might partition the data.

One way that we might partition the data is by land and ocean. This particularly makes sense for our application since there are obviously no rooftop solar panels or solar farms in the ocean. Another, perhaps less obvious, way to partition the data is by elevation. There are two main motivations behind partitioning by elevation. First, more of the population lives at lower elevation. Therefore, there will likely be more rooftop solar panels in that region. The second motivation has a meteorological basis; due to warm air rising along the mountains, cloud formation is more likely at higher elevations as the air cools and condenses.

We obtained elevation data from the Google Maps Elevation API. From this we can easily partition each grid point by elevation, but we can also use this to approximate which grid points are on the land or ocean. We consider any point with an elevation of 0 m or less to be part of the ocean and any point with greater than 0 m elevation to be part of the land.

4.3   Data Transformation

In this section we describe a method for processing the GHI data which provides an alternative method to account for differences in time of day and location that does not reduce the amount of data that we have to create the model as was the case with partitioning. Let $\hat{S}(x, y, t)$ denote the transformed value. After we apply the transformation, the data can be used as before. For example, Eq. 5 defines the linear regression model equivalent to the one give by Eq. 1.

$$\hat{S}(x, y, t) = c_1 \hat{S}(x, y, t - n) + c_0 \qquad (5)$$

Our transformation will be based on the deviation from some average value. Consider the following scenario. Suppose that the GHI at some location is 500 W/m^2. If this is in the afternoon, then this might be a normal value for that time of day, so we might expect that it will follow typical patterns. However, if this is in the middle of the day, then it might be lower than we expect, so we probably would not expect it to follow typical patterns. This is the motivation behind this model. We also take into account the fact that the typical value at a given time of day might vary from one location to the next.

Following the reasoning from the example above, our averaging should take into account both temporal and spatial information. This is accomplished by computing the average for each grid point at each time of day. Let $\bar{S}(x, y, hh{:}mm)$ represent the average GHI for a given grid point at a time of day specified by $hh{:}mm$.

The data transformation simply subtracts the corresponding average value from the actual average. For example,

$$\hat{S}(x, y, 2013\text{-}01\text{-}01\text{T}12{:}00) = S(x, y, 2013\text{-}01\text{-}01\text{T}12{:}00) - \bar{S}(x, y, 12{:}00).$$

Figure 5 shows the process visually. Figure 5a shows the data for one specific day at noon and Fig. 5b shows the average that was computed from all the data at noon. Lastly, Fig. 5c shows the deviation from the average for one specific day at noon, obtained by subtracting the values in 5b from 5a. This is data that will be used for creating the linear regression model.

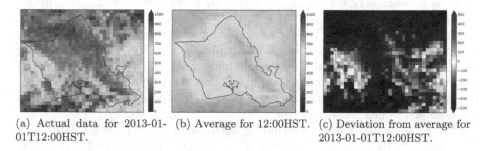

(a) Actual data for 2013-01-01T12:00HST.   (b) Average for 12:00HST.   (c) Deviation from average for 2013-01-01T12:00HST.

Fig. 5. Process for computing deviation

5   Results

Due do the number of combinations that are possible as well as the number of parameters that can be adjusted, it would be unreasonable to test all possible models. Also, due to our limited data set, it would not make sense to try all possible combinations to find one that is the best as it would likely be specific to our data set. Rather, it is more important to find which techniques seem to reduce errors in general.

This section will describe the performance of a number of different models. Each model is created using 2013 data only and predictions are made for 2014. It is important to note that when applying the data transformation, the average is based only on 2013 and when computing the deviation from the average, even for 2014 data, we will use the 2013 average. The performance will be measured by mean absolute error (MAE). In other words, the average of the absolute difference between our prediction and the actual irradiance. In the tables listing the results, we will also report the standard deviation in parentheses.

5.1   Accuracy vs. Spatial and Temporal Resolution

Tables 1, and 2 show the performance of our method as we increase the amount of spatial or temporal data used. The labels on the top and left describe how many predictor variables are used in each model. The spatial data is labeled as $n \times n$ which describes the size of the surrounding region that we will use. The temporal data is labeled as a list of times used, relative to the target time. "(DT)" indicates that our data transformation was applied to that particular model.

From Table 1 we can see that the error of our model decreases consistently up to a 13×13 region. However, the improvement is largest when moving from 1×1 to 3×3 and anything beyond 5×5 seems to have very minimal impact. We have not tested using regions larger than 13×13 so it is not clear what will happen beyond that point. However, we suspect that at some point it will include too much information from too far away and performance will degrade.

Table 1 also shows the impact of increasing from 30 to 60-min predictions. The result is not very surprising. As we try to forecast farther into the future, the error increases.

Table 2 also shows the impact of including more temporal data. What is interesting here is that when we do not apply the data transformation, using up to 90 min of temporal data does not have much impact, but using up to 120 min of temporal data reduces the prediction error by a significant margin. In contrast, if we do apply the data transformation, adding temporal data does not help and in fact increases error.

Table 2 shows the effect of including both temporal and spatial data. This table suggests that the two factors work mostly independently of each other. Adding spatial data helps in all cases, as it did in Table 1, and adding temporal data helps in the same way as it did in Table 2. Specifically, if the data transformation was not applied, then the additional temporal data seems to help.

Table 1. MAE with increasing spatial resolution. Standard deviation in parenthesis.

	[t−30]	[t−30] (DT)	[t−60]	[t−60] (DT)
1×1	109.16 (140.89)	89.83 (127.52)	149.66 (178.17)	109.18 (146.64)
3×3	103.15 (133.08)	83.15 (119.87)	146.11 (173.45)	103.55 (140.32)
5×5	101.96 (131.35)	81.65 (117.89)	145.38 (172.36)	101.99 (138.34)
7×7	101.39 (130.57)	80.91 (116.89)	145.00 (171.82)	101.07 (137.20)
9×9	101.13 (130.20)	80.53 (116.36)	144.82 (171.54)	100.90 (136.48)
11×11	101.01 (130.03)	80.33 (116.06)	144.72 (171.40)	100.08 (135.98)
13×13	100.95 (129.93)	80.21 (115.90)	144.67 (171.31)	99.78 (135.64)

Table 2. MAE with increasing spatial resolution and temporal window.

	1 × 1	1 × 1 (DT)	3 × 3	3 × 3 (DT)
[t−60]	149.66 (178.17)	109.18 (146.64)	146.11 (173.45)	103.55 (140.32)
[t−60, t−90]	150.33 (180.29)	109.93 (146.96)	141.27 (172.41)	105.69 (142.49)
[t−60, t−75, t−90]	149.05 (180.93)	110.15 (147.89)	140.50 (173.17)	106.45 (143.93)
[t−60, t−90, t−120]	145.70 (177.52)	113.16 (150.09)	134.95 (167.95)	108.82 (145.81)
[t−60, t−75, t−90, t−105, t−120]	136.94 (172.04)	118.32 (156.83)	130.94 (166.13)	114.53 (153.03)

5.2   Accuracy Using Temporal and Elevation Partitioning

The results of applying temporal and elevation partitioning are shown in Tables 3 and 4. These results are based on a model which uses a single predictor variable for 60-min forecasts. Table 3 shows the performance of various combinations of daily and yearly partitioning and Table 4 shows the performance for various elevation partitions. In addition to the mean absolute error and standard deviation, we also report—in square brackets and italics—the mean absolute error of the equivalent non-partitioned model, for the partition in question. In particular, we use the results from the non-partitioned, non-transformed, single predictor variable model and rather than looking at the error across all predictions, we look at the error specifically for only morning hours, or only afternoon hours, etc. This will allow us to see if the performance is truly improving.

We can see from Table 3 that temporal partitioning is useful in all cases except for the "summer" partition. We can also see that partitioning by morning and afternoon reduces errors much more than partitioning by seasons. This could be due to the fact that seasonal differences are not very significant in Hawaii.

Table 3. MAE with temporal and seasonal partitioning. Standard deviation in parenthesis and MAE of non-partitioned baseline in square brackets.

	Full day	Morning	Afternoon
Full year	149.66 (178.17)	109.65 (141.52) *[144.17]*	131.33 (163.59) *[152.53]*
"Winter"	144.38 (172.74) *[145.06]*	106.56 (138.74) *[134.36]*	127.13 (158.05) *[150.55]*
"Summer"	155.31 (183.12) *[153.40]*	112.64 (143.15) *[154.05]*	136.08 (169.39) *[154.58]*

Table 4. MAE with elevation partitioning.

"Ocean" (elevation ≤ 0 m)	152.31 (180.76) *[152.78]*
"Land" (elevation > 0 m)	144.37 (172.98) *[144.75]*
0 m < elevation ≤ 50 m	146.95 (174.96) *[145.81]*
50 m < elevation ≤ 100 m	146.19 (174.15) *[145.65]*
100 m < elevation ≤ 150 m	146.68 (175.56) *[146.78]*
150 m < elevation ≤ 200 m	147.53 (176.12) *[147.01]*
Elevation > 200 m	140.90 (170.34) *[143.32]*
Elevation > 500 m	129.06 (159.73) *[137.28]*

Table 5. MAE with temporal, seasonal partitioning and data transformation.

	Full day	Morning	Afternoon
Full year	109.18 (146.64)	104.31 (140.41) *[110.90]*	101.16 (137.18) *[108.27]*
"Winter"	107.14 (145.49) *[108.74]*	101.10 (137.32) *[109.91]*	100.62 (137.57) *[108.14]*
"Summer"	111.58 (147.40) *[109.62]*	107.80 (142.51) *[111.91]*	101.95 (138.02) *[108.41]*

Table 4 shows us that spatial partitioning is not very useful for our data set. While, in most cases, the partitioning does improve the error relative to the average error of the original model, when we compare it to the error for only that partition (the number in square brackets), the improvement is much less significant and in fact often performs slightly worse. The one exception is when elevation is greater than 500 meters. However, that only accounts for less than 10% of the total land and likely an even smaller portion of the population and rooftop solar panels.

Table 5 contains the results of applying temporal partitioning as well as data transformation. Again we see that the "summer" partition performs worse while the others perform better. However, the improvements are much less significant than applying those seen in Table 3. This is likely due to the fact that the data transformation already captures the same patterns that temporal partitioning tries to account for.

6   Conclusion

In this paper we discussed a method for short-term gridded solar irradiance forecasting using linear regression as well as several techniques for improving the linear regression model. We found that adding predictor variables was useful in reducing errors. In particular including additional spatial data improved predictions in all cases that we tested, while adding temporal data only improved predictions under certain circumstances. We used regions up to 13×13 grid points, but the rate of improvement was greatly reduced beyond a 5×5 region. Partitioning the data and creating separate models for each partition was also helpful in certain cases. Spatial partitioning turned out not to be very helpful except at high elevations which accounts for only a small portion of Oahu. Temporal partition was more useful with dividing the data into morning and afternoon partitions reducing the errors the most. All of the above methods were out-performed by first applying a data transformation which takes into account different patterns based on the time of day and location. In addition, this can be further improved by including additional spatial data.

References

1. Brinkworth, B.: Autocorrelation and stochastic modelling of insolation sequences. Solar Energy **19**(4), 343–347 (1977)
2. Cao, J., Cao, S.: Study of forecasting solar irradiance using neural networks with preprocessing sample data by wavelet analysis. Energy **31**(15), 3435–3445 (2006)
3. Cao, J., Lin, X.: Application of the diagonal recurrent wavelet neural network to solar irradiation forecast assisted with fuzzy technique. Eng. Appl. Artif. Intell. **21**(8), 1255–1263 (2008)
4. Cao, S., Cao, J.: Forecast of solar irradiance using recurrent neural networks combined with wavelet analysis. Appl. Therm. Eng. **25**(2), 161–172 (2005)
5. Chow, C.W., Urquhart, B., Lave, M., Dominguez, A., Kleissl, J., Shields, J., Washom, B.: Intra-hour forecasting with a total sky imager at the UC San Diego solar energy testbed. Solar Energy **85**(11), 2881–2893 (2011)
6. Diagne, M., David, M., Lauret, P., Boland, J., Schmutz, N.: Review of solar irradiance forecasting methods and a proposition for small-scale insular grids. Renew. Sustain. Energy Rev. **27**, 65–76 (2013)
7. Dudhia, J., Gill, D., Henderson, T., Klemp, J., Skamarock, W., Wang, W.: The weather research and forecast model: software architecture and performance. In: Proceedings of the Eleventh ECMWF Workshop on the Use of High Performance Computing in Meteorology, pp. 156–168. World Scientific (2005)
8. National Centers for Environmental Information: Global forecast system (GFS). http://www.ncdc.noaa.gov/data-access/model-data/model-datasets/global-forcast-system-gfs
9. Guarnieri, R., Martins, F., Pereira, E., Chou, S.C.: Solar radiation forecast using artificial neural networks. Nat. Inst. Space Res. 1–34 (2008)
10. Hammer, A., Heinemann, D., Lorenz, E., Lückehe, B.: Short-term forecasting of solar radiation: a statistical approach using satellite data. Solar Energy **67**(1), 139–150 (1999)
11. Heinemann, D., Lorenz, E., Girodo, M.: Forecasting of Solar Radiation. Solar Energy Resource Management for Electricity Generation from Local Level to Global Scale. Nova Science Publishers, New York (2006)
12. Hocaoğlu, F.O., Gerek, Ö.N., Kurban, M.: Hourly solar radiation forecasting using optimal coefficient 2-D linear filters and feed-forward neural networks. Solar Energy **82**(8), 714–726 (2008)

13. Hokoi, S., Matsumoto, M., Kagawa, M.: Stochastic models of solar radiation and outdoor temperature. ASHRAE Transactions (American Society of Heating, Refrigerating and Air-Conditioning Engineers); (United States) 96(CONF-9006117-) (1990)
14. Huang, J., Korolkiewicz, M., Agrawal, M., Boland, J.: Forecasting solar radiation on an hourly time scale using a coupled autoregressive and dynamical system (cards) model. Solar Energy 87, 136–149 (2013)
15. Ji, W., Chee, K.C.: Prediction of hourly solar radiation using a novel hybrid model of arma and TDNN. Solar Energy 85(5), 808–817 (2011)
16. Lorenz, E., Hammer, A., Heinemann, D.: Short term forecasting of solar radiation based on satellite data. In: EUROSUN2004 (ISES Europe Solar Congress), pp. 841–848 (2004)
17. Martins, F.R., Pereira, E.B., Guarnieri, R.A.: Solar radiation forecast using artificial neural networks. Int. J. Energy Sci. 2(6) (2012)
18. European Centre for Medium-Range Weather Forecasts: Modeling and prediction. http://www.ecmwf.int/en/research/modelling-and-prediction
19. Mellit, A., Benghanem, M., Kalogirou, S.: An adaptive wavelet-network model for forecasting daily total solar-radiation. Appl. Energy 83(7), 705–722 (2006)
20. Perez, R., Moore, K., Kmiecik, M., Chain, C., Ineichen, P., George, R., Vignola, F.: A new operational satellite-to-irradiance model-description and validation. In: Proceedings of the Solar Conference, pp. 315–322 (2002)
21. Zhang, G.P.: Time series forecasting using a hybrid arima and neural network model. Neurocomputing 50, 159–175 (2003)

An Efficient Framework for the Analysis of Big Brain Signals Data

Supriya[✉], Siuly, Hua Wang, and Yanchun Zhang

Centre for Applied Informatics, College of Engineering and Science,
Victoria University, Melbourne, VIC 8001, Australia
Supriya.Supriya@live.vu.edu.au,
{Siuly.Siuly,Hua.Wang,Yanchun.Zhang}@vu.edu.au

Abstract. Big Brain Signals Data (BBSD) analysis is one of the most difficult challenges in the biomedical signal processing field for modern treatment and health monitoring applications. BBSD analytics has been recently applied towards aiding the process of care delivery and disease exploration. The main purpose of this paper is to introduce a framework for the analysis of BBSD of time series EEG in biomedical signal processing for identification of abnormalities. This paper presents a data analysis framework combining complex network and machine learning techniques for the analysis of BBSD in time series form. The proposed method is tested on an electroencephalogram (EEG) time series database as the implanted electrodes in the brain generate huge amounts of time series data in EEG. The pilot study in this paper has examined that the proposed methodology has the capability to analysis massive size of brain signals data and also can be used for handling any other biomedical signal data in time series form (e.g. electrocardiogram (ECG); Electromyogram (EMG)). The main benefit of the proposed methodology is to provide an effective way for analyzing the vast amount of BBSD generated from the brain to care patients with better outcomes and also help technicians for making intelligent decisions system.

Keywords: Big data · Biomedical signal · EEG · Complex network
Machine learning · Feature extraction · Classification

1 Introduction

Big Brain Signals Data (BBSD) analytics in the biomedical signal processing is a growing area with the potential to provide useful insight in health and medical applications. BBSD is basically EEG signals coming from the different 19 locations of the brains (10-20 system). The current medical technologies produce huge quantities of complex and high-dimension brain signal data such as Electroencephalogram (EEG), Electroneurogram (ENG) etc., which are important sources for diagnosing diseases and treatment and therapy planning [1, 2]. Big Data and brain signal processing have always been companions. Brain signal processing involves the analysis of the measurements to provide useful information upon which clinicians can make decisions. Current diagnosis from BBSD is a strenuous challenge for modern medicine because they produce huge quantity data (in size and dimension). Analyzing these sheer volumes of data sets is still exemplifying a big challenge because of its complexity, diversity, and the rich context of the data. As brain signals are also an important epitomize of information, therefore, BBSD processing is of great value.

The main goal of BBSD processing is to extract important information from the brain signals for distinguishing abnormality from original EEG data. Owing to a huge amount and complexity nature, the analytics face challenges to analyze big brain signal data in diagnosis, treatment, and planning. The analytics demand to have authentic, accurate, and reliable information for good decision making in disease diagnosis and heath monitoring applications. In this research paper, we have used EEG signals for analysis. As we know the human brain is the most complicated biological structure in the universe. It is a database of the billions of distinct kinds of neurons and hence a source of big data with diverse morphologies, functions, patterns of connectivity, and forms of communication. Moreover, EEG signals is a fast growing field nowadays because EEG helps to measure the brain electrical activity and most of the neurological disorder like Brain Tumors, Epilepsy, Stroke, Sleep disorder Dementia and Autism etc. leaves their signature in the EEG signals.

In recent years, several approaches have been proposed for processing of large volume biomedical signal data with complicated structure [3–6]. As the present methodologies for the analysis of bio-medical signal data are based on time or frequency features and due to the non-stationary nature of big brain signals, the existing approaches may not be adequate for the analysis of big brain EEG data. Also the existing technique does not fulfill the gap between non-linear time series and dynamical systems. As per our knowledge, there is no efficient analysis methodology available which can preserve all the important and significant characteristic properties of dynamic big EEG signals. Moreover, the adoption rate and research development in this space are still hindered by some fundamental problems inherent within the big data paradigm. Furthermore, to detect an abnormality in the brain, comprises of visual inspection of long term EEG recoding of several days by the expert neurologist. All of these points motivate us to introduce a new graph theory based framework for the analysis of big brain EEG data.

Thus, this research aims to present an efficient big data analysis framework for Big Brain Signals Data in biomedical signal processing. In this study, we developed a new method based on a complex network technique and named as 'weighted horizontal visibility graph' to discover canceled patterns from big time-varying EEG signal data. Two complex network measures named as Average Weighted Degree, and Average degree are extracted to characterize the new complex method. And afterward, six machine learning classifiers: Naive Bayes, Linear Discriminant Analysis, Quadratic Discriminant Analysis, Support Vector Machine (SVM) classifier with Linear, Rbf and Polynomial kernel function using 10-fold cross validation have been used to check the validity of proposed algorithm. The reason behind of using the weighted horizontal visibility graph instead of natural horizontal visibility graph is to detect the sudden changes happening in big brain EEG signal. As the weight of the edges known as edge strength helps to recognize the sudden fluctuation in Big EEG signals because different edges have different strength in the network. The proposed methodology is tested on two different benchmark EEG signal database: Epileptic related EEG database and Alcohol related EEG database. The investigational results demonstrate that our proposed approach is capable of the analysis of Big Brain Signals Data. It is our belief that this proposed algorithm will help in making decision support system for diseases diagnosis and treatments by reducing cost and time. We also expected that this approach could be applied to other big biomedical signal data such as ECG, EMG, ENG etc.

This remaining paper has been structured as: Sect. 2 includes a detailed description of the proposed approach with the experimental data. Section 3 provides the experimental results and discussion. Concluding remarks are specified in Sect. 4.

2 Proposed Framework

In this research work, a novel technique based on the complex network approach is proposed for the analysis of Big EEG signals. The technique is very efficient for the classification of different kinds of EEG signals. Figure 1 illustrates the structural diagram of the proposed technique. The proposed framework is comprised of different processing modules: Mapping of time series EEG signals into the Complex network by using links weight of network, extraction of measures of a complex network, classification on the basis of extracted feature set and performance measures.

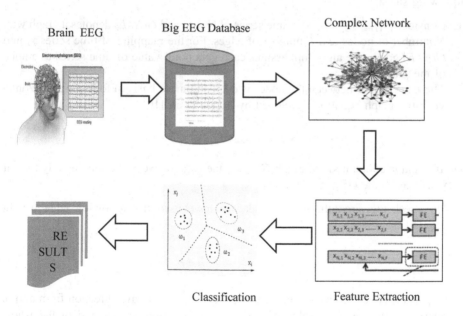

Fig. 1. Structural diagram of the proposed algorithm

2.1 Experimental Data

In this paper, we have used the following two different EEG database collected from two different sources.

2.2 Epileptic Related EEG Database

This experimental data is developed and issued by the department of epilepsy in Bonn University Germany. This data is publically online available. This EEG database is a collection of five sets symbolized as Z, S, O, F and N. Each set comprise 100 single channel EEG signals of 23.6 s. This EEG recording has sampling rate as 173.61 Hz. Andrezejak et al. [7] describes in detail about the data collection process.

2.3 Alcohol Related EEG Database

This experimental EEG data used for analysis is made available by the University of California, Irvine Knowledge Discovery in Databases Archive UCI KDD [8]. This data is also publically online available. This database is basically the EEG recordings of control and alcoholic subjects. This data is obtained from 122 subjects and each subject completed 120 trials where three type of stimuli were displayed. This EEG recording has sampling rate as 256 Hz. The detail explanation about this database is available in [9].

2.4 Mapping of Time Series EEG Signals to the Complex Network

For the mapping of time series EEG signals to the complex network, we have used the following steps:

1. Consider $\{x_t\}_{t=1,2,3,.....,N}$ be a time series of N data and $G(N, E)$ denotes a graph with N number of nodes and E number of edges. For the mapping of time series x_t into $G(N, E)$ graph, the algorithm assigns each data point value of time series to a node of the graph.
2. The edge or link between the nodes is decided on the basis of following horizontal visibility graph equation developed by Luque et al. [10]:

$$x_a, x_b > x_n, \forall n | a < n < b \tag{1}$$

i.e. if a and b are the node of graph $G(N, E)$, the edge between these node only exits if they will fulfill the criteria of Eq. (1).

3. To check the strength of edge link, we have used the following edge weight Eq. [11]:

$$w_{ab} = \frac{x_b - x_a}{b - a}, a < b \tag{2}$$

i.e. w_{ab} is the edge weight between the node x_a and x_b and have direction from a to b. Furthermore, the absolute value of edge weight has been considered in the whole experimentation.

4. Finally a weighted horizontal visibility graph is built from the above steps.

The reasons behind using horizontal visibility graph instead of visibility graph are [10]: (i) The horizontal visibility graph can easily make a difference of random series from chaotic ones. (ii) The horizontal visibility graph is a geometrically simpler and analytically solvable version of visibility graph algorithm.

2.5   Extraction of Complex Network Measures

The complex network measures have been extracted as a feature vector for classification. The Extraction of complex network measures helps in the analysis of graph of big brain EEG by dimensional reduction on the basis of minimum the loss of original information. In the research work, we have used two complex network measures named as an Average weighted degree (AWD) and Average degree (AD) for extracting the features and used for classification.

2.5.1   Average Weighted Degree
The Average Weighted Degree (AWD) of the graph is defined as the average mean of the total weights of the incident edges on all the nodes in the graph [12]. And weighted degree [13] of a node l of the graph is the total weights of all the edges attached to node l and is denoted by:

$$wd_l = \sum_{k \varepsilon C(l)} w_{lk} \tag{3}$$

Where, $C(l)$ denotes the neighborhood of node l and w_{lk} indicate the edge weight between the nodes l and k.

2.5.2   Average Degree
The Average Degree (AD) of a graph $G = (N, E)$ measures the total links in set E as compared to how many nodes in set N. As our proposed methodology is directional in nature and count the degree in one direction. As a result AD of a graph $G = (N, E)$ is

$$AD = \frac{|E|}{|N|} \tag{4}$$

2.6   Classification

To check the performance of the extracted features, we have used different machine learning classifiers named as Naive Bayes (NB), Linear Discriminant Analysis (LDA), Quadratic Discriminant Analysis (QDA), Support Vector Machine (SVM) classifier with Linear, Rbf and Polynomial kernel function. The reason behind using these classifiers are as SVM classifier is the most popular classifier in biomedical signals processing [14] whereas, NB offers a flexible approach for dealing with any number of features or classes and fastest algorithm that examines all its training input [15, 16] and LDA and QDA are fast, very simple and easy to implement. A brief review about all of these classifiers is available in [17].

2.7   Classification Performance Measures

The classification outcome is measured by using the Accuracy parameters [18]:

$$Accuracy = \frac{TruePositive\ (TP) + TrueNegative\ (TN)}{TP + FalseNegatie + FalsePositive + TN} \tag{5}$$

3   Experimental Results and Discussion

To investigate the capability and consistency performance of the proposed framework, we have employed experiments on two different kinds of EEG database (Epileptic EEG database and Alcohol related EEG database) and both the databases are available online. This section describes the experimental results of the proposed framework with different classifiers. All experiments are carried out on the MATLAB R2016b (Version 9.1). In order to achieve consistent and reliable results, we have performed all classification experiments by considering a k-fold classification for each classifier with k = 10.

3.1   Experimental Results for Epileptic EEG Database

Figures 2 and 3 illustrates the boxplot diagram of all of the five sets of Epileptic EEG database. The below figures clearly demonstrates that the extracted feature AWD and AD of our proposed methodology have different values for all of the five sets and also it will help in classification.

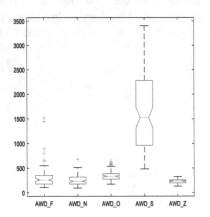
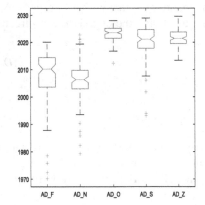

Fig. 2. Boxplot diagram of AWD of different (F, N, O, S, Z) sets of Epileptic EEG database.

Fig. 3. Boxplot diagram of AD of different (F, N, O, S, Z) sets of Epileptic EEG database.

As we have already mentioned that in case of Epileptic EEG database, we have 5 sets of different kind of EEG signals. Set S is the EEG recording during an epileptic seizure activity therefore it is compared with other four (Z, O, N and F) EEG data sets. The proposed technique is tested on the below four different classification problems constructed upon this data set:

- Set Z versus Set S
- Set O versus Set S
- Set N versus Set S
- Set F versus Set S

Table 1 describe the classification accuracy of all the six classifiers for the different classification problems of Epileptic EEG database by using combined feature set (AWD + AD). From Table 1, it is clearly visible that among all the six classifier (Naive Bayes, LDA, QDA, SVM Linear, SVM Rbf and SVM Poly), the SVM classifier with Polynomial kernel function produce most promising results with 100% classification accuracy for Set Z vs Set S, 97% for Set O vs Set S, 98.50% for Set N vs Set S and 95.50% for the Set F vs Set S. However the other two classifier Naive Bayes and QDA also provide classification accuracy close to SVM Poly. From this Table 1 we can say that SVM Poly provide better results with our proposed methodology for Epileptic EEG database.

Table 1. The accuracy performance of the different classifiers for the combined feature set (AWD + AD) in case of Epileptic EEG database.

Different test cases	Naive Bayes (%)	LDA (%)	QDA (%)	SVM Linear (%)	SVM Rbf (%)	SVM Poly (%)
Set Z vs Set S	100	93	100	97	95.5	100
Set O vs Set S	97	93	97	94	95	97
Set N vs Set S	97.50	89.50	98	95.50	95	98.50
Set F vs Set S	91.50	87	94.50	92	92.50	95.50

3.2   Experimental Results for Alcohol Related EEG Database

We further investigate our proposed methodology with other EEG database known as Alcohol related EEG database. Figures 4 and 5 demonstrate the boxplot diagram of AWD and AD feature set of the Alcoholic and healthy subject in case of Alcohol related EEG database. The difference in the value of feature set also depicts that our proposed framework can discriminate among different kind of EEG signals.

Table 2 displays the experimental outcomes of the proposed algorithm in case of Alcohol related EEG database with different classifiers. Table 2 depict that in case of Alcohol related EEG database, the SVM classifier with Polynomial kernel function produces most promising results with 90.42% classification accuracy as compared to other classifiers.

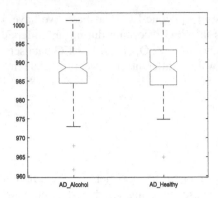

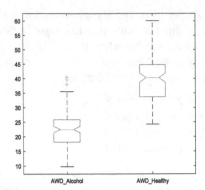

Fig. 4. Boxplot diagram of AWD of Alcoholic and healthy subject in case of Alcohol related EEG database.

Fig. 5. Boxplot diagram of AD of Alcoholic and healthy subject in case of Alcohol related EEG database.

Table 2. The accuracy performance of the different classifiers for the combined feature set (AWD + AD) in case of Alcohol related EEG database.

Test cases	Naive Bayes (%)	LDA (%)	QDA (%)	SVM Linear (%)	SVM Rbf (%)	SVM Poly (%)
Alcohol group vs healthy control group	87.08	84.21	87.08	88.33	89.17	90.42

In summary, on the basis of experimental results illustrated in Tables 1 and 2, it is positive to say that our proposed framework is the best for the analysis of different kinds of big brain EEG signals. It is our belief that our proposed algorithm can easy the problem of medical professionals of manual analysis of the huge volume of big brain EEG signals, assistance in the diagnosis of brain disorders, also helps in research and can be applicable to other time series biomedical signals.

4 Concluding Remark

This article presents an efficient framework for the analysis of Big Brain Signals Data with the help of graph theory approach. Firstly, the time series EEG signals are mapped to weighted horizontal visibility graph. Afterwards Average Weighted Degree and Average Degree measures of the complex network are used as parameters for feature extraction. The efficiency of the proposed framework is evaluated with the help of six machine learning algorithms named as Naive Bayes, Linear Discriminant Analysis, Quadratic Discriminant Analysis, Support Vector Machine (SVM) classifier with Linear, Rbf and Polynomial kernel function using 10-fold cross validation. The research results show that is promising for the analysis of Big Brain Signals Data and also helps to differentiate between different kinds of EEG signals.

References

1. Siuly, S., Li, Y., Zhang, Y.: EEG Signal Analysis and Classification: Techniques and Applications. Health Information Science. Springer Nature, Heidelberg (2016). https://doi.org/10.1007/978-3-319-47653-7. (ISBN 978-3-319-47653-7)
2. Siuly, S., Zhang, Y.: Medical big data: neurological diseases diagnosis through medical data analysis. Data Sci. Eng. **1**(2), 54–64 (2016)
3. Derlatka, M., Pauk, J.: Data Mining in Analysis of Biomechanical Signals. Solid State Phenom. **147–149**, 588–593 (2009)
4. Belle, A., Thiagarajan, R., Soroushmehr, S.M.R., Navidi, F., Beard, D.A., Najarian, K.: Big data analytics in healthcare. Biomed. Res. Int. **2015**, 16 (2015). Article ID 370194
5. Rakthanmanon, T., Campana, B., Mueen, A., Batista, G., Westover, B., Zhu, Q., et al.: Addressing big data time series. ACM Trans. Knowl. Discov. Data **7**(3), 1–31 (2013)
6. Herland, M., Khoshgoftaar, T., Wald, R.: A review of data mining using big data in health informatics. J. Big Data **1**(1), 2 (2014)
7. Andrzejak, R., Lehnertz, K., Mormann, F., Rieke, C., David, P., Elger, C.: Indications of nonlinear deterministic and finite-dimensional structures in time series of brain electrical activity: dependence on recording region and brain state. Phys. Rev. E **64**(6), 061907 (2001)
8. Bache, K., Lichman, M.: UCI machine learning repository. University of California, Irvine, School of Information and Computer (2013). http://archive.ics.uci.edu/ml
9. Zhang, X., Begleiter, H., Porjesz, B., Wang, W., Litke, A.: Event related potentials during object recognition tasks. Brain Res. Bull. **38**(6), 531–538 (1995)
10. Luque, B., Lacasa, L., Ballesteros, F., Luque, J.: Horizontal visibility graphs: exact results for random time series. Phys. Rev. E **80**(4), 046103 (2009)
11. Supriya, S., Siuly, S., Wang, H., Zhuo, G., Zhang, Y.: Analyzing EEG signal data for detection of epileptic seizure: introducing weight on visibility graph with complex network feature. In: Cheema, M., Zhang, W., Chang, L. (eds.) Databases Theory and Applications. LNCS, vol. 9877, pp. 56–66. Springer, Cham (2016). https://doi.org/10.1007/978-3-319-46922-5_5
12. Supriya, S., Siuly, S., Zhang, Y.: Automatic epilepsy detection from EEG introducing a new edge weight method in the complex network. Electron. Lett. **52**(17), 1430–1432 (2016)
13. Antoniou, I., Tsompa, E.: Statistical: analysis of weighted networks. Discrete Dyn. Nat. Soc. **2008**, 1–16 (2008)
14. Zhang, B., Zhang, Y., Begg, R.: Gait classification in children with cerebral palsy by Bayesian approach. Pattern Recogn. **42**(4), 581–586 (2009)
15. Cao, J., Wu, Z., Mao, B., Zhang, Y.: Shilling attack detection utilizing semi-supervised learning method for collaborative recommender system. World Wide Web **16**(5–6), 729–748 (2012)
16. Siuly, Wang, H., Zhang, Y.: Detection of motor imagery EEG signals employing Naïve Bayes based learning process. Measurement **86**, 148–158 (2016)
17. Kotsiantis, S.B., Zaharakis, I., Pintelas, P.: Supervised machine learning: a review of classification techniques. Emerg. Artif. Intell. Appl. Comput. Eng. **160**, 3–24 (2007)
18. Supriya, S., Siuly, S., Wang, H., Cao, J., Zhang, Y.: Weighted visibility graph with complex network features in the detection of epilepsy. IEEE Access **4**, 6554–6566 (2016)

Full Research Papers: Theories and Methodologies

TSAUB: A Temporal-Sentiment-Aware User Behavior Model for Personalized Recommendation

Qinyong Wang[1], Hongzhi Yin[1(✉)], Hao Wang[2], and Zi Huang[1]

[1] School of Information Technology and Electrical Engineering,
The University of Queensland, Brisbane, Australia
{qinyong.wang,h.yin1}@uq.edu.au, huang@itee.uq.edu.au
[2] 360 Search Lab, Beijing, China
cashenry@126.com

Abstract. Personalized recommender system has become an essential means to help people discover attractive and interesting items. We find that to buy an item, a user is influenced not only by her intrinsic interests and temporal contexts, but also by the crowd sentiment to this item. Users tend to refuse to accept the recommended items whose most reviews are negative. In light of this, we propose a temporal-sentiment-aware user behavior model (TSAUB) to learn personal interests, temporal contexts (i.e., temporal preferences of the public) and crowd sentiment from user review data. Based on the learnt knowledge from TSAUB, we design a temporal-sentiment-aware recommender system. To improve the training efficiency of TSAUB, we develop a distributed learning algorithm for model parameter estimation using the Spark framework. Extensive experiments have been performed on four Amazon datasets, and the results show that our recommender system significantly outperforms the state-of-the-arts by making more effective and efficient recommendations.

Keywords: Temporal recommendation · User behavior modeling
Crowd sentiment

1 Introduction

With increasing choices online, recommender systems can help matching items (e.g., books and movies) with potential users. Many recommender systems are based on Collaborative filtering (CF) that employs a user-item matrix to infer users' interests regarding each unrated item However, CF methods suffer from severe data sparsity problem since most users leave few interaction histories, making the recommender system quite difficult to accurately learn their preferences. For example, in the Electronics category of Amazon datasets [9], up to 68% of users have generated only 1 review. An accurate modeling of user behaviors[1] is the key for the system to make correct recommendations.

---

[1] We use "behaviors" to refer to a broad range of user actions such as purchases, clicks and writing reviews.

© Springer International Publishing AG, part of Springer Nature 2018
J. Wang et al. (Eds.): ADC 2018, LNCS 10837, pp. 211–223, 2018.
https://doi.org/10.1007/978-3-319-92013-9_17

In this paper, we explore three factors that affect user behaviors and decision-making. **User Preferences.** It is intuitive that users choose a product because they are intrinsically interested in it. Most existing works such as [2,16] exploit the user preferences to account for user behaviors. **Temporal Contexts.** User behaviors are not only affected by their intrinsic preferences but also significantly influenced by temporal contexts [22,23]. e.g., a user is more likely to buy a T-shirt than a coat in the summer, and prefers to buy a best-selling book on Amazon. **Crowd Sentiments.** Besides these factors, another observation is that user behaviors are also influenced by the word-of-mouth effect or crowd sentiments [5]. For instance, if a user concluded from the overall history reviews by previous buyers (crowd sentiment) of the item recommended to her as negative, it is most likely that she will not accept it although the underlying topics of this item match the user's personal preferences or the temporal context.

No existing models exploit and integrate all those three factors in a unified way to improve recommendation. To this end, we propose a probabilistic generative model called temporal-sentiment-aware user behavior model (TSAUB) to learn user interests, temporal contexts and crowd sentiments from user review data in a unified way, inspired by the success of graphical model applied in the recommendation task [21,24,27]. Based on the learnt knowledge, we develop a temporal-sentiment-aware recommender system. In TSAUB, both user interests and the temporal contexts reflected by the temporal preferences of the public are characterized by latent topics, inspired by [20,22]. As a review contains both topic-related words (e.g., words used to describe the functions or aspects of the product) and sentiment-related words (i.e., words used to express the user's sentiment polarity), we introduce another latent variable to represent user sentiment and then couple it with the latent topic variable as a joint latent factor. We assume that user reviews are generated by the joint latent variable pair instead of only the latent topic variable, which distinguishes TSAUB from most existing works [20,22]. To the best of our knowledge, we are the first to model user behaviors and make recommendations by integrating user preferences, temporal contexts and user sentiments in a unified way.

The major contributions of this paper are summarized as follows. Firstly, we propose a novel probabilistic generative model TSAUB to account for user reviewing behaviors by simultaneously considering the influences of user preference, temporal contexts and user sentiments in a unified way. Secondly, we make the model parameter estimation process scalable with Spark framework to adapt to large-scale user review data by harnessing the powers of clusters. Thirdly, based on the knowledge learnt by TSAUB model, we design a temporal-sentiment-aware recommender system. Finally, we conduct extensive experiments to evaluate the performance of our TSAUB model on four Amazon datasets. The experimental results show the superiority of our TSAUB in both recommendation effectiveness and model training efficiency.

2   Temporal-Sentiment-Aware User Behavior Model

In this section, we first present our objectives to build the temporal-sentiment-aware user behavior model (TSAUB). To achieve these goals, we present several intuitions based on which we build our model. We then describe the details of the model, and develop a model estimation method.

2.1   Intuitions

In this paper, we aim at building a probabilistic generative model for mining user review data that is able to (1) discover latent topics of items or products; (2) uncover personal preferences and temporal preferences of the general public over topics; (3) detect the crowd sentiment to items under each topic; and (4) reveal the interdependencies among time, users, topics, crowd sentiments, items and reviews. To achieve these objectives, we exploit the following intuitions in designing our model:

Intuition 1: A user buys an item because its topics (e.g., categories or functions) satisfy hie/her personal interests. Each user has her own preferences on the topics, which can be discovered from her historical reviewing data. We assume that a user is interested in the topics of a product as long as she/he provides a review for that product, whether the review is positive or negative. If the review is positive, it means that the user is interested in the topics and also likes the specific product. Otherwise, it means that the user is still interested in the topic of the item and just dislikes the specific product.

Intuition 2: Another reason a user buys an item is that its topics are currently most popular and attract much attention at the moment (e.g., best-sellers), which we call temporal contexts representing the temporal preferences of the general public.

Intuition 3: When a user writes a review on an item, she will use words for both the topics of the item and her sentiments about the item. For example, a review for a suncream product may say "It's the best suncream products I've ever used." where "suncream products" and "best" are used for describing the *topic* and *personal sentiment,* respectively. For a specific product, we can obtain the crowd sentiment to it by accumulating the sentiments from all its history reviewers. The crowd sentiment is an effective indicator of the item quality, which will be greatly helpful to improve the item recommendation.

2.2   Model Description

First, we introduce the relevant notations used in this paper. We use D to denote the dataset consisting of user reviews. Each review in D contains four elements: user u, item v, time for generating the review t and review content $\mathbf{w}$, that is, $(u, v, t, \mathbf{w}) \in D$. All review records generated by user u are grouped into D_u as u's profile. Following [22], a time slice t can be obtained by transforming the original raw timestamps according to a predefined granularity (e.g., a week, a month or a season). Other notations are listed in Table 1. Note that all vectors or distributions in this paper are denoted by bold case letters. Then we describe our model in details following the three intuitions and present its graphical representation in Fig. 1.

Table 1. Notations for TSAUB

Symbol	Description	Symbol	Description
u, t	User and time slice	N, M	# of users and time slice
E, K	# of sentiment labels and topics	ψ_{zsw}	Probability of w generated by (z, s)
V, J	# of unique items and review words	$v, \mathbf{w}, w$	Item and its review, word in the review
$|\mathbf{w}|$	# of words in v's review	z, s	Topic, sentiment
θ_u	Personal interests of u	θ_t'	Temporal contexts at time slice t
Ω_{zs}	Probability of s generated by z	ϕ_{zsv}	Probability of v generated by (z, s)

Based on **Intuition 1**, we model a user's personal interests as a multinomial distribution over topics (i.e., θ_u), and $P(z|u)$ represents the probability of u preferring topic z (i.e., $\theta_{uz} = P(z|u)$). This factor is activated when $l = 1$. Besides users' personal interests, their purchasing behaviors are also influenced by the temporal preferences of the general public (i.e., the temporal contexts), as analyzed in [22]. Thus, we exploit the temporal contexts to account for our **Intuition 2**. For each time slice t, the trending preferences of the public are also modeled as a multinomial distributions over topics (i.e., θ_t'). This factor, however, is activated when $l = 0$. Another advantage of introducing the temporal background model to account for dynamic user purchasing behaviors is to alleviate the sparsity of the review data generated by individual users. We employ a personalized mixing weight ξ_u to measure the influence from the two factors, i.e., $l = 1$ with probability ξ_u and $l = 0$ with probability $1 - \xi_u$:

$$P(z|\theta_u, \theta_t') = \xi_u P(z|\theta_u) + (1 - \xi_u) P(z|\theta_t'). \tag{1}$$

Based on **Intuition 3**, a user review for an item often contains both topical and sentimental words, thus we use a joint latent factor *topic-sentiment* to generate the review words and the item, i.e., $P(\mathbf{w}|z, s, \psi)$ and $P(v|z, s, \phi)$ where z and s are topic and sentiment, respectively. ψ_{zsw} is the probability of the topic-sentiment pair (z, s) generating word w, and ϕ_{zsv} is the probability of the joint latent variable pair (z, s) generating item v. This model design enables us to obtain the crowd sentiment to each item by accumulating the sentiments from all its reviewers, as the model parameters ϕ_{zsv} and ψ_{zsw} are global and shared by all users. Thus, we can further distinguish items with the same topics but different crowd sentiments. In other words, the topics in our model are sentiment-aware. The assumption of simultaneously generating both item and its review words by (z, s) drives parameter estimation process to discover sentiment-aware topics that capture both item co-occurrence, content word co-occurrence and sentiment word co-occurrence patterns. This encodes our prior knowledge that items having many common users, similar content and crowd sentiments should be clustered into the same sentiment-aware topic with high probability. We assume that the sentiment label s is sampled from the user generated topic z, i.e., $P(s|\Omega_z)$, considering that user sentiments often depend on topics.

The generative process of our TASUB model is summarized in Algorithm 1. To avoid overfitting, we place Dirichlet priors $\alpha, \alpha', \beta, \eta, \lambda$ and Beta priors γ, γ'

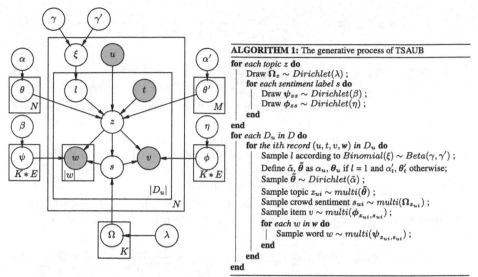

ALGORITHM 1: The generative process of TSAUB

for *each topic z* **do**
    Draw $\Omega_z \sim Dirichlet(\lambda)$;
    for *each sentiment label s* **do**
        Draw $\psi_{zs} \sim Dirichlet(\beta)$;
        Draw $\phi_{zs} \sim Dirichlet(\eta)$;
    end
end
for *each D_u in D* **do**
    for *the ith record (u, t, v, w) in D_u* **do**
        Sample l according to $Binomial(\xi) \sim Beta(\gamma, \gamma')$;
        Define $\tilde{\alpha}, \tilde{\theta}$ as α_u, θ_u if $l = 1$ and α'_t, θ'_t otherwise;
        Sample $\tilde{\theta} \sim Dirichlet(\tilde{\alpha})$;
        Sample topic $z_{ui} \sim multi(\tilde{\theta})$;
        Sample crowd sentiment $s_{ui} \sim multi(\Omega_{z_{ui}})$;
        Sample item $v \sim multi(\phi_{z_{ui},s_{ui}})$;
        for *each w in w* **do**
            Sample word $w \sim multi(\psi_{z_{ui},s_{ui}})$;
        end
    end
end

Fig. 1. The graphical representation

over the multinomial distributions $\theta, \theta', \Omega, \phi, \psi$ and the binomial distribution ξ in TSAUB respectively. For example, the multinomial distribution θ is parameterized by α:

$$P(\boldsymbol{\theta}_u|\alpha) = \frac{\Gamma(\sum_z \alpha_z)}{\prod_z \Gamma(\alpha_z)} \prod_z \theta_{uz}^{\alpha_z - 1} \tag{2}$$

where $\Gamma(.)$ denotes the gamma function. The joint probability of both observed and hidden variables with priors is shown in Eq. (3).

$$P(v, w, l, z, s|\alpha, \alpha', \gamma, \gamma', \beta, \eta, \lambda) = P(l|\gamma, \gamma')P(z|l, \alpha, \alpha')P(s|z, \lambda)P(w|z, s, \beta)P(v|z, s, \eta)$$

$$= \int \dots \int P(\xi|\gamma, \gamma')P(l|\xi)P(\theta|\alpha)P(\theta'|\alpha')P(z|\theta, \theta', l)P(\Omega|\lambda)P(s|\Omega, z)P(\psi|\beta)P(w|\psi, z, s) \tag{3}$$

$$P(\phi|\eta)P(v|\phi, z, s)d\theta d\theta' d\phi d\psi d\Omega d\xi$$

2.3 Model Inference

Following the studies [17,25,28], we use collapsed Gibbs sampling to obtain samples of the hidden variable assignment and to estimate unknown parameters $\{\theta, \theta', \phi, \psi, \Omega, \xi\}$ in our model. As for the hyper-parameters $\alpha, \alpha', \gamma, \gamma', \beta, \eta, \lambda$, we take fixed values.

In the sampling procedure, we begin with the joint probability of all user profiles in the dataset. Next, using the chain rule, we obtain the posterior probability of sampling topics and sentiments for each four-tuple (u, v, t, w). Specifically, we employ a two-step Gibbs sampling procedure. Due to space constraints, we show only the derived Gibbs sampling formulas, omitting the detailed derivation process. We first sample the coin l according to the posterior probability in Eqs. (4) and (5), and the sampled value of l determines which factor will be activated: user personal interests ($l = 1$) or the temporal context ($l = 0$).

$$P(l_{ui} = 1|l_{\neg ui}, \boldsymbol{z}, u, .) \propto \frac{n_{u,z_{ui}}^{\neg u,i} + \alpha_{z_{ui}}}{\sum_z^K (n_{u,z}^{\neg ui} + \alpha_z)} \times \frac{n_{u,l_1} + \gamma}{n_{u,l_1} + \gamma + n_{u,l_0} + \gamma'} \qquad (4)$$

$$P(l_{ui} = 0|l_{\neg ui}, \boldsymbol{z}, u, .) \propto \frac{n_{t_{ui},z_{ui}}^{\neg ui} + \alpha'_{z_{ui}}}{\sum_z^K n_{t_{ui},z}^{\neg ui} + \alpha'_z} \times \frac{n_{u,l_0} + \gamma'}{n_{u,l_1} + \gamma + n_{u,l_0} + \gamma'} \qquad (5)$$

where n_{u,l_1} is the number of times that $l = 1$ has been sampled in the user profile D_u; n_{u,l_0} is the number of times that $l = 0$ has been sampled in the user profile D_u; $n_{u,z}$ is the number of times that topic z has been sampled from the personal interests of user u; $n_{t,z}$ is the number of times that latent topic z has been sampled from the temporal context at t; the number n with superscription $\neg ui$ denotes a quantity excluding the current instance.

Then, following [13], we simultaneously sample topic z and sentiment s according to the following posterior probability, when $l_{ui} = 1$ and when $l_{ui} = 0$:

$$P(z_{ui} = k, s_{ui} = e|l_{ui} = 1, \boldsymbol{z}_{\neg ui}, \boldsymbol{s}_{\neg ui}, u, .) \propto \frac{n_{u,k}^{\neg ui} + \alpha_k}{\sum_z^K n_{u,z}^{\neg ui} + \alpha_z} \times \Pi \qquad (6)$$

$$P(z_{ui} = k, s_{ui} = e|l_{ui} = 0, \boldsymbol{z}_{\neg ui}, \boldsymbol{s}_{\neg ui}, u, .) \propto \frac{n_{t_{ui},k}^{\neg ui} + \alpha'_k}{\sum_z^K n_{t_{ui},z}^{\neg ui} + \alpha'_z} \times \Pi \qquad (7)$$

where

$$\Pi = \frac{n_{k,e}^{\neg ui} + \lambda_s}{\sum_s^E n_{k,s}^{\neg ui} + \lambda_s} \times \frac{n_{k,e,v_{ui}}^{\neg ui} + \eta_{v_{ui}}}{\sum_v^V n_{k,e,v}^{\neg ui} + \eta_v} \times \prod_{w \in \mathbf{w}} \frac{n_{k,e,w}^{\neg ui} + \beta_w}{\sum_{w'}^J n_{k,e,w'}^{\neg ui} + \beta_{w'}} \qquad (8)$$

and $n_{k,e}$ is the number of times that sentiment e has been sampled from topic k, and $n_{k,e,w}$ and $n_{k,e,v}$ are the numbers of times that word w and item v have been sampled from the topic-sentiment pair (k, e), respectively.

After a sufficient number of sampling iterations, we apply the expectation of the Dirichlet distribution (e.g., $Dir(\boldsymbol{\alpha}) = \alpha_i / \sum_i \alpha_i$) on those samples and yield the estimation of the model parameters as follows:

$$\hat{\theta}_{uz} = \frac{n_{u,z} + \alpha}{\sum_{z'}^K n_{u,z'} + \alpha}; \hat{\theta}'_{tz} = \frac{n_{t,z} + \alpha'}{\sum_{z'}^K n_{t,z'} + \alpha'}; \hat{\psi}_{zsw} = \frac{n_{z,s,w} + \beta}{\sum_{w'}^J n_{z,s,w'} + \beta}$$

$$\hat{\Omega}_{zs} = \frac{n_{z,s} + \lambda}{\sum_{s'}^E n_{z,s'} + \lambda}; \hat{\xi}_u = \frac{n_{u,l_1} + \gamma}{n_{u,l_1} + \gamma + n_{u,l_0} + \gamma'}; \hat{\phi}_{zsv} = \frac{n_{z,s,v} + \eta}{\sum_{v'}^V n_{z,s,v'} + \eta}$$

2.4   Scalable Inference Algorithm

The rapid growth of review data scale poses a significant challenge for model parameter estimation in terms of both computation time and memory requirements. It is crucial to take advantage of the computation power and memory capacity of clusters. We propose a distributed TSAUB inference algorithm based on Spark [30], a general and scalable processing system specifically targeted at machine-learning iterative workloads.

First, we create a type of RDD (Resilient Distributed Data) [29] named $userRDD$ to store D_u for each user u. For a $userRDD$, every item or every word holds the last topic assignment z, the last sentiment assignment s and the last binary state l (i.e., $l = 1$ or $l = 0$). Each $userRDD$ contains local counts $n_{u,z}, n_{t,z,u}, n_{l,u}, n_{z,s,u}, n_{z,s,v,u}$ and $n_{z,s,w,u}$. Note that all counts with subscript u (except $n_{u,z}$) indicate that they are local to a specific user u and do not need to be shared across $userRDDs$. Finally, we can get the global counts by aggregating the local counts over all $userRDDs$, e.g., aggregating the local count $n_{t,z,u}$ over all $userRDDs$ to obtain a global count $n_{t,z} = \sum_u n_{t,z,u}$.

Inspired by [1], we present a transformation operation named GibbsSampler that is applied to every $userRDD$ to get a new $userRDD$. GibbsSampler first decreases the local counts and their corresponding global counts according to their last assignments, then computes the new distributions for latent variables l, z and s by Eqs. (4) to (7), and finally assigns new values to those latent variables and increases the local counts and global counts.

Note that each worker node has a same copy of global counts at the beginning of each iteration so that every $userRDD$ has access to them, but after GibbsSampler transformations are performed, the local counts are modified so that the global counts are not in synchronization until the start of the next iteration, where all local counts are accumulated to get global counts for broadcast.

3   TSAUB-Based Recommender System

The TSAUB-based recommender system consists of two components: offline modeling component (i.e., TSAUB) and online recommendation component. Once we have estimated TSAUB model parameters in the offline modeling phase, the online recommendation component computes a ranking score for each item based on the learnt knowledge and returns top-k ones with the highest scores. A user tends to choose items which have both topics or functions that match the user's personal interests or the current temporal context and positive crowd sentiments. For example, a user may want to buy a suncream product (topic) in summer (temporal context), and she is most likely to choose the one with very good overall feedbacks from previous reviewers (crowd sentiments). Based on this intuition, given a query $q = (u, t)$, we first construct a query vector for q as follows:

$$\hat{\vartheta}_q = \xi_u \hat{\theta}_u + (1 - \xi_u)\hat{\theta}'_t \tag{9}$$

The ranking score $score(u, t, v)$ for item v is computed as the inner product in the K-dimensional topic space between the query's vector $\hat{\vartheta}_q$ and the item's vector $\hat{\phi}_{s_1 v}$:

$$score(u, t, v) = \sum_{z=1}^{K} \hat{\vartheta}_{qz} \hat{\phi}_{zs_1 v} \tag{10}$$

where we are only interested in positive crowd sentiment (i.e., s_1).

The straightforward method of generating top-k recommendations needs to compute the ranking scores for all items according to Eq. (10) and select the k

ones with highest ranking scores, which is, however, computationally inefficient, especially when the number of available items becomes large. To improve the online recommendation efficiency based on the observation of query preference sparsity that a query q only prefers a small number of topics (say 5–10 latent dimensions) and the query weights on most dimensions are extremely small, we adopt the TA-based query processing technique developed in [22,28]. Since $\hat{\vartheta}_{qz}$ is non-negative, the proposed ranking function in Eq. (10) is monotonically increasing given a query q, which meets the requirement of the TA-based query processing technique. This technology has the nice property of finding top-k results correctly by examining the minimum number of items without scanning all ones, which enables our recommender system scalable to large-scale datasets.

4   Experimental Results

4.1   Datasets

The Amazon dataset [9] contain many categories, from which we select four: electronic equipments, clothings, kitchen products and movies (for simplicity, we name them Electronics, Clothings, Kitchens and Movies). Each record in a category contains five elements: user, item, time, review, rating.

4.2   Comparative Approaches

We compare TSAUB with the following state-of-the-art recommendation techniques: TCAM, FM, EFM and ItemKNN.

TCAM: [22] proposed a probabilistic generative model named TCAM that models both user preferences and temporal contexts over user-oriented topics and time-oriented topics, respectively. The recommendation method based on TCAM we used first generates a list of $5 * k$ recommended items, then we select the *top-k* items whose average item ratings are higher than that of the other $4 * k$ items.

FM: Factorization Machines [12] are generic approaches that allow to mimic most factorization models by feature engineering, i.e., FM models all interactions between variables (e.g., user, item and auxiliary information). With FM, temporal factors could be automatically taken into account as a feature.

EFM: EFM [31] is a matrix factorization method based explicit factor model which extracts aspects and sentiment from reviews, and models the relation among user, item, aspect and personal sentiment for recommendation. It is the state-of-the-art CF method that integrates sentiments.

ItemKNN: ItemKNN [14] is the most straightforward idea for recommendations, which applies the collaborative filtering method directly over the items.

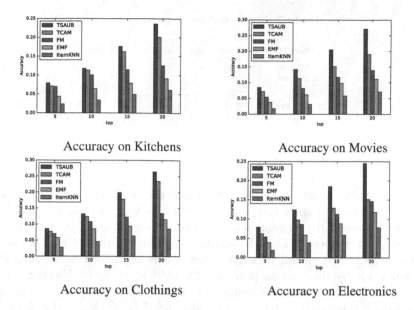

Accuracy on Kitchens   Accuracy on Movies

Accuracy on Clothings   Accuracy on Electronics

Fig. 2. Recommendations on four Amazon datasets

4.3 Evaluation Methods and Metrics

Given a user profile D_u in terms of a collection of review records, we first sort these review records by their generated time stamps, then use the $80th$ percentile as the cutoff point such that the part before this point is used for training and the rest recordsfor testing. According to this splitting strategy, we divide the whole dataset D into a training set D_{train} and a test set D_{test}.

We adopt the evaluation methodology and measurement Accuracy@k applied in [2,3,6,25] to evaluate the top-k recommendation accuracy. Specifically, for each user review record $(u, v, t, \mathbf{w})$ in the test set D_{test}, we first randomly select 1000 unrated items by user u at time slice t, and then compute the score for item v as well as all other 1000 items. Then, we form a top-k recommendation list by picking the k ones with the highest scores. If item v (i.e., the ground truth item) appears in top-k recommendations, we have a hit, otherwise we have a miss. Accuracy@k is computed as the hit ratio in the test set D_{test}, as follows:

$$Accuracy@k = \frac{\#Hit@k}{|D_{test}|} \qquad (11)$$

where $\#Hit@k$ and $|D_{test}|$ denote the number of hits in the test set and the number of all test cases, respectively.

4.4 Recommendation Effectiveness

In this subsection, we present the effectiveness of our proposed TSAUB and all other comparison methods with well-tuned hyper-parameters listed in Table 2.

Table 2. Fine-tuned hyper-parameters

	Electronics	Clothings	Movies	Kitchens
K	130	120	120	100
E			2	
Timeslice	3 days	4 days	1 week	2 weeks
Iterations	600	500	400	400
Priors	$\alpha = \alpha' = 50/K, \beta = \eta = \lambda = 0.01, \gamma = \gamma' = 0.5$			

Due to the space limitation, we do not present the sensitivity analysis of these hyper-parameters. We show the performance where k is set to 5, 10, 15, 20.

Figure 2 presents the recommendation accuracy on the four Amazon datasets. Obviously, our proposed TSAUB significantly outperforms other competitor methods consistently on all datasets. Several conclusion can be reached from the results: Firstly, TSAUB outperforms TCAM, especially for Electronics and Movies whose sales are more easily affected by word-of-mouth, which verifies the significance of the crowd sentiment. Secondly, TSAUB, TCAM and FM outperform EMF and ItemKNN, justifying the benefits brought by exploiting and integrating temporal contexts (i.e., the temporal preferences of the public) which can effectively alleviate the sparsity of individual users' review data. Thirdly, EMF shows higher recommendation accuracy than ItemKNN due to the incorporation of user sentiments. Finally, we need to carefully choose the length of time slice, because different category of product manifests different life span. For instance, electronic products usually upgrade very fast, so the length of time slice should be short.

4.5   Model Training Efficiency

We perform this experiment to evaluate the training efficiency of TSAUB on those four datasets. We ran the sequential implementation on a server equipped with 4 processors of Intel Xeon E5-v3, 64 cores and 124 GB memory, and ran the scalable Spark implementation on a cluster of 10 servers where each server is equipped with 2 processors of Intel Xeon E5-v3, 32 cores and 32 GB memory.

We demonstrate the running time w.r.t. different implementations (i.e., sequential and scalable) in Fig. 3. As expected, the sequential implementation of TSAUB is very time-consuming (hundreds of hours), while the Spark implementation can gain 3x–5x speed-up. For example, for every iteration running on Electronics, the sequential implementation takes 21 min on average while the Spark implementation takes 4.6 min, obtaining 4.5x speed-up. With the scalable and fast inference implementation, it becomes practical for TSAUB to be deployed in the real environment.

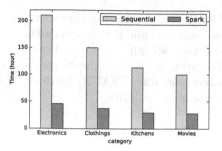

Fig. 3. Training efficiency

5 Related Works

5.1 Recommendation Using Temporal Information

The temporal effect for user behaviors analysis has attracted much attention recently [7,8,18,19,22,26]. TimeSVD [7] is a model that can capture local changes to user preferences, which is important for recommendation performance. [19] introduced Bayesian probabilistic tensor factorization model (BPTF) which represents users, items, and time in a low-dimensional space and predicts the rating score that user u will assign to item v at time t. To make top-k recommendation, [22] proposed a temporal context-aware recommender system based on TCAM model to simultaneously model user-oriented topics related to users' preferences and time-oriented topics related to temporal contexts. TSAUB distinguishes from TCAM mainly in: (1) TCAM ignores the crowd sentiment factor, which TSAUB considers important for item recommendation; and (2) TSAUB exploits the textual reviews that contain rich information but TCAM only focuses on ratings.

5.2 Recommendation Using Sentiment Analysis

Sentiment analysis has been integrated into recommender systems by many studies. [4] proposed to classify users into two distinct categories (i.e., optimists and pessimists) by averaging the sentiment polarity of remarks and then use the categories as features in CF. [15] explored to incorporate a sentiment classifier for movie recommendation. First, CF is used to generate a list of candidates, then each movie is labeled with sentiment polarity by the sentiment classifier, finally only the "positive" movies are recommended to users. [10] introduced a neighbor-based CF that utilizes the predicted sentiment scores to fill in the missing ratings. [11] investigated to combine the sentiment score of a review and the real ratings in a biased matrix factorization model. [31] proposed a matrix factorization model EFM which extracts explicit product features and user sentiments by phrase-level sentiment analysis on reviews, then generates both recommendations and disrecommendations based on the predicted user's preferences and sentiments. TSAUB distinguishes from the aforementioned methods in several points. First, they only focus on the sentiment without considering topics in the texts. Second, TSAUB accumulates the sentiment for an item from all its reviewers instead of from only one, and this design can help obtain a more reliable crowd sentiment. Third, they all fall into the category of supervised learning, which requires a labeled corpus for training, and this requirement severely limits their applications in other domains. TSAUB, however, is a fully unsupervised method to extract the sentiment polarity.

6 Conclusions

We proposed a novel probabilistic graphical model TSAUB to learn user interests, temporal contexts and crowd sentiments from user review data, based on which a novel temporal-sentiment-aware recommender system was built. Extensive experiments were conducted and the experimental results showed that our proposed model significantly improves the prediction accuracy over the state-of-the-arts. We also developed a scalable implementation for estimating the model parameters to cope with large-scale datasets, which shows superior performance over the sequential implementation.

Acknolwledgement. This work was supported by ARC Discovery Early Career Researcher Award (Grant No. DE160100308), ARC Discovery Project (Grant No. DP170103954) and New Staff Research Grant of The University of Queensland (Grant No.613134).

References

1. Bi, B., Tian, Y., Sismanis, Y., Balmin, A., Cho, J.: Scalable topic-specific influence analysis on microblogs. In: WSDM, pp. 513–522 (2014)
2. Chen, W.Y., Chu, J.C., Luan, J., Bai, H., Wang, Y., Chang, E.Y.: Collaborative filtering for orkut communities: discovery of user latent behavior. In: WWW, pp. 681–690 (2009)
3. Cremonesi, P., Koren, Y., Turrin, R.: Performance of recommender algorithms on top-n recommendation tasks. In: RecSys, pp. 39–46 (2010)
4. García-Cumbreras, M.Á., Montejo-Ráez, A., Díaz-Galiano, M.C.: Pessimists and optimists: improving collaborative filtering through sentiment analysis. Expert Syst. Appl. **40**(17), 6758–6765 (2013)
5. Herr, P.M., Kardes, F.R., Kim, J.: Effects of word-of-mouth and product-attribute information on persuasion: an accessibility-diagnosticity perspective. J. Consum. Res. **17**(4), 454–462 (1991)
6. Koren, Y.: Factorization meets the neighborhood: a multifaceted collaborative filtering model. In: KDD, pp. 426–434 (2008)
7. Koren, Y.: Collaborative filtering with temporal dynamics. Commun. ACM **53**(4), 89–97 (2010)
8. Li, L., Chu, W., Langford, J., Schapire, R.E.: A contextual-bandit approach to personalized news article recommendation. In: WWW, pp. 661–670 (2010)
9. McAuley, J., Leskovec, J.: Hidden factors and hidden topics: understanding rating dimensions with review text. In: RecSys, pp. 165–172 (2013)
10. Pappas, N., Popescu-Belis, A.: Sentiment analysis of user comments for one-class collaborative filtering over ted talks. In: SIGIR, pp. 773–776 (2013)

11. Pero, Š., Horváth, T.: Opinion-driven matrix factorization for rating prediction. In: Carberry, S., Weibelzahl, S., Micarelli, A., Semeraro, G. (eds.) UMAP 2013. LNCS, vol. 7899, pp. 1–13. Springer, Heidelberg (2013). https://doi.org/10.1007/978-3-642-38844-6_1
12. Rendle, S.: Factorization machines. In: ICDM, pp. 995–1000 (2010)
13. Rosen-Zvi, M., Griffiths, T., Steyvers, M., Smyth, P.: The author-topic model for authors and documents. In: UAI, pp. 487–494 (2004)
14. Sarwar, B., Karypis, G., Konstan, J., Riedl, J.: Item-based collaborative filtering recommendation algorithms. In: WWW, pp. 285–295 (2001)
15. Singh, V.K., Mukherjee, M., Mehta, G.K.: Combining collaborative filtering and sentiment classification for improved movie recommendations. In: Sombattheera, C., Agarwal, A., Udgata, S.K., Lavangnananda, K. (eds.) MIWAI 2011. LNCS (LNAI), vol. 7080, pp. 38–50. Springer, Heidelberg (2011). https://doi.org/10.1007/978-3-642-25725-4_4
16. Stoyanovich, J., Amer-Yahia, S., Marlow, C., Yu, C.: Leveraging tagging to model user interests in del. icio. us. In: AAAI, pp. 104–109 (2008)
17. Tang, J., Wu, S., Sun, J., Su, H.: Cross-domain collaboration recommendation. In: KDD, pp. 1285–1293 (2012)
18. Xie, M., Yin, H., Wang, H., Xu, F., Chen, W., Wang, S.: Learning graph-based poi embedding for location-based recommendation. In: CIKM, pp. 15–24 (2016)
19. Xiong, L., Chen, X., Huang, T.K., Schneider, J.G., Carbonell, J.G.: Temporal collaborative filtering with bayesian probabilistic tensor factorization. In: SDM, pp. 211–222 (2010)
20. Xu, Z., Zhang, Y., Wu, Y., Yang, Q.: Modeling user posting behavior on social media. In: SIGIR, pp. 545–554 (2012)
21. Yin, H., Cui, B., Chen, L., Hu, Z., Zhang, C.: Modeling location-based user rating profiles for personalized recommendation. TKDE 9(3), 19 (2015)
22. Yin, H., Cui, B., Chen, L., Hu, Z., Zhou, X.: Dynamic user modeling in social media systems. TOIS 33(3), 10 (2015)
23. Yin, H., Cui, B., Lu, H., Huang, Y., Yao, J.: A unified model for stable and temporal topic detection from social media data. In: ICDE, pp. 661–672 (2013)
24. Yin, H., Cui, B., Zhou, X., Wang, W., Huang, Z., Sadiq, S.: Joint modeling of user check-in behaviors for real-time point-of-interest recommendation. TOIS 35(2), 11 (2016)
25. Yin, H., Sun, Y., Cui, B., Hu, Z., Chen, L.: LCARS: a location-content-aware recommender system. In: KDD, pp. 221–229 (2013)
26. Yin, H., Wang, W., Wang, H., Chen, L., Zhou, X.: Spatial-aware hierarchical collaborative deep learning for poi recommendation. TKDE 29(11), 2537–2551 (2017)
27. Yin, H., Zhou, X., Cui, B., Wang, H., Zheng, K., Nguyen, Q.V.H.: Adapting to user interest drift for poi recommendation. TKDE 28(10), 2566–2581 (2016)
28. Yin, H., Zhou, X., Shao, Y., Wang, H., Sadiq, S.: Joint modeling of user check-in behaviors for point-of-interest recommendation. In: CIKM, pp. 1631–1640 (2015)
29. Zaharia, M., Chowdhury, M., Das, T., Dave, A., Ma, J., McCauley, M., Franklin, M.J., Shenker, S., Stoica, I.: Resilient distributed datasets: a fault-tolerant abstraction for in-memory cluster computing. In: NSDI, p. 2 (2012)
30. Zaharia, M., Chowdhury, M., Franklin, M.J., Shenker, S., Stoica, I.: Spark: cluster computing with working sets. In: HotCloud, p. 10 (2010)
31. Zhang, Y., Lai, G., Zhang, M., Zhang, Y., Liu, Y., Ma, S.: Explicit factor models for explainable recommendation based on phrase-level sentiment analysis. In: SIGIR, pp. 83–92 (2014)

Finding Maximal Stable Cores
in Social Networks

Alexander Zhou[1]([envelope]), Fan Zhang[2], Long Yuan[2], Ying Zhang[3],
and Xuemin Lin[2]

[1] The University of Queensland, Brisbane, Australia
`alexander.zhou@uqconnect.edu.au`
[2] The University of New South Wales, Sydney, Australia
`fan.zhang3@unsw.edu.au`, {`longyuan,lxue`}`@cse.unsw.edu.au`
[3] The University of Technology Sydney, Sydney, Australia
`ying.zhang@uts.edu.au`

Abstract. Maximal Stable Cores are a cohesive subgraph on a social
network which use both engagement and similarity to identify stable
groups of users. The problem is, when given a query user and a similarity threshold, to find all Maximal Stable Cores relative to the user.
We propose a baseline algorithm and as the problem is NP-Hard, an
improved heuristic algorithm which utilises linear time k-core decomposition. Experiments how that when the two algorithms differ, the improved
algorithm significantly outperforms the baseline.

Keywords: Social networks · Graph databases · Maximal Stable Core
(k, r)-core

1 Introduction

Social networks may be modelled as attributed graphs with users denoted as
vertices and connections as edges, where each vertex contains attributes such as
liked pages or location. On these graphs, detecting communities through structural models allows for a deeper understanding as to which users are likely to
stay inside the network. As opposed to most models (such as the k-core [11] or
k-truss [10]) which only consider the structural cohesiveness of the subgraph, the
(k, r)-core [15] also considers attributes inherent in the system and may therefore
highlight groups of users with an increased likelihood to stay.

The (k, r)-core focuses on two key variables: Engagement (k) and Similarity
(r). Much research has been conducted on the engagement of users regarding
graphical representations, in particular how certain structures may identify stable groups of users. Engagement can be modelled by the k-core, where each
vertex in a cohesive subgraph has at least k neighbours [11].

Following suit, users in social networks contain a certain set of attributes
depending on the system (such as location, liked pages, age, sex etc.). Given two
users and their corresponding attributes, it is possible to assign a numerical value

© Springer International Publishing AG, part of Springer Nature 2018
J. Wang et al. (Eds.): ADC 2018, LNCS 10837, pp. 224–235, 2018.
https://doi.org/10.1007/978-3-319-92013-9_18

(such as the Jaccard Similarity Coefficient) to measure the similarity between them. Given a similarity threshold r, we can then build a similarity graph where an edge connection between two vertices implies that they are similar. Similarity among these vertices may be modelled by a clique [8,9], where each vertex in a cohesive subgraph is a neighbour to every other vertex on the similarity graph.

The (k, r)-core combines these two notions. A (k, r)-core is a connected subgraph which is both a k-core on the original graph and also a clique on the corresponding similarity graph. Whilst research has been conducted on finding maximal (k, r)-cores with fixed values of k and r this paper aims to find the maximal k-value in which a (k, r)-core containing that user still exists (given a query vertex q and fixed value for r). We name such a structure the Maximal Stable Core(s) (MSC(s)) containing q.

In terms of applications for this research, finding the maximum k value leads us to groups of users who are most tightly connected to the target user with similar interests. Given this information, social networks such as Facebook would be able to recommend friends to a query user in order to set up an active group. Additionally, location-based games such as Pokémon Go would be able to direct a targeted user to potential friends also in the nearby area.

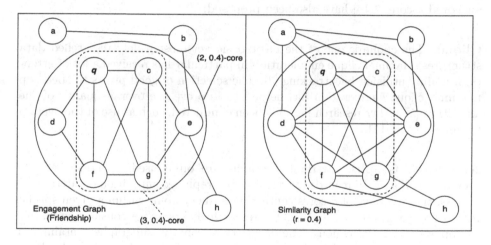

Fig. 1. Friendship and liked pages based example

Example 1 *Social Network*. *In Fig. 1 we have the Engagement on the left, in which an edge represents "friend" status between the two users it connects. On the right we have a graphical representation of the Similarity, with an edge indicating the Jaccard Coefficient being greater than the similarity threshold r on the set of liked pages for both users. In this example, $r = 0.4$. A node with the same label on both graphs corresponds to the same user. For the query vertex q, there exists a $(2, 0.4)$-core (indicated by the solid circle) and a $(3, 0.4)$-core (indicated by the dashed space). As no $(4, 0.4)$-core exists, we call the $(3, 0.4)$-core the MSC containing q.*

Whilst there exists a linear-time algorithm for k-core computation [1], clique discovery and consequently maximal (k, r)-core enumeration is NP-Hard [4,15]. As a result, the problem of finding all MSC(s) for a query user is also NP-Hard, as established in Sect. 3. In Sect. 4, this paper introduces a baseline, trivial approach to solve the problem using both incremental and binary search methods. Then an improved algorithm is proposed in Sect. 5 which attempts to minimize the running time by avoiding similarity constraints as much as possible through the use of k-core decomposition. Key to all techniques, we prove the nested nature of the MSC and (k, r)-cores which helps to avoid accessing unnecessary vertices and edges. We also provide pruning techniques to further reduce runtime.

2   Related Work

k-core. The k-core as a model for identifying cohesive subgraphs was first proposed by Seidman [11] but has since been widely recognised in part due to the linear time algorithm proposed by Batagelj and Zaversnik [1] as well as a single PC decomposition method [12]. Multiple extensions of this structure such as the anchored k-core [2,14] have also been proposed.

Clique. The clique is one of the most basic yet most widely researched data structures. Maximal clique enumeration in particular has received a lot of attention, mainly utilising backtracking [3]. The selection of good pivots to speed up maximal clique enumeration has helped to improve the overall quality of the algorithm [5]. Other research has also been conducted, such as use of the overlap to improve speed [13].

Attributed Graphs. Attributed graphs are often used to model real-life social networks [7]. In regards to cohesive subgraph decomposition on attributed graphs, the discovery of k-cores containing a query point within a given special region has been researched [16]. Our research differs as we consider similarity as opposed to spatial regions. The discovery of cohesive subgraphs containing a query point in regards to both structure and keyword similarity has also been researched [6]. However, their work aims in maximizing the number of shared keywords among vertices, whereas ours only cares for a fixed similarity.

(k, r)-core. Currently, the (k, r)-core is the only structure to use both the k-core and clique to help discover stable communities on networks [15]. This research has demonstrated the challenges in computing maximal (k, r)-cores. No attempt has been made to apply this to a query user or the discovery of Maximal Stable Cores.

3 Preliminaries

3.1 Problem Definition

Let us consider an undirected, unweighted and attributed graph $G = (V, \mathcal{E}, A)$ with $V(G)$ representing the set of vertices, $\mathcal{E}(G)$ representing the set of edges and $A(G)$ denoting the attributes of the vertices. We may denote the similarity of two vertices $u, v \in V(G)$ by $sim(u, v)$, derived from the attribute values of each of the vertices utilising an appropriate measure such as the Jaccard Similarity Coefficient for sets or Euclidean Distance for distance. When given a similarity threshold r, we say two vertices are similar if $sim(u, v) \geq r$ (otherwise we say they are dissimilar).

We denote a subgraph S of G by the notation $S \subseteq G$, implying $V(S) \subseteq V(G)$, $\mathcal{E}(S) \subseteq \mathcal{E}(G)$ and $A(S) \subseteq A(G)$. For a vertex u, we use $deg(u, V)$ to denote the number of adjacent vertices of u that exist in $V(S)$. We also use $DP(u, S)$ to denote the number of other vertices in $V(S)$ which are dissimilar to u ($sim(u, v) < r, \forall v \in S$) for the given r. Alternatively, we may also use $SP(u, S)$ to denote the number of similar vertices.

Definition 1 *(k, r)-core.* *Given a connected subgraph $S \subseteq G$, a positive integer k and a given value of similarity threshold r, S is a (k, r)-core if:*

(i) $deg(u, S) \geq k$ holds true for all $u \in V(S)$.
(ii) $DP(u, S) = 0$ holds true for all $u \in V(S)$

Additionally, we wish to discover the maximum k value and its corresponding (k, r)-core as defined below.

Definition 2 *Maximal (k, r)-core.* *Given a connected subgraph $S \subseteq G$ with a given positive integer k and similarity threshold r, S is a maximal (k, r)-core of G if there exists no (k, r)-core S' of G in which $S \subset S'$.*

Definition 3 *Stable Core (SC) and Maximal Stable Core (MSC).* *Given a connected graph G with given similarity threshold r, we say the (k, r)-core S in G is the Stable Core containing q if there exists no value $k' > k$ in which a (k', r)-core exists. We call S a Maximal Stable Core (MSC) if it is also a maximal (k, r)-core.*

Problem Statement. Given an undirected, unweighted and attributed graph G, a fixed similarity threshold r and a query vertex $q \in V(G)$, we wish to find all MSCs that contain q.

Problem Complexity. As established previously, the problem of finding maximal (k, r)-cores with fixed k and r values is NP-Hard due to the necessity of discovering maximal cliques on the similarity. As the proposed problem is an extension upon this and can also be reduced to finding maximal cliques on the graph containing q, it is also NP-Hard (Table 1).

Table 1. Key notation and definitions

Notation	Definition
G	Undirected, unweighted, attributed graph
S	Subgraph of G
r	Similarity threshold
k	Engagement threshold
k_{max}	Maximum possible engagement for given graph
q	Query vertex
MSC	Maximal stable core
$deg(u, S)$	Number of adjacent vertices in S compared to u
$sim(u, v)$	Similarity between vertices u and v
$DP(u, S)$	Number of dissimilar vertices in S compared to u
$SF(S)$	Every vertex $u \in S$ has $DP(u, S) = 0$

4 Baseline Approach

4.1 Incremental Approach

Perhaps considered a trivial solution, the core notion of this approach is to start at a value of k guaranteed to produce a (k, r)-core and then iteratively incrementing the value of k until we cannot find a (k, r)-core in our graph. Thus, the maximal value is $k - 1$ and the MSCs have been discovered. To find the (k, r)-cores, we will utilise the current best algorithm which is the Enumeration Approach detailed by Zhang et al. [15].

Algorithm 1 presents the Enumeration Method pseudocode. Lines 1–4 examine all candidate vertices C, and moves them to the relevant excluded vertices E if they cannot form a (k, r)-core with the current chosen vertices M. Lines 5 and 6 decide if the current search should be terminated. The algorithm then checks if C is similar (Line 7). If so, the union of M and C is a (k, r)-core. A check is conducted to see if the union is maximal and if so it is added to R, a set of maximal (k, r)-cores (Lines 8–10). Otherwise, the algorithm continues to search (Lines 11–14).

Theorem 1. In regards to k, (k, r)-cores obey the nested property. That is, (k_1, r)-core $S \subseteq (k_2, r)$-core S' where $k_1 \geq k_2$. Additionally, all $MSC(s)$ are contained in (k, r)-core(s) where $k \leq k_{max}$.

Proof: Firstly, note that each vertex $v \in V(S)$ has $deg(v, S) \geq k > k - 1$. By finding all vertices in $G \backslash S$ which create a $(k - 1, r)$-core in union with S, we discover S'. As a result, each maximal (k, r)-core in G can be expanded to a maximal $(k-1, r)$-core. By induction, we can also see that all $MSC(s)$ in G can be expanded into a (k, r)-core where $k \leq k_{max}$.

As a result of Theorem 1 when using the Incremental Approach, when we have found all (k, r)-cores S containing q we need only perform a search for the

---

Algorithm 1. EnumMethod(k, M, C, E)

   Input   : k: Engagement Value, M: Chosen Vertices, C: Candidate Vertices,
                E: Relevant Excluded Vertices
   Output: R: Maximal (k, r)-cores
1 **for** *each vertex* $u \in C$ **do**
2   **if** $deg(u, M \cup C) < k$ *or* $DP(u, M) > 0$ **then**
3        $C = C \setminus u$;
4        $E = E \cup u$;

5 **if** *there exists* $u \in SF_C(E)$ *with* $deg(u, M) \geq k$ **then**
6   **return**

7 **if** C *is* $SF(C)$ **then**
8     $M := M \cup C$;
9   **if** M *is maximal* **then**
10       $R := R \cup M$;

11 **else**
12     $u = $ a vertex in $C \setminus SF(C)$;
13   **EnumMethod**($M \cup u, C \setminus u, E$);
14   **EnumMethod**($M, C \setminus u, E \cup u$);

$(k + 1, r)$-core on the vertices of each individual core in S in order to improve our algorithm.

Observation 1. We may ignore all vertices which are dissimilar to q.

Observation 2. We may ignore an edge if the two vertices it connects are dissimilar.

These observations help to reduce the number of vertices and edges required to search, which can be crucial in reducing the running time of the algorithm when applied accordingly.

4.2 Binary Search Approach

In general, but especially when many vertices are similar to each other, the Incremental Approach is too slow to even consider. The Incremental Approach requires the use of the Enumeration Approach $deg(q, G)$ times in the worst case. Instead, we may perform Binary Search on the k-value between $k = 1$ and $k = deg(q, G)$, which will in a worst case scenario require $log(deg(q, G))$ uses of the Enumeration Approach.

Observation 3. For any given vertex $q \in G$, q can only exist in a (k, r)-core where $k \leq deg(q, G)$. Therefore, the k_{max} leading to the MSC(s) containing q must lie between 1 and $deg(q, G)$.

Proof: Suppose we have a (k, r)-core containing q, where $deg(q, G) < k$. There exists an immediate contradiction as, per the definition of the (k, r)-core, all vertices v in the (k, r)-core must have $deg(v, G) \geq k$.

Algorithm 2. BinarySearch(G, r, q)

Input : G: Undirected Graph, r: Similarity Threshold, q: Query Vertex
Output: k_{max}: Maximum k-value, R: All Maximal (k, r)-cores

1 **for** *each vertex $v \neq q$ in $V(G)$* **do**
2   Remove v and all its edges if $sim(q, v) < r$;

3 **for** *each edge(u, v) in $\mathcal{E}(G)$* **do**
4   Remove edge(u, v) if $sim(u, v) < r$;

5 $botCap$ = value guarenteed to produce valid result; $topCap = deg(q, G)$; $R = \emptyset$;
6 **while** *true* **do**
7     $k = (topCap + botCap)/2$; **SetUpMCE()**;
8   **if** $R = $ ***EnumMethod(k, M, C, E)*** *is non empty* **then**
9        $k+ = 1$; **SetUpMCE()**;
10   **if** $R = $ ***EnumMethod(k, M, C, E)*** *is empty* **then**
11   **return** $k_{max} = (k - 1)$, *Previous non-empty R*;
12   **else**
13           $botCap = k$;

14   **else**
15        $k- = 1$; **SetUpMCE()**;
16   **if** $R = $ ***EnumMethod(k, M, C, E)*** *is non empty* **then**
17   **return** $k_{max} = k$, R;
18   **else**
19           $topCap = k$;

Algorithm 2 presents the pseudocode for the Binary Search Approach. Lines 1–4 prune vertices and edges as per Observations 1 and 2. In Line 5, we set up $topCap$ and $botCap$, which we will use for the binary search. We select a value for $botCap$ guaranteed to produce a result. As per Observation 3, $topCap = deg(q, G)$. We then perform the binary search (Lines 6–19). Notably, if the search succeeds for a value of k we must then check if $k + 1$ would fail (Lines 9–13). Similarly, if the search fails for k we check if $k - 1$ would succeed (Lines 15–19). These checks ensure algorithm correctness. **SetUpMCE()** sets M as q, C as all vertices not removed already and E as $\emptyset$.

5   Core Decomposition Approach

Ultimately, in an attempt to lower the running time of the query, we wish to avoid the Enumeration Method as much as possible. Using this as motivation, we propose the following Core Decomposition Approach.

Theorem 2. For any (k, r)-core S containing query vertex q, where $k \leq k_{max}$, it will produce one and only one MSC candidate containing q when k-core decomposition is conducted on S. We define a MSC candidate as the Maximal Stable Core considering only S.

Proof: From Theorem 1 previously we have established that at least one MSC candidate must exist in any given S, even if the MSC is S itself. By performing k-core decomposition to find the maximum k-value and the corresponding k-core containing q on S, we can verify that the decomposition produces the relative MSC of S as we know that all vertices in S are already similar as per the definition of the (k, r)-core. Finally, there may only be exactly one MSC containing q in S since if there are multiple k-cores on a graph, they must be disjoint as established in previous research.

By combining Theorems 1 and 2, we can determine that should we find all maximal (k, r)-cores containing q where $k \leq k_{max}$, if we perform k-core decomposition on each of these cores we are guaranteed to find the MSC(s) and k_{max}.

Algorithm 3. CoreDecompositionMethod(G, r, q)

Input : G: Undirected Graph, r: Similarity Threshold, q: Query Vertex
Output: k_{max}: Maximum k-value, MSC: Maximal Stable Core(s)
1 **for** *each vertex $v \neq q$ in $V(G)$* **do**
2 | Remove v and all its edges if $sim(q, v) < r$;

3 **for** *each edge(u, v) in $\mathcal{E}(G)$* **do**
4 | Remove edge(u, v) if $sim(u, v) < r$;

5 k = value guaranteed to produce a result; **SetUpMCE()**;
6 R = **EnumMethod**(k, M, C, E);
7 **foreach** *(k, r)-core $S \in R$* **do**
8 | $MSC = MSC \cup$ **CoreDecomposition**(S);

9 Scan MSC to find k_{max} and delete any cores where $k_S < k_{max}$;
10 **return** MSC

Algorithm 3 presents the pseudocode for the Core Decomposition Approach. Lines 1–4 are the pruning rules established by Observations 1 and 2. We then perform the Enumeration Method with a value of k guaranteed to produce a valid result which defaults to $k = 1$ when nothing is known about existing (k, r)-cores discovered previously (Lines 5–6). For each (k, r)-core produced, we perform k-core decomposition upon it to find its MSC candidate (Lines 7–8). Given all candidates, we simply examine them to determine k_{max} and all MSC(s) in G containing q (Lines 9–10).

As there exists a linear time algorithm to discover k-cores in a graph, this method may significantly reduce the total running time of the algorithm in comparison to the Incremental and Binary Search Approaches.

6 Performance

6.1 Experimental Setting

Algorithms. In regards to (k, r)-core computation, the current baseline is the algorithm proposed by Zhang et al. [15] taking fixed k and r values. This algorithm however does not consider a query point. As such, to the best of our knowledge, there exists no work that deals with MSC. The following two algorithms were tested:

The *BinarySearch* Method (BS) utilising the Enumeration Algorithm as described in Sect. 4.2 On the case of a successful EnumMethod, subsequent searches would use the currently discovered (k, r)-cores as the only vertices needed to be examined.

The *CoreDecomposition* Method (CD) as described in Sect. 5 utilises a single run of the Enumeration Algorithm followed by k-core decomposition.

Datasets. The two datasets utilised, *Brightkite* and *Gowalla*, were acquired from http://snap.stanford.edu/data/index.html. Both of these datasets contain location information and thus for simplicity we use a vertex's latitude information as a means of determining similarity (the distance between two points). Table 2 displays additional information on these datasets:

Table 2. Dataset information

Dataset	Nodes	Edges
Brightkite	58,228	214,078
Gowalla	196,591	950,237

Parameters. The datasets were analysed and evaluated with R to discover values of r which would allow for the quantile of vertices being similar (i.e. $r = 3$ means 3% of vertices are similar to each other). To avoid experiments that would take an unreasonable amount of time to terminate, we set a baseline of $k = 5$. That is *CoreDecomposition* started by finding a $(5, r)$-core and terminated if none were found. *BinarySearch* with the first search being $k = 5$ as opposed to the usual search value and terminated if none were found. For each experiment, one hundred random query points were selected consistent across both methods tested.

All programs were implemented in standard C++ and compiled utilising G++ in Redhat Linux. All experiments were performed using Intel Xeon 2.3GHz CPUs.

6.2   Efficiency Comparison

Total Running Time. Figure 2 depicts the total running time of both algorithms on the same set of query vertices. During the experiments, *CoreDecomposition* consistently outperformed *BinarySearch*, although not in any overtly meaningful manner. However, as we delve further into the data we can observe the following.

First Enumeration. As both methods used $k = 5$ as the first enumeration, it becomes possible to compare the specific areas in which the algorithms differed. In Fig. 3 we can visibly see that as the similarity increases, the first enumeration

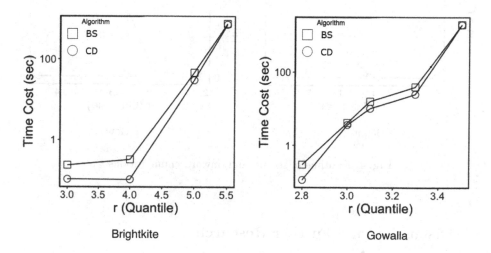

Fig. 2. Total running time

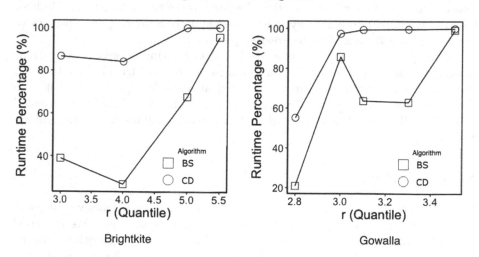

Fig. 3. First enumeration percentage of total runtime

takes a greater percentage of the total runtime of the algorithm. Additionally, the reasoning as to why the runtime of both algorithms is similar in Fig. 2 becomes clear as both algorithms run the same first enumeration for any given query vertex. Figure 4 displays the subsequent runtime of both algorithms after the first enumeration. Notably, *CoreDecomposition* is significantly more efficient than *BinarySearch* as the similarity increases.

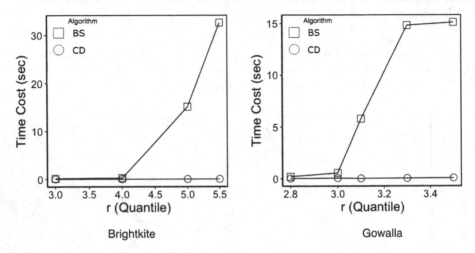

Fig. 4. Runtime of second and onward enumerations

7   Discussion and Further Research

As expected, the running time of all approaches is heavily dominated by the first, and in the case of *CoreDecomposition* the only, use of the Enumeration Method. Currently, in order to make any significant way into improving the efficiency of this query, this is area with the greatest potential.

Nonetheless, $MSC(s)$ may prove to be an interesting alternative to current subgraph data structures which aim to discover groups of friends for a targeted user. Additionally, whilst currently targeted at a specific query vertex, it does not appear unreasonable to believe that the current algorithm could be extended to finding all $MSC(s)$ on a graph though this would require further experimentation.

8   Conclusion

In this paper, we proposed the Maximal Stable Core as a cohesive subgraph model and aimed to discover all $MSC(s)$ for a given query user. We proposed a baseline algorithm using binary search and an improved algorithm utilising k-core decomposition after discovering existing(k, r)-cores, having proved the nested property regarding k for the (k, r)-core. We also implemented both algorithms and noted that both algorithms were dominated by the first enumeration, though Core Decomposition outperformed Binary Search in all other areas.

References

1. Batagelj, V., Zaversnik, M.: An O(m) algorithm for cores decomposition of networks. CoRR, cs.DS/0310049 (2003)
2. Bhawalkar, K., Kleinberg, J., Lewi, K., Roughgarden, T., Sharma, A.: Preventing unravelling in social networks: the anchored k-core problem. SIAM J. Discrete Math. **29**(3), 1452–1475 (2015)
3. Bron, C., Kerbosch, J.: Finding all cliques of an undirected graph (algorithm 457). Commun. ACM **16**(9), 575–576 (2006)
4. Cheng, J., Zhu, L., Ke, Y., Chu, S.: Fast algorithms for maximal clique enumeration with limited memory. In: KDD, pp. 1240–1348 (2012)
5. Eppstein, D., Strash, D.: Listing all maximal cliques in large sparse real-world graphs. In: Pardalos, P.M., Rebennack, S. (eds.) SEA 2011. LNCS, vol. 6630, pp. 364–375. Springer, Heidelberg (2011). https://doi.org/10.1007/978-3-642-20662-7_31
6. Fang, Y., Cheng, R., Luo, S., Hu, J.: Effective community search for large attributed graphs. PVLDB **9**(12), 1233–1244 (2016)
7. Fang, Y., Zhang, H., Ye, Y., Li, X.: Detecting hot topics from twitter: a multiview approach. J. Inf. Sci. **40**(5), 578–593 (2014)
8. Goldberg, M.K., Kelly, S., Magdon-Ismail, M., Mertsalov, K., Wallace, A.: Finding overlapping communities in social networks. In: SocialCom/PASSAT, pp. 104–113 (2010)
9. Hristova, D., Musolesi, M., Mascolo, C.: Keep your friends close and your facebook friends closer: a multiplex network approach to the analysis of offline and online social ties. In: ICWSM (2014)
10. Huang, X., Lu, W., Lakshmanan, L.V.S.: Truss decomposition of probabilistic graphs: semantics and algorithms. In: SIGMOD, pp. 77–90 (2016)
11. Seidman, S.B.: Network structure and minimum degree. Soc. Netw. **5**(3), 269–287 (1983)
12. Khaouid, W., Barsky, M., Srinivasan, V., Thomo, A.: K-core deomposition of large networks on a single PC. PVLDB **9**(1), 13–23 (2015)
13. Wang, J., Cheng, J., Fi, A.W.: Redundancy-aware maximal cliques. In: KDD, pp. 122–130 (2013)
14. Zhang, F., Zhang, W., Zhang, Y., Qin, L., Lin, X.: OLAK: an efficient algorithm to prevent unravelling in social networks. PVLDB **10**(6), 649–660 (2017)
15. Zhang, F., Zhang, Y., Qin, L., Zhang, W., Lin, X.: When engagement meets similarity: efficient (k, r)-core computation on social networks. PVLDB **10**(10), 998–1009 (2017)
16. Zhu, Q., Hu, H., Xu, J., Lee, W.: Geo-social group queries with minimum acquaintance constraint. CoRR, abs/1406.7367 (2014)

Feature Extraction for Smart Sensing Using Multi-perspectives Transformation

Sanad Al-Maskari[1,2(✉)], Ibrahim A. Ibrahim[1], Xue Li[1], Eimad Abusham[2], and Abdulqader Almars[1]

[1] School of Information Technology and Electrical Engineering,
The University of Queensland, Brisbane, Australia
{s.almaskari,i.ibrahim,xueli,a.almars}@uq.edu.au
[2] Faculty of Computing and Information Technology,
Sohar University, Sohar, Oman

Abstract. Air quality sensing systems, such as e-nose, are one of the complex dynamic systems; due to their sensitivity to electromagnetic interference, humidity, temperature, pressure and airflow. This yield to a Multi-Dependency effect over the output signal. To address the Multi-Dependency effect, we propose a multi-dimensional signal transformation for feature extraction. Our idea is analogous to viewing one huge object from different angles and arriving at different perspectives. Every perspective is partially true, but the final picture can be inferred by combining all perspectives. We evaluated our method extensively on two data sets including a publicly available e-nose dataset generated over a three-year period. Our results show higher performance in term of accuracies, F-measure, and stability when compared to standard methods.

Keywords: E-nose · Air quality · Feature extraction · Time series
Pattern recognition · Classification · Sensors

1 Introduction

A large-scale environmental sensor network generates huge time series data, which are used to monitor the air quality. Smartphones sensors are used to monitor personal health, behaviours, and activities. Furthermore, sensors have been used for water leakage, food spoilage and earth quack detection. For such applications to be successful, it requires the identification of patterns, detection of abnormal behaviours, and the prediction of future and unknown patterns. Sensor signal pre-processing and feature extractions are an essential step for these applications to be successful.

In this study, we selected e-nose system due to its wide applications such as air quality monitoring, food spoilage detection, medical diagnostics, and odour measurement in packaging [1–4]. The e-nose is made off an array of different chemical sensors, resulting in a higher system complexity for modelling dynamic behaviours. Furthermore, gas samples are introduced with various concentrations and different known and unknown types. Moreover, each sensor is sensitive to

© Springer International Publishing AG, part of Springer Nature 2018
J. Wang et al. (Eds.): ADC 2018, LNCS 10837, pp. 236–248, 2018.
https://doi.org/10.1007/978-3-319-92013-9_19

electromagnetic interference, humidity, temperature, pressure and air flow. All of the above would point to a Multi-Dependency (MD) effect over the output signal rather than just chemical information.

Feature extraction goal is to extract highly discriminant and relevant information from the original signals while reducing data dimensionality. The performance of any pattern recognition system is highly dependent on the effectiveness of the extracted features. A feature set is generated to summarize, describe and reduce the high dimensionality of the original signals. Our problem considers a continuous time series data generated by multiple sensors S where $S = s_1, s_2, \ldots, s_n$ and each sensor generate T samples. Data generated by these sensors are noisy due to the dynamic environment and Multi-Dependency effect. Our main objective is to extract highly discriminant and effective features to improve the classification performance. To date, a handful of feature extraction methods have been used in the literature for e-nose pattern recognition. A recent work by Vergara *et al.* [5] proposed to use an exponential moving average for feature extraction. Other methods such as Fast Fourier Transform (FFT) and Discrete Wavelet Transform (DWT) have been proposed [6,7]. These proposed methods will have satisfactory results in a closed and predefine environment. Unfortunately, none of these works considered dynamic, complex environment and the Multi-Dependency effect. Furthermore, using alternative methods can provide a more optimal solution.

To address the MD effect discussed previously, a new feature extraction method is proposed to improve the sensor pattern recognition performance. The main idea of our model is to capture multiple perspectives of the signal using transformation function rather than relying on the original signal space. After that, different views or perspectives of the same signal are created. Finally, all the created perspectives are used to generate new discriminant features. Each perspective contains different information, and combining all perspectives together can provide a more insightful picture.

The primary contributions of our work are as follows: (1) A Multi-Perspective Transformation (MPT) model is proposed for feature extraction. (2) We focus more on improving system performance when an MD effect exist on the sensor data. (3) Our proposed method is applicable for various sensing technologies. (4) Furthermore, we conducted extensive experiments with multiple evaluation metrics including accuracies, F-measure, and stability. (5) Finally, our proposed method is suitable for online pattern recognition systems.

The rest of the paper is organized as follows. Section 2 discusses the related work. Section 3 describes the methodology and proposed approach of multidimensional signal transformation for feature extraction will be discussed. Section 4 describes the experiments and evaluates the results. Finally, Sect. 5 concludes our paper.

2   Related Work

The main goal of e-nose sensing system is to identify gases or odour in the ambient air [2,8,9]. The e-nose consists of an array of sensors that interacts selectively with predefined gases. These sensors can identify gases with acceptable accuracies in a closed environment. However, installing e-nose in an outdoor environment produce a far more complex modelling system, due to noise, drift, high uncertainties and dynamic environment. We refer to such a challenge as a Multi-Dependency effect. One critical step to reduce the effect of MD is to create robust features from the original signal. In this section, we briefly discussed standard and state of the art methods related to e-nose feature extraction and demonstrate how our approach can improve e-nose pattern recognition by considering multiple perspectives of the raw signal.

2.1 Standard Feature Extraction Methods

In the literature, steady-state and **dynamic-based** chemo-sensory feature extraction methods have been discussed. Steady-state features are extracted from the steady-state response produced by a gas sensor; refer to Fig. 1a. When gas is emitted with different concentration $c(t)$ the sensor generates an output measured in resistance $R(t)$ [6]. The change in resistance of a semiconductor gas sensor ΔR is the difference between the maximal resistance change and the base line as shown in this equation $||\Delta R|| = \frac{R_{gas} - R_{air}}{R_{air}}$. R_{gas} is the sensor response to a given gas in steady-state, R_{air} is the sensor response to pure air, which is used as a baseline. The steady-state feature ΔR has two major issues. Firstly, it becomes available late in the response as shown in Fig. 1a. Secondly, it is susceptible to drift. Therefore dynamic features have been proposed to capture the transient phase of the signal. Dynamic-based features are extracted from transient chemical gas sensor response (adsorption and desorption). In the adsorption stage of gas sensor responses, the resistance R increases, while in the desorption stage, the resistance R decreases, as shown in Fig. 1a. Dynamic features can provide information about the analyte that can't be extracted using steady-state methods. Furthermore, steady-state values are rarely reached due to gas sensors slow response and environmental complexity (e.g. airflow turbulence). Therefore, dynamic features are used to capture transient features to reduce the effect of the dynamic real environment. Recent work by [5] proposed the use of exponential moving average (EMA) combined with steady-state features to improve the classification performance of e-nose with drift Fig. 1b.

Various types of features extraction methods have been proposed in the literature. The first type include the use of as maximum values, integrals, differences, primary derivatives $f(x)' = \frac{dx(t)}{d(t)}$, $f(x)'' = \frac{d^2x(t)}{d^2(t)}$, the adsorption slope [8,10–12] refer to Figs. 1a and 2b. Other proposed to use signal transformation methods such as Fast Fourier Transform (FFT) and Discrete Wavelet Transform (DWT) [6,8,13]. The Fourier Transform is calculated by summing all observations for each frequency f_k $\mathcal{X}_k = \sum_{n=0}^{N} \mathcal{X}_n e^{i2\pi k \frac{n}{N}}$ where $i^2 = 1$. Unfortunately, transforming signals from the time domain to the frequency domain fails to preserve important transient characteristics of the original signal. Therefore, using a method that can preserve the signal's transient characteristics is very important. The third category of methods is based on curve fitting where an attempt is made to fit the data in a model and the fitting parameters are extracted. In [11,14] different curve fitting models are compared, including single exponential, double exponential, sigmoid, and Lorentzian model. Curve fitting dynamic signals can be complex, difficult and time-consuming. Furthermore, attempting to fit unknown dynamic function is deemed to be complex and challenging.

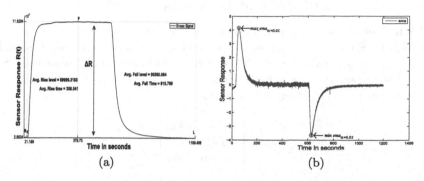

(a)   (b)

Fig. 1. (a) Row sensors features. (b) Shows the exponential moving average analysis when $\alpha = 0.01$.

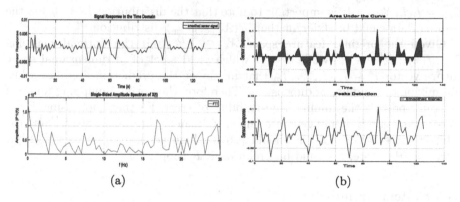

(a)   (b)

Fig. 2. (a) FFT transformation for raw sensor signal. (b) Area under the curve for a given sensor signal.

In this study, we propose a new feature extraction method that can extract a highly stable, and discriminant features while reducing the number of dimensions. Our idea is to consider different perspectives rather than relying only on the raw signal. To generate different perspectives, we use a transformation function based on Hilbert transform [15]. Once all perspectives are generated, a small set of descriptors are extracted from each perspective.

3   Methodology

In this section, we formulate a feature extraction research problem which is applicable for real-world sensing applications such as air quality monitoring. Secondly, we present our Multi-Perspective Transformation model for feature extraction. Finally, we derive our concrete MPT algorithm which will be evaluated extensively against standard and state of the art methods.

Problem Definition. Consider a continuous time-series data generated by multiple sensors S where $S = s_1, s_2, \ldots, s_n$ and each sensor generate T samples $s_1 = x_1, x_2, \ldots, x_t$ where $t \in T$. At time t a discriminative subsequences S of length n is extracted using a fixed window size w. The subset S can be represented as a matrix consisting of k time series.

$$S_t = \begin{bmatrix} x_{11} & x_{21} & .. & x_{k1} \\ x_{12} & x_{22} & .. & x_{k2} \\ x_{1t} & x_{2t} & .. & x_{kt} \end{bmatrix}$$

The $i-th$ observation can be defined as $\mathcal{X}_i = [x_i^1, x_i^2, \ldots, x_i^k]$; therefore, our training set can be represented as $L = \{\mathcal{X}_i, y_i\}_{i=1}^{t}$. The main objective of a learning algorithm is to learn a prediction function h using L that maximize the prediction accuracy for any new input $\mathcal{X}_{new}, h(L, \mathcal{X}_{new})$ will predict y_{new}, hence $y_{new} = h(L, \mathcal{X}_{new})$. It is important to note that the distribution $P(\mathcal{X}_i, y_i)$ in the training data could be different than $P(\mathcal{X}_{new}, y_{new})$ distribution.

Given the original feature space $\mathcal{X}_i \in R^D$, find the optimal mapping $F = f(x) : R^D \rightarrow R^d$ while $d < D$ which yield a set of m dimensional space feature vector $F = f_1, f_2, \ldots, f_m$ that maximize the prediction accuracy while minimizing the number of dimensions. Therefore, the optimal mapping function F should provide the minimum probability of error. Furthermore, using F the decision function h should generate same results in the original space R^D and the reduced space R^d. Finally, F should provide high generalisation over multiple functions; therefore, h should be irrelevant if F is optimal.

3.1   System Architecture

Gas type detection and identification for an outdoor system is an unsolved challenge due to MD effect. The MD effect can be caused by low sensor selectivity which makes discrimination between different gases difficult when they co-exist. Furthermore, as explained previously, sensors are subject to high uncertainties due to environmental changes, drift, noise and unknown factors which contributes to MD effect. Therefore, any pattern recognition system should consider all the variabilities surrounding the sensing system. In our approach, we propose to reduce the impact of MD at the feature extraction layer. Considering MD effect only at the learning layer will not provide an optimal solution. Figure 3 illustrates the full life cycle of the proposed approach.

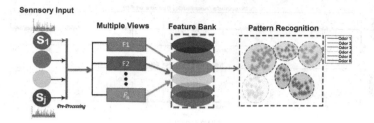

Fig. 3. The proposed e-nose pattern recognition using MPT.

3.2 Multi-perspectives Transformation

The sensor signal data are discrete and measured at a fixed interval. The samples are collected every T_s s, or a frequency of $F_s = 1/T_s$ referred to as Hertz, or cycle per second. Consider we need to apply a 90° phase shift to our signal using a transfer function $\mathcal{H}$ and signum function $sign(f)$:

$$\mathcal{H}(f) = \begin{cases} -i, f > 0 \\ 0, f = 0 \\ i, f < 0 \end{cases} \tag{1}$$

$$sign(f) = \begin{cases} 1, f > 0 \\ 0, f = 0 \\ -1, f < 0 \end{cases} \tag{2}$$

From Eular Formal we know that:

$$e^{ix} = \cos x + i \sin x \text{ where } i = \sqrt{-1}, \ i = e^{i\frac{\pi}{2}} \text{ and } -i = e^{-i\frac{\pi}{2}} \tag{3}$$

From the above we have: $\mathcal{H}(f) = \begin{cases} e^{-i\frac{\pi}{2}}, f > 0 \\ e^{i\frac{\pi}{2}}, f < 0 \end{cases}$ \hfill (4)

From (1) and (2), we can rewrite $\mathcal{H}(f)$ as: $\mathcal{H}(f) = -isgn(f)$ \hfill (5)

This is equivalent to the Fourier Transform of $\frac{1}{\pi t}$. The multiplication operator in a frequency domain is equivalent to convolution in the time domain. A Hilbert transform [15] in a time domain is the convolution between real signal s(t) and $\frac{1}{\pi}$ operator. From above, H transform can be computed in a time domain and frequency domain as follow (Fig. 4):

$$\mathcal{H}[s(t)] = s(t) * \frac{1}{\pi t} = \frac{1}{\pi} \int_{-\infty}^{+\infty} \frac{s(\tau)}{t - \tau} d\tau = \frac{1}{\pi} \int_{-\infty}^{+\infty} \frac{s(t - \tau)}{\tau} d\tau \tag{6}$$

The edge detection (Fig. 5) can be performed using the magnitude of a complex signal $s_c(t)$

$$s_c(t) = s_r(t) + is_i(t) \tag{7}$$

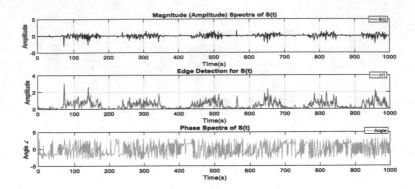

Fig. 4. The figure shows multiple views of the original signal S(t).

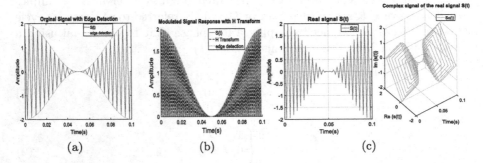

(a)   (b)   (c)

Fig. 5. (a) Real signal with H transform and lower and upper edge detection. (b) Absolute signal with edge detection. (C) Left is the real signal of S(t), right is the complex signal for S(t)

$$|s_c(t)| = \sqrt{s_r(t)^2 + is_i(t)^2} \tag{8}$$

Phase calculated using inverse tangent (9). (10) is the instantaneous frequency

$$\theta(t) = \tan^{-1}\left(\frac{s_i(t)}{s_r(t)}\right) \tag{9}$$

$$q(t) = \frac{1}{2\pi}\frac{\Delta\theta(t)}{\Delta t} \tag{10}$$

4   Experiments and Evaluation

The main objective of our experiments is to evaluate MPT classification performance, efficiency and stability. We use two different data sets generated from different real-world sensor technologies. The first data collected from outdoor sensors, which exhibit the Multi-Dependency effect. The second dataset contains drift caused by sensor ageing and electromagnetic interference. In this section, we describe the experimental setup, design and results.

Algorithm 1. Multi-Perspectives Transformation Model

1: **Input:**
  S: Row sensors signals $S(1) = (Xs_1, Xs_2, \ldots, Xs_d)$
  w: window length SR: Sampling Rate
2: **Output:** *new feature space F.*
3: *Normalize Row Sensor S.*
4: *Generate t_{new} using the new resemble rate $\frac{1}{SR}$.*
5: *Use interpolation to generate S_{new}.*
6: *From $k = 1$ to the last possible window frame in S_{new}*
7: *Extract W_k frame of size w*
8: *Apply data transformation per frame on W_k according to (6).*
9: *Generate the edge view V for W_k based on (7).*
10: *Generate the phase view θ for W_k according to (9).*
11: *Extract features from S, V and θ.*
12: *Populate the feature bank F*
13: **return** *F*

4.1 Experimental Design

The experiments are divided into two parts. The first part thoroughly evaluates an outdoor sensor system. Secondly, MPT model is evaluated against a large number of features and classifiers including Neural Net, Decision Trees, Ensembles, KNN, SVM and others [1, 16]. Furthermore, we tested the performance of MPT using different K-fold cross-validation including leave one out, 3, 5, 10, 30, 50, and 70 folds. We use this experimental setup to evaluate the stability, generalisation and performance of our MPT model. We evaluate our method in term of Classification Accuracies (A), Precision (P), Recall (R), F-Measure (F1), extraction efficiency, training efficiency and stability.

$$A = \frac{(TP+TN)}{(TP+FN+FP+TN)}, \ P = \frac{TP}{(TP+FP)}, \ R = \frac{TP}{(TP+FN)}, \ F_1 = \frac{2*P*R}{(P+R)}$$

where, True Positive (TP): correct positive decisions is made; True Negative (TN): correct negative decision is made; False Positive (FP): wrong positive decisions is made; False Negative (FN): wrong negative decisions is made.

Baselines. In our experiments, we compared our method with standard and state of the art methods including MNAP which contains max, min, and AUC extracted from raw sensor signal. SMSP contains features extracted from smoothed sensor response such as mean, max, the standard deviation and PCA. RFSFD features are extracted from the first derivative including max, min, mean, peaks, AUC, rise time τ_r, decay time τ_d [12]. RFSSD is the second derivative feature set. MNAPSD contains max, min, and AUC features from first derivative. PPFA and PPFMNA are features extracted based on curve fitting [11]. SMSP basic statistics combined with PCA [17]. RSTP contains features extracted from smoothed raw sensor signal including max, min, mean, standard deviation, AUC and PCA features. RSM contains different statistics extracted from raw sensor response such as average signal magnitude, different signal percentiles, sum squares of signal magnitudes. WDT contains features such as wave energy, coefficients statistics, entropy and other features [6]. FFT contains features such as absolute amplitude, mean, max, standard deviation of highest peaks and other features. FFT_PF contains FFT based features with curve based fitting features. EMA contains steady state features combined with exponential moving average features [5]. For more details refer to the related work section.

4.2 Outdoor Sensing Dataset

This dataset was generated using sensors with high susceptibility to noise, interference and outdoor environment. The dataset contains sex classes with over than 120 dimensions and more than 7000 training samples. We tested this dataset according to Sect. 4.1 and on 15 feature extraction methods. The experimental results are shown on Figs. 6 and 7. In both 10 and 30 folds, MPT achieved the best performance, with over than 93% for accuracies, precision and F-measure. Interestingly, only MPT maintained the highest performance for Neural Net based classifiers when compared to EMA($\sim$71%), DWT around ($\sim$52%), RSTP and SMSP (<90%) and FFT and other features (<30%). Moreover, we evaluated the generalisation and stability of MPT method across all folds and classifiers as shown in Fig. 7. Finally, MPT model outperforms all other methods, which empirically prove it is effectiveness.

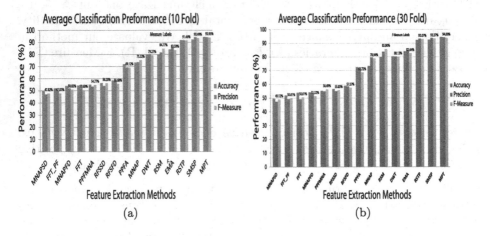

Fig. 6. The proposed model performance indicators using sixteen MOX sensors.

From Fig. 8a, we can see that MPT is one of the top 6 fastest feature extraction method. To test the speed of different methods we set the window size to 1000. MPT approximately requires 2 s to extract features from 1000 samples with 128 dimensions. Because only a few features are extracted from different

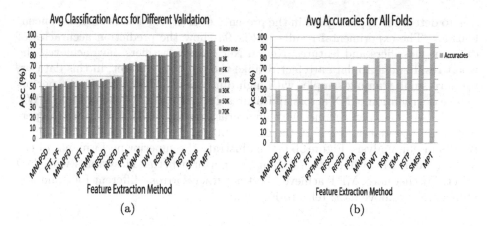

Fig. 7. (a) Average classification accuracies for different validation (b) Average Accuracies across all validation.

views MPT generate small dimensions per sensor (six features per sensor). However, EMA extracts eight features per sensor. The number of extracted features reflects MPT training time speed when compared to other approaches. PPFMNA is the slowest method, due to a large number of features used. It is interesting to note that having a large number of features doesn't provide optimal classification performance as we see clearly from RSFSSD, RFSFD, MNAPFD, and MNAPSD; refer to Figs. 8b and 7b.

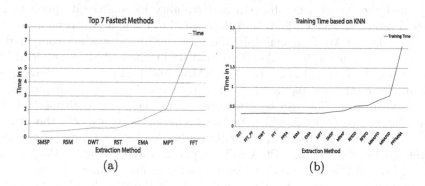

Fig. 8. (a) Feature extraction time for top 7 fastest methods. (b) Training time for different features based on KNN.

4.3   Indoor Sensing Dataset

In this experiment, the data set based on Vergara *et al.* was used. This dataset was designed to analyse drift generated by e-nose sensors [5]. Different type of gases was emitted to the sensors with varying concentrations including Acetone, Ethanol, Toluene, Acetaldehyde, Ethylene, and Ammonia. The main objective was to detect the type of gases in the presence of drift, regardless of their concentrations. The experimental results in Fig. 9a show the prediction accuracies of different classifiers and features. Neural Net based classifiers have achieved the worst results, due to data artefact. Unlike the previous dataset, in this dataset, we have small training samples with high dimensions, which explain the performance degradation of NN across all features. Nevertheless, we can see that DWT provided the best performance with an average result of 77.7%. Because the performance degradation is due to the data artifacts, we don't consider NN models results in our analysis. Figure 9b and c illustrate the superior performance of the MPT model, which indicate its ability to perform better in systems with MD effect. Furthermore, MPT achieved best accuracies across different folds, having all accuracies above 93%; refer to Fig. 9b.

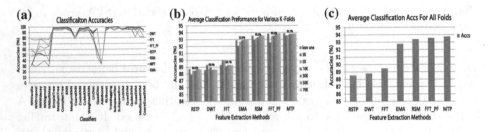

Fig. 9. (a) Classifier Acc (b) Folds Accs (c) Average Accs per fold

To test the model generalisation and stability we analyse its performance across different classifiers, folds and data set. From the above results, we can see the ability of MPT to maintain the best performance when compared to other extraction methods. Unlike SMSP and RSTP method MPT provided best accuracies in all fold and both datasets. SMSP and RSTP have produced good performance in the first dataset but failed to maintain this performance in the second experiment. This can be attributed to the fact that both methods use PCA. Unfortunately, PCA will not always guarantee to preserve the original shape of the data. For instance, if the discrimination between different classes is not reflected in the variance, PCA will not perform well. Secondly, PCA performance suffers if the data is not linearly separable. Furthermore, in the feature reduction process, some useful data can be lost. On the other hand, MPT doesn't attempt to reduce the original signal dimensionality, instead, it will firstly create new views which maximize information gain. After that, from each view, a set of descriptors that capture and preserve the shape of the signal are extracted.

5   Conclusions and Future Work

Feature extraction is a very critical step in any learning system. The MPT model was found to provide higher performance, efficiency and stability when compared to state of the art methods. MPT was able to provide higher resistance to Multi-Dependency effects which is associated with complex uncontrolled factors. The consideration of multiple views of the raw signal proved to be useful when dealing with complex and dynamic signals. Furthermore, MPT provides a very fast feature extraction process with a low number of dimensions, which makes it appropriate for online pattern recognition systems. Our future work we will apply our MPT model on various types of sensor applications. Secondly, we would like to know which set of features can be combined with MPT to provide optimal performance, efficiency, stability while minimizing dimensionality.

References

1. Al-Maskari, S., Li, X., Liu, Q.: An effective approach to handling noise and drift in electronic noses. In: Wang, H., Sharaf, M.A. (eds.) ADC 2014. LNCS, vol. 8506, pp. 223–230. Springer, Cham (2014). https://doi.org/10.1007/978-3-319-08608-8_21
2. Al-Maskari, S., Saini, D., Omar, W.: Cyber infrastructure and data quality for environmental pollution control in Oman. In: Proceedings of the 2010 DAMD International Conference on Data Analysis, Data Quality and Metada, vol. 71 (2010)
3. Al Maskari, S., Kumar, D., Chiffings, T.: Data mining for environment monitoring. In: International Conference on Software Technology and Engineering, ICSTE 2012. ASME Press (2012)
4. Al Maskari, S., Li, X.: E-nose pattern recognition and drift compensation methods. In: Electronic Nose Technologies and Advances in Machine Olfaction, pp. 38–57. IGI Global (2018)
5. Vergara, A., Vembu, S., Ayhan, T., Ryan, M.A., Homer, M.L., Huerta, R.: Chemical gas sensor drift compensation using classifier ensembles. Sens. Actuators B: Chem. **166–167**, 320–329 (2012)
6. Llobet, E., Brezmes, J., Ionescu, R., Vilanova, X., Al-Khalifa, S., Gardner, J., Brsan, N., Correig, X.: Wavelet transform and fuzzy ARTMAP-based pattern recognition for fast gas identification using a micro-hotplate gas sensor. Sens. Actuators B: Chem. **83**(13), 238–244 (2002). Selected Papers from TRANSDUCERS 2001 EUROSENSORS XV
7. Nakata, S., Nakamura, H., Yoshikawa, K.: New strategy for the development of a gas sensor based on the dynamic characteristics: principle and preliminary experiment. Sens. Actuators B: Chem. **8**(2), 187–189 (1992)
8. Al-Maskari, S., Bélisle, E., Li, X., Le Digabel, S., Nawahda, A., Zhong, J.: Classification with quantification for air quality monitoring. In: Bailey, J., Khan, L., Washio, T., Dobbie, G., Huang, J.Z., Wang, R. (eds.) PAKDD 2016. LNCS, vol. 9651, pp. 578–590. Springer, Cham (2016). https://doi.org/10.1007/978-3-319-31753-3_46
9. Al-Maskari, S., Xu, Z., Guo, W., Zhao, X., Li, X.: Bio-inspired learning approach for electronic nose. Computing **100**, 387–402 (2018)
10. Llobet, E., Brezmes, J., Vilanova, X., Sueiras, J.E., Correig, X.: Qualitative and quantitative analysis of volatile organic compounds using transient and steady-state responses of a thick-film tin oxide gas sensor array. Sens. Actuators B: Chem. **41**(1), 13–21 (1997)

11. Carmel, L., Levy, S., Lancet, D., Harel, D.: A feature extraction method for chemical sensors in electronic noses. Sens. Actuators B: Chem. **93**(13), 67–76 (2003). Proceedings of the Ninth International Meeting on Chemical Sensors

12. Zhang, S., Xie, C., Zeng, D., Zhang, Q., Li, H., Bi, Z.: A feature extraction method and a sampling system for fast recognition of flammable liquids with a portable E-nose. Sens. Actuators B: Chem. **124**(2), 437–443 (2007)

13. Yin, Y., Yu, H., Zhang, H.: A feature extraction method based on wavelet packet analysis for discrimination of Chinese vinegars using a gas sensors array. Sens. Actuators B: Chem. **134**(2), 1005–1009 (2008)

14. Yan, J., Guo, X., Duan, S., Jia, P., Wang, L., Peng, C., Zhang, S.: Electronic nose feature extraction methods: a review. Sensors **15**(11), 27804–27831 (2015)

15. Lohmann, A.W., Mendlovic, D., Zalevsky, Z.: Fractional Hilbert transform. Opt. Lett. **21**(4), 281–283 (1996)

16. Nahar, V., Al-Maskari, S., Li, X., Pang, C.: Semi-supervised learning for cyberbullying detection in social networks. In: Wang, H., Sharaf, M.A. (eds.) ADC 2014. LNCS, vol. 8506, pp. 160–171. Springer, Cham (2014). https://doi.org/10.1007/978-3-319-08608-8_14

17. Sophian, A., Tian, G.Y., Taylor, D., Rudlin, J.: A feature extraction technique based on principal component analysis for pulsed Eddy current NDT. NDT & E Int. **36**(1), 37–41 (2003)

Finding Influential Nodes by a Fast Marginal Ranking Method

Yipeng Zhang[1(✉)], Ping Zhang[2], Zhifeng Bao[1], Zizhe Xie[3], Qizhi Liu[3],
and Bang Zhang[4]

[1] RMIT University, Melbourne, Australia
s3582779@student.rmit.edu.au
[2] Wuhan University, Wuhan, China
[3] State Key Laboratory for Novel Software Technology,
Nanjing University, Nanjing, China
[4] CSIRO, Canberra, Australia

Abstract. The problem of Influence Maximization (IM) aims to find a
small set of k nodes (seed nodes) in a social network G that could maximize the expected number of nodes. It has been proven to be #P-hard,
and many approximation algorithms and heuristic algorithms have been
proposed to solve this problem in polynomial time. Those algorithms,
however, either trade effectiveness for practical efficiency or vice versa.
In order to make a good balance between effectiveness and efficiency,
this paper introduces a novel ranking method to identify the influential
nodes without computing their exact influence. In particular, our method
consists of two phases, the influence ranking and the node selection. At
the first phase, we rank the node's influence based on the centrality of
the network. At the second phase, we greedily pick the nodes of high
ranks as seeds by considering their marginal influence to the current
seed set. Experiments on real-world datasets show that the effectiveness
of our method outperforms the state-of-the-art heuristic methods by 3%
to 25%; and its speed is faster than the approximate method by at least
three orders of magnitude (e.g., the approximate method could not com-
plete in 12 h even for a social network of $|V| = 196{,}591$ and $|E| = 950{,}327$,
while our method completes in 100 s).

1 Introduction

In this paper we study the Influence Maximization (IM) problem over social networks, which is first formulated as a discrete optimization problem by Kempe
et al. [9]. Formally, its goal is to find a set of k nodes (seed nodes) in a social
network G that could maximize the expected number of nodes under a given
stochastic influence model. With the increasing popularity of social media, such
as Facebook and Twitter, the influence maximization problem plays a critical
role in effectively enabling large-scale viral marketing online. In the rest of this
section, we will investigate the literature, identify the existing methods' drawbacks, and propose our solution.

© Springer International Publishing AG, part of Springer Nature 2018
J. Wang et al. (Eds.): ADC 2018, LNCS 10837, pp. 249–261, 2018.
https://doi.org/10.1007/978-3-319-92013-9_20

1.1   Related Work

Independent Cascade (IC) model and Linear Threshold (LT) model are two common influence models to capture the influence spread process. Under the two models, Kempe et al. [9] show that IM is NP-hard and present a MC greedy approximation algorithm (Greedy) guaranteeing that the influence spread is within $(1 - 1/e)$ of the optimal influence spread. In particular, the core idea is to calculate the influence of each individual node and take turns to choose the node maximizing the marginal influence until k nodes are selected. As computing the exact marginal gain (or the exact expected spread) under both the IC and LT models is #P-hard [3,4], Greedy tries to estimate the influence spread by running Monte Carlo (MC) simulations.

However, such a greedy method suffers from two major sources of inefficiency: (i) it has to repeatedly compute the influence for various seed sets, (ii) it needs to run a large number of Monte Carlo (MC) simulations to obtain a high-confidence result. Thereby, a plethora of algorithms are proposed to reduce the computation overhead [2,12,14], and they can be divided into two main categories.

Approximate Method. Approximate methods mainly focus on how to reduce the influence computation cost under certain models, while it can also provide $(1 - 1/e - \varepsilon)$-approximation. For IC and LT models, Leskovec et al. [12] present a 'lazy-forward' optimization for selecting new seeds, which greatly reduces the number of evaluations on the influence spread of nodes. Under IC model, Tang et al. [14] and Borgs et al. [2] use a reverse sampling approach to get the approximate influence and thus reduce the number of (MC) simulations greatly. However, these methods are time-consuming on large networks, e.g., the state-of-the-art method [14] needs to take four hours to find one seed from a graph $G(V, E)$ whose $|V| = 41.6 * 10^6$ and $|E| = 1.5 * 10^9$.

Heuristic Method. In general, heuristic methods are much faster than approximate methods since they only estimate the influence according to some simple heuristic rules; however, they cannot achieve an approximation ratio guarantee or a high influence value as approximate methods. In particular, Chen et al. [3] assume that the influence spread increases with the degree of nodes and present a degree discount heuristic method. Kimura and Saito [10] propose shortest-path based influence models and provide efficient algorithms for estimating influence under these models. Chen et al. [5] utilize the community structure to aggregate the features of nodes to reduce the number of nodes they need to check. PageRank [13] measures the centrality (or importance) of a node in a network, which is also used for selecting seeds in Influence Maximization. Chen et al. [3] show that it can achieve a competitive result compared to other heuristics. However, the heuristic rule cannot guarantee the effectiveness, thus the performance of a heuristic method would fluctuate dramatically on different networks.

1.2   Contributions

In this paper, we focus on the influence maximization problem under the IC model. In order to achieve a better trade-off between efficiency and effectiveness, we propose a novel ranking method to select the influential nodes heuristically. Different from existing heuristic methods, our ranking metric is to measure the marginal influence of candidates rather than the influence itself. As a result, our proposed metric can help avoid the high influence overlap of the selected seeds to some extent, thus leading to a better effectiveness against existing heuristic measures. In particular, our contributions are summarized as follows.

- We measure the marginal influence of candidates iteratively based on PageRank and Personalized PageRank, and propose a ranking based greedy algorithm, called IRank, to identify the influential nodes. IRank achieves a better effectiveness on large-scale data than the heuristic methods (without losing much efficiency), which meets our primary goal of achieving an accurate seed selection. Meanwhile, its efficiency is at least three orders of magnitude faster than that of the approximate methods, which usually could not be completed in reasonable time. E.g., in our experiment, Greedy takes 2.4 h to run in the Email-Enron dataset at $k = 250$, while IRank only takes 8 s.
- We conduct a time complexity analysis and find that the computation cost of Personalized PageRank would increase as the growth of S. Thereby, in order to reduce the ranking cost, we propose InLocalPush to compute the Personalized PageRank incrementally and the cost of InLocalPush is independent of the size of S.
- We conduct extensive experiments on various real datasets to verify the efficiency, effectiveness and scalability of the proposed method.

2   Problem Formulation

2.1   Preliminaries

Independent Cascade (IC) Model. A social network can be represented by a (directed and undirected) graph $G(V, E)$, where V and E denote the users and their friendships respectively. To model the influence between users, we use a parameter p_{ij} ($0 \leq p_{ij} \leq 1$) to represent the influence probability of node v_i to v_j. Note that, many studies [6,11] show that p_{ij} can actually be inferred from the historical influence cascade data. As this paper only focuses on the seed selection, we assume that p_{ij} is given in advance. The default p_{ij} is set as 0.01.

Given a seed set $S \subset V$, the IC model describes the influence spread by a discrete process as follows. Each node in the IC model has two states, active and inactive. Initially at time $t = 0$, we activate the nodes in S, while setting all other nodes inactive. At a time $t > 0$, any node v_i activated at time $(t - 1)$ has a single chance to influence each currently inactive neighbor v_j independently: it succeeds with the probability p_{ij} and fails with the probability $1 - p_{ij}$. If v_i succeeds, v_j will become active at time $t + 1$. This process runs until no more activations are possible. Here, the expected number of nodes activated by the process is the influence of S.

Let $\delta(S)$ denote the expected influence of S under IC model. Chen et al. [3] show that computing $\delta(S)$ is #P-hard by a reduction from the counting problem of *s-t* connectedness [15]. As approximating the probability of *s-t* connectivity remains a long-standing open problem, it implies that we cannot expect to compute or even approximate $\delta(S)$ efficiently.

PageRank (PR). Let D and A be the degree matrix and the adjacency matrix of a graph $G(V, E)$ respectively. Given a subset $S \in V$, PageRank [13] can be described by the following equation:

$$pr(\alpha, \pi) = \alpha\pi + (1 - \alpha)\, pr(\alpha, \pi)W \tag{1}$$

where $pr(\alpha, \pi)$ is the pagerank vector of G, α is a constant in $(0, 1]$ called the *teleportation constant*, π is a uniform distribution of V, and W is equal to $(I + D^{-1}A)$.

Personalized PageRank (PPR). A PageRank vector whose distribution π is concentrated on a smaller set of (targeted) nodes is called Personalized PageRank vector [1,7]. Therefore, Personalized PageRank is more generalized than PageRank and can be also described by Eq. 1. Given a target set S, we denote the Personalized PageRank vector of S as $pr(\alpha, S)$. Since our focus is to maximize the influence spread in social networks, please find more details of PageRank and Personalized PageRank in [1,7,13].

2.2   Problem Definition and Our Framework

Based on the IC model, we present the formal problem definition of IM as below.

Definition 1. *Given a social network $G(V, E)$ and a budget k, the problem of influence maximization is to find a k-size set S in V, such that S can maximize the expected influence spread $\delta(S)$.*

By Definition 1, our goal is to maximize the objective function $\delta(S)$ heuristically. As described in Sect. 1.1, PageRank is a good heuristic method for IM but far behind the MC greedy in term of effectiveness [3]. The main bottleneck is that the top-k ranking nodes can have large influence overlaps. It leads to the case that the influence of the union of seeds is much less than the sum of the influence of each seed.

In order to further improve the effectiveness of the current heuristic methods without sacrificing much efficiency degrade, we propose a ranking based greedy method to avoid selecting seeds with high overlaps. Given an initial seed set $S = \phi$, the core idea of our method is to select the influential nodes ranking by their marginal influence to S iteratively. Let $\mathcal{R}_s(v)$ ($v \in V$) denote the ranking of the marginal influence of v to S. We note that the marginal influence can be decided by two parts: (1) the influence of v and (2) the overlap between v and S. According to this observation, we introduce a hybrid metric (as shown in Eq. 2) to measure $\mathcal{R}_s(v)$ by considering both parts aforementioned. In particular, the metric is represented by a linear combination of two items: the first item is PageRank (PR) of v which measures v's influence; the second item is the Personalized PageRank (PPR) of v (to S) which measures the overlap of v and S (in Sect. 3.1).

Table 1. Notations

Symbol	Description
$G(V, E)$	The social network
p_{ij}	The immediate influence from v_i to v_j
$\delta(S)$	The exact influence of S under the IC model
$\mathcal{R}_s(v)$	The marginal ranking of v (to S)

3   Our Solution

3.1   Influential Node Selection by Marginal Influence Ranking

In this section, we first introduce the ranking based algorithm called IRank and then present our ranking strategy. Important notations are presented in Table 1.

Algorithm 1 describes how our method works. It first initializes $S = \phi$ (line 1.3). In each iteration, IRank computes $\mathcal{R}_s(v)$ for each $v \in V \backslash S$ and picks the node with the highest ranking into S (lines 1.4 to 1.6). Here, CalMagRank(G, S) is used to compute $\mathcal{R}_s(v)$ for $\forall v \in V \backslash S$ (line 1.5). The algorithm repeats this process k times, and then returns S as the final solution. Our ranking metric of $\mathcal{R}_s(v)$ is defined as:

$$\mathcal{R}_s(v) = r(v) - \lambda r_s(v) \tag{2}$$

where $r(v)$ is to capture v's influence; $r_s(v)$ is to capture the overlap of v and S; and λ is a given parameter to balance the two items.

The Measurement of $r(v)$. Chen et al. [3] have shown that the nodes with the high influence usually have high PageRank values, which indicates that PageRank is a good indicator to measure the influence of nodes. Therefore, we compute $r(v)$ for each $v \in V$ by the PageRank of v.

The Measurement of $r_s(v)$. In general, most individuals tend to trust the person who is important to their trusted ones. Given a seed set S and a candidate $v \in V \backslash S$, it indicates that the audiences of S tend to be influenced by v if v is very important to S, which implies that the influence overlap of v and S should be large. As a result, we compute $r_s(v)$ by the Personalized PageRank of v to S (Step 2), since PPR reflects the importance of v to S [1].

In this paper, we choose two most important algorithms, PageRank [13] and LocalPush [1], to compute the PR and PPR respectively. As PageRank is well-known, we only discuss how LocalPush works.

The core idea of LocalPush is to compute a pair of distributions p and e with the following property.

$$pr(\alpha, S) = p + pr(\alpha, e) \tag{3}$$

If p and e are two distributions with this property, Andersen et al. [1] indicate that p is close to the PPR vector $p(\alpha, S)$ when each element of $pr(\alpha, e)$ is sufficiently small. Note that, this claim is true because of the *Linearity* property of PPR which is discovered by Jeh and Widom [8].

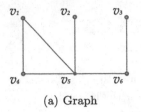

V	v_1	v_2	v_3	v_4	v_5	v_6
e	0	0	0	0	1	0
p	0	0	0	0	α	0

Move α from e to p

(a) Graph   (b) LocalPush Setting $S=\{v_1\}$

Fig. 1. An example of LocalPush

Algorithm 1. IRank(G, k)

1.1 **Input:** a graph $G(V, E)$ and k
1.2 **Output:** a set S
1.3 $S \leftarrow \phi$
1.4 **for** $i \leftarrow 1$ *to* k **do**
1.5   Invoke CalMagRank(G, S) to rank nodes in $V \backslash S$.
1.6   Select the node with the highest ranking and add it into S.
1.7 **return** S

To obtain the PPR vector $pr(\alpha, S)$, LocalPush computes the p of Eq. 3 according to the following process. Each node $v \in V$ is assigned a pair of parameters: an *approximate ranking* $p(v)$ and a *residue* $e(v)$. Given a target set S as shown in Fig. 1a. Figure 1b shows how to initialize vectors p and e. Each $p(v)$ which $\forall v \in V$ is initialized by 0; and $e(v) = 1$ if $v \in S$, otherwise $e(v) = 0$. p (e) is the distribution of the approximate rankings (residues) of V. Note that, e are corresponding to $pr(\alpha, e)$ of Eq. 3. LocalPush maintains p and e by applying a series of push operations. Each push operation takes an arbitrary node v, moves an α fraction of the value from $e(v)$ into $p(v)$, and then spreads the remaining $(1-\alpha)$ fraction value to v's neighbors. Let d_v be the degree of v, each neighbor u of v receives $(1-\alpha)e(v)/d_v$ value from v and add it into $e(u)$. LocalPush returns p as the PPR vector of S when each element of e is less than a threshold ε.

Algorithm 2 is to compute $\mathcal{R}_s(v)$ for $\forall v \in V \backslash S$. In this algorithm, we use PageRank(G) [13] and LocalPush(G, S) [1] to compute $r(v)$ (PR) and $r_s(v)$ (PPR) respectively. It is worth noting that $r(v)$ is independent of S and does not change during the whole iterative process. Therefore, during implementation, we can store it in an n-dimension vector to avoid redundant computations.

The Time Complexity Analysis. The complexity of Algorithm 2 is determined by PageRank and LocalPush. Suppose PageRank should be terminated after a constant number of iterations. In each iteration, PageRank needs to traverse G and updates the ranking of each node, thus it takes $O(m + n)$ time. Moreover, the time complexity of LocalPush is the same as the PageRank at the worst case. Therefore Algorithm 2 takes $O(m + n)$ time. As Algorithm 1 invokes CalMagRank k times and k is a small constant, the complexity of IRank is $O(m + n)$.

Algorithm 2. CalMagRank

2.1 **Input:** a graph $G(V,E)$, a set S and λ
2.2 **Output:** a vector R
2.3 Initialize two vectors r and r_s.
    /* `PageRank`(G) algorithm is used to compute the pagerank in [13]. */
2.4 Compute r by PageRank(G).
    /* `LocalPush`(G,S) algorithm is used to compute the PPR in [1]. */
2.5 Compute r_s by LocalPush(G,S).
2.6 $R = r - \lambda r_s$
2.7 **return** R

Algorithm 3. InLocalPush(G, v, r_s)

3.1 **Input:** a graph $G(V,E)$, a node v and an n-dimension vector r
3.2 **Output:** a vector R
3.3 Initialize a vector r_v.
    /* `LocalPush`(G,S) algorithm is used to compute the PPR in [1]. */
3.4 $r_v \leftarrow$ LocalPush(G,v).
3.5 $R \leftarrow r_v + r_s$
3.6 **return** R

---

4   Optimization

Incremental PPR Computation. According to Algorithm 1, when a new seed is added into S, IRank has to update $\mathcal{R}_s(v)$ for each node by calling CalMagRank. As mentioned above, as PR can be stored for reusing, the efficiency of IRank is mainly decided by LocalPush. To accelerate our method, we modify LocalPush to an incremental method (called InLocalPush) to further reduce the computation cost. In this section, we first show how InLocalPush works and then explain why it can reduce the cost.

InLocalPush is inspired by the following theorem introduced in [8].

Theorem 1. *Given two sets $S, S' \subseteq V$, and $S \cap S' = \phi$. Let $T = S \cup S'$, we have:*

$$pr(\alpha, T) = pr(\alpha, S) + pr(\alpha, S') \tag{4}$$

Let S_i be the seed set that is generated by IRank in the first ith iteration and $S_{i+1} = S_i \cup v$. According to Theorem 1, we have $pr(\alpha, S_{i+1}) = pr(\alpha, S_i) + pr(\alpha, v)$. As $pr(\alpha, S_i)$ is already obtained in the previous iteration, we only need to compute $pr(\alpha, v)$ to obtain $pr(\alpha, S_{i+1})$ rather than computing $pr(\alpha, S_{i+1})$ directly. It actually indicates that S can be computed incrementally.

Based on Theorem 1, we introduce InLocalPush to compute PPR incrementally, which is shown as Algorithm 3. Besides G, it has two extra input parameters, a node v and a vector r_s. When $r_s = pr(\alpha, S_i)$, InLocalPush returns the PPR vector of S_{i+1} as the result.

A Comparison of LocalPush and InLocalPush. Recall the description of LocalPush in Sect. 3.1, given a target set S, LocalPush initializes the two distributions p and e (according to S) and continues pushing the residues from e to p until each element of e is smaller than ε. Therefore, the cost of LocalPush is determined by the number of push operations. Intuitively, when ε is fixed, the larger the total residues are, the more push operations are needed to ensure the residue of each element in e small enough. As the sum of residues equals the cardinality of S, the cost of LocalPush should raise with the increase of the size of S. On the other hand, InLocalPush computes $pr(\alpha, S)$ incrementally and its cost is independent of the size of S. It implies that InLocalPush should be faster than LocalPush when $|S|$ is large, and thus Algorithm 2 can be benefited by replacing LocalPush by InLocalPush (line 3.4)[1].

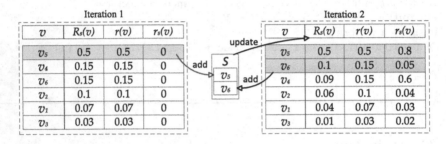

Fig. 2. A running example of IRank ($\lambda = 1$)

Example 1. *Figure 2 gives a running example of IRank for the instance of $G(V, E)$ in Fig. 1a. We initialize $S = \phi$, and assume $\lambda = 1$ and $k = 2$. At Step 1, $\mathcal{R}_s(v)$, $r(v)$ and $r_s(v)$ for each node $v \in V$ are listed in the left table. Note that, $\mathcal{R}_s(v) = r(v)$ and $r_s(v) = 0$ since the PPR of ϕ equals to 0. According to this table, v_5 is selected into S since it has the largest influence rank in this step. At Step 2, we update the rank of each $v \in V \backslash S$ and show the result in the right table. Therefore, v_6 is the optimal candidate and added into S. Since $k = 2$, IRank stops and returns $\{v_5, v_6\}$ as the final result.*

5   Experiments

In this section, we conduct four sets of experiments to evaluate: the impact of λ in effectiveness, the effectiveness, the efficiency, and the scalability of our method in real-life datasets.

---

[1] This modification also needs to vary the input parameters of Algorithm 2 from (G, S, λ) to (G, v, λ, r_s).

Table 2. Statistics of datasets

Datasets	Type	#Vertices	#Edges
Email-Enron	Undirected	36,692	183,831
Gowalla	Undirected	196,591	950,327
Twitter	Directed	11,316,811	85,331,846

Table 3. Parameter setting.

Parameter	Values
k	10, 20, 30, $\ldots$, 240, **250**
p	**0.01**, 0.02, $\ldots$, 0.09, 0.1
λ	1300, $\ldots$, **1350**, $\ldots$, 1400

5.1 Experimental Setup

Datasets. We use three real datasets, Email-Enron, Gowalla and Twitter. Email-Enron and Gowalla are two benchmark datasets that are obtained from http://snap.stanford.edu; Twitter is downloaded from http://socialcomputing. asu.edu/. All of them are social network datasets. The statistics of those datasets are shown in Table 2.

Algorithms. We compare our method against three algorithms: MC based greedy [9] (Greedy), Pagerank [13] (PR) and DegreeDiscount [3] (DD). To verify the effectiveness and efficiency of all algorithms, for each selected seed set, we run MC simulation 20000 times on the network

Setup. All algorithms are implemented using Java. and take the average of the influence spread as the benchmark. All experiments are conducted on a computer with two Intel(R) Xeon(R) E5630 3.0 GHZ processors and 48 GB RAM, running Ubuntu 10.04.

Parameter Setting. Table 3 shows the settings of all parameters, and the default one is highlighted in bold. In all experiments, we vary one parameter while the rest parameters are kept default unless specified otherwise. Note that, these networks do not capture the influence between the nodes explicitly. Therefore, we assume that the influence probability for each pair of neighboring nodes is 0.01, that is $p_{ij} = 0.01$ for $\forall v_i, \forall v_j \in V$, $e_{ij} \in E$.

Impact of λ. As we described in Sect. 3.1, λ is used to balance $r(v)$ and $r_s(v)$. In LocalPush, the sum of $e(v)$ and $p(v)$ equal to 1. Moreover, in these two vectors, the node that is the start point has the main part of possibility; it leads to a consequence that $r(v)$ is much bigger than $r_s(v)$. Therefore, we need a big λ for balance purpose. Figure 3 shows the influence of our method in Email-Enron and Gowalla by varying λ from 1,300 to 1,400. In both datasets, we find that the performance of IRank first increases as the growth of λ and then drops notably when λ is larger than 1360. It implies that our metric gets a good balance at $\lambda = 1350$ and thus we choose $\lambda = 1350$ as the default value.

5.2 Effectiveness

We study how the influence spread is affected by varying k. Figure 4a shows that Greedy achieves the best performance, and it is followed by IRank, PR and DD. IRank is only at most 9% less than Greedy. Comparing to PR and DD respectively, IRank is 6.5% and 24.9% better at most. The reason is that, both

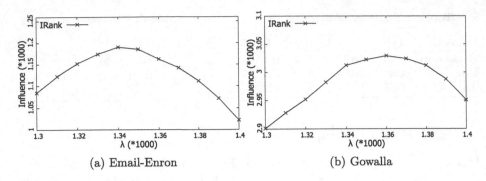

(a) Email-Enron   (b) Gowalla

Fig. 3. Effectiveness of varying λ

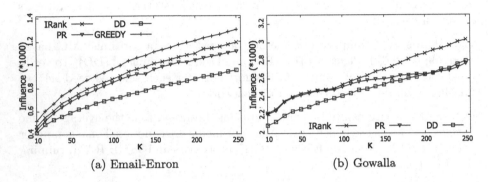

(a) Email-Enron   (b) Gowalla

Fig. 4. Effectiveness of varying seed number k

PR and DD select the seeds according to the influence rank, and the influential nodes may have a high influence overlap between them. Clearly, the high overlap should diminish the total influence spread significantly. In contrast, IRank can avoid this issue because it is based on measuring the marginal influence.

Figure 4b reports the results for Gowalla dataset. After running 8 h, Greedy can only get 8 candidate nodes. As Greedy is too slow to complete in 12 h, we omit it. When k is small, IRank and PR have similar influence spread and both of them outperform DD by 10%. Note that when k increases, the influence of PR drops down and is close to that of DD, which is different to the observation in Fig. 4a; while IRank still beats PR and DD by around 8%. It indicates that PR is sensitive to k and its performance fluctuates in different datasets.

Figure 5 shows the results of increasing influence spread with increasing p. In Email-Enron dataset, although IRank is worse than Greedy by 6.6%, it is still much better than PR and DD. For example, at $p = 0.01$, the influence of PR is 93.5% of that of IRank, while the influence of DD is only 79.8% of that of IRank. In the Gowalla dataset, Fig. 5b shows that the influence spread of all seed sets as expected turns out to be a linear growth as the increasing of p. It is because that a higher influence possibility should increases influence spread of S. The performance of all algorithms is very close and IRank is slightly better

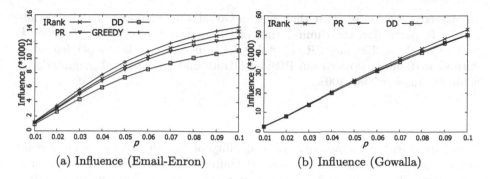

(a) Influence (Email-Enron)   (b) Influence (Gowalla)

Fig. 5. Effectiveness of varying p

than the two heuristics by 5.4% and 6.8% respectively. It indicates that IRank is very robust to p and always better than PR and DD during the varying of p.

5.3   Efficiency

Figure 6 presents the efficiency results when k varies from 10 to 250. In Fig. 6a, we can see that Greedy is feasible to run in the Email-Enron dataset and takes 2.4 h at $k = 250$. In contrast, IRank only takes 8 s, which significantly outperforms Greedy by three orders of magnitude. We note that the running time of IRank and DD are proportional to the seed size k. For example, IRank and DD only take 1.2 and 0.05 s respectively at $k = 10$. However, when $k = 250$, their running time both increase one order of magnitude and are 8.0 and 0.73 s respectively. In contrast, the running time of PR does not change because its ranking process is independent of k. It indicates that when k is large, PR is more scalable than IRank and DD, although its influence spread is lower than the others.

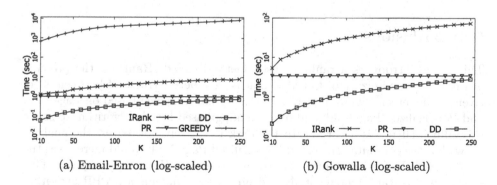

(a) Email-Enron (log-scaled)   (b) Gowalla (log-scaled)

Fig. 6. Efficiency of varying seed number k

The observation is also verified in Gowalla dataset and its result is shown in Fig. 6b. Note that Greedy is out of this test since Gowalla is too large to run Greedy. We can see that the result in Gowalla are similar to that in Email-Enron. In particular, the running time of DD ranges from 0.21 to 2.7 s when k varies from 10 to 250, and PR only takes 3.4 s since its cost is independent of k. Although IRank is slower than PR and DD around one order of magnitude, it is able to finish within 100 s.

5.4 Scalability

This experiment is to evaluate the scalability of the algorithms in large scale network Twitter. Figure 7a and b show the influence spread and the running time respectively. The result of Fig. 7a is consistent with the previous experiments that the effectiveness of IRank is better than that of PR and DD. Moreover, we can see the influence spread of IRank is relatively stable when k is varying. As shown in Fig. 7b, the runtime of both IRank and DD increases with the increase of k; although IRank is slower than DD, it still can handle million-sized graphs well.

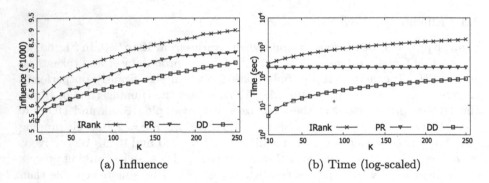

(a) Influence   (b) Time (log-scaled)

Fig. 7. Efficiency and effectiveness for Twitter

6   Conclusions

This paper introduces a ranking based method called IRank for the problem of Influence Maximization. In order to achieve a better trade-off between effectiveness and efficiency, we first rank the marginal influence based on PageRank and Personalized PageRank and use a ranking based greedy algorithm to select the influential nodes according to the rank iteratively. Moreover, the analysis show that the computation cost of Personalized PageRank would increase as the growth of S. To further reduce the cost, we accelerate IRank by computing Personalized PageRank incrementally and propose an incremental PPR algorithm InLocalPush. Empirical studies on a large real-world network show that IRank achieves a better effectiveness than the heuristic methods, which meets our primary goal of achieving an accurate seed selection. Meanwhile, its efficiency is at least three orders of magnitude faster than that of the approximate method.

Acknowledgement. This work is partially supported by the ARC (DP170102726, DP180102050), NSF of China (61728204, 91646204), and China National Key Research and Development Program (2016YFB1000700).

References

1. Andersen, R., Chung, F., Lang, K.: Local graph partitioning using pagerank vectors. In: FOCS, pp. 475–486. IEEE (2006)
2. Borgs, C., Brautbar, M., Chayes, J., Lucier, B.: Maximizing social influence in nearly optimal time. In: Proceedings of the Twenty-Fifth Annual ACM-SIAM Symposium on Discrete Algorithms, pp. 946–957. SIAM (2014)
3. Chen, W., Wang, C., Wang, Y.: Scalable influence maximization for prevalent viral marketing in large-scale social networks. In: SIGKDD, pp. 1029–1038. ACM (2010)
4. Chen, W., Yuan, Y., Zhang, L.: Scalable influence maximization in social networks under the linear threshold model. In: ICDM, pp. 88–97. IEEE (2010)
5. Chen, Y.-C., Peng, W.-C., Lee, S.-Y.: Efficient algorithms for influence maximization in social networks. Knowl. Inf. Syst. **33**(3), 577–601 (2012)
6. Gomez Rodriguez, M., Leskovec, J., Krause, A.: Inferring networks of diffusion and influence. In: SIGKDD, pp. 1019–1028. ACM (2010)
7. Haveliwala, T.H.: Topic-sensitive pagerank: a context-sensitive ranking algorithm for web search. IEEE Trans. Knowl. Data Eng. **15**(4), 784–796 (2003)
8. Jeh, G., Widom, J.: Scaling personalized web search. In: WWW, pp. 271–279. ACM (2003)
9. Kempe, D., Kleinberg, J., Tardos, É.: Maximizing the spread of influence through a social network. In: SIGKDD, pp. 137–146. ACM (2003)
10. Kimura, M., Saito, K.: Tractable models for information diffusion in social networks. In: Fürnkranz, J., Scheffer, T., Spiliopoulou, M. (eds.) PKDD 2006. LNCS (LNAI), vol. 4213, pp. 259–271. Springer, Heidelberg (2006). https://doi.org/10.1007/11871637_27
11. Kurashima, T., Iwata, T., Takaya, N., Sawada, H.: Probabilistic latent network visualization: inferring and embedding diffusion networks. In: SIGKDD, pp. 1236–1245. ACM (2014)
12. Leskovec, J., Krause, A., Guestrin, C., Faloutsos, C., VanBriesen, J., Glance, N.: Cost-effective outbreak detection in networks. In: SIGKDD, pp. 420–429. ACM (2007)
13. Page, L., Brin, S., Motwani, R., Winograd, T.: The pagerank citation ranking: bringing order to the web. Technical report, Stanford InfoLab (1999)
14. Tang, Y., Xiao, X., Shi, Y.: Influence maximization: near-optimal time complexity meets practical efficiency. In: SIGMOD, pp. 75–86. ACM (2014)
15. Valiant, L.G.: The complexity of enumeration and reliability problems. SIAM J. Comput. **8**(3), 410–421 (1979)

Maximizing Reverse k-Nearest Neighbors for Trajectories

Tamjid Al Rahat$^{(\boxtimes)}$, Arif Arman$^{(\boxtimes)}$, and Mohammed Eunus Ali$^{(\boxtimes)}$

Department of Computer Science and Engineering,
Bangladesh University of Engineering and Technology, Dhaka, Bangladesh
{tamjid,arman}@cse.uiu.ac.bd, eunus@cse.buet.ac.bd

Abstract. In this paper, we address a popular query involving trajectories, namely, the Maximizing Reverse k-Nearest Neighbors for Trajectories (**MaxRkNNT**) query. Given a set of existing facility trajectories (e.g., bus routes), a set of user trajectories (e.g., daily commuting routes of users) and a set of query facility trajectories (e.g., proposed new bus routes), the MaxRkNNT query finds the proposed facility trajectory that maximizes the cardinality of reverse k-Nearest Neighbors (NNs) set for the query trajectories. A major challenge in solving this problem is to deal with complex computation of nearest neighbors (or similarities) with respect to multi-point queries and data objects. To address this problem, we first introduce a generic similarity measure between a query object and a data object that helps us to define the nearest neighbors according to user requirements. Then, we propose some pruning strategies that can quickly compute k-NNs (or top-k) facility trajectories for a given user trajectory. Finally, we propose a filter and refinement technique to compute the MaxRkNNT. Our experimental results show that our proposed approach significantly outperforms the baseline for both real and synthetic datasets.

1 Introduction

With the widespread use of GPS enabled mobile devices, we have witnessed an unprecedented growth of real trajectory data (e.g., taxi or uber trajectories) capturing the daily movements of people. Such availability has enabled us to address many real life problems by developing a new range of applications based on the trajectory data. For example, let us consider a scenario where a trajectory database consists of user's daily commuting routes with their private vehicles or taxis. To improve the traffic condition and to encourage more people to use public transports, the city authority may want to introduce new facilities (e.g., bus routes) so that they can attract the maximum number of users currently using private vehicles for their regular commute. Similarly, a tourist operator may want to design its routes based on the popularity of users' visiting preferences to different points of interest (POIs). In all these applications, a user may want to avail the proposed bus service if a proposed bus route is one of k nearest bus routes (or top-k bus routes) from user trajectory. To find the best k routes for

© Springer International Publishing AG, part of Springer Nature 2018
J. Wang et al. (Eds.): ADC 2018, LNCS 10837, pp. 262–274, 2018.
https://doi.org/10.1007/978-3-319-92013-9_21

a user trajectory, we need to define an appropriate scoring function that ranks facility trajectories with respect to the user trajectories. Moreover, this scoring function may vary across applications. Thus we first devise scoring functions that can handle a wide range of practical applications (See Sect. 3).

In each of the above scenarios the goal is to find a new facility trajectory that best suits for the maximum number of user trajectories. In this case, a facility trajectory is suitable for a user if the trajectory is one of the k-NN (or top-k) facilities with respect to the user trajectory. This problem can be mapped to a *reverse query* problem on a trajectory database since the underlying problem is to find the facility trajectory which is among the k-nearest neighbors (k-NN) of maximum user trajectories[1]. Therefore, in this paper we first explore the RkNN query on trajectories, which we refer to as RkNNT. Formally, we can define the RkNNT query as follows. Given a set of user trajectories $\mathcal{D}_\mathcal{U}$ and another set of existing facility trajectories $\mathcal{D}_\mathcal{F}$, an RkNNT query returns all users that take $q \in \mathcal{Q}$ as one of their k-nearest neighbors, where $\mathcal{Q}$ is the set of query facility trajectories.

Figure 1 illustrates an example of the RkNNT query with two query facilities $\mathcal{Q}_1$ and $\mathcal{Q}_2$, five user trajectories $\mathcal{U}_1, \mathcal{U}_2 \ldots \mathcal{U}_5 \in \mathcal{D}_\mathcal{U}$, two existing facilities, $\mathcal{F}_1$ and $\mathcal{F}_2 \in \mathcal{D}_\mathcal{F}$ and $k = 1$. Facility $\mathcal{F}_2$ is the 1-NN (or top-1) for users $\mathcal{U}_2, \mathcal{U}_3, \mathcal{U}_4, \mathcal{U}_5$ and $\mathcal{F}_1$ is the NN for $\mathcal{U}_1$. When a new facility $\mathcal{Q}_2$ arrives, $\mathcal{Q}_2$ becomes the NN for $\mathcal{U}_3, \mathcal{U}_4, \mathcal{U}_5$. Thus, R1NNT($\mathcal{Q}_2$) = $\{\mathcal{U}_3, \mathcal{U}_4, \mathcal{U}_5\}$. Similarly, R1NNT($\mathcal{Q}_1$) = $\{\mathcal{U}_1\}$.

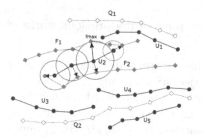

Fig. 1. An example of the **RkNNT** query, with $Q = \{\mathcal{Q}_1, \mathcal{Q}_2\}$, $U = \{\mathcal{U}_1, \mathcal{U}_2 \ldots \mathcal{U}_5\}$ and $F = \{\mathcal{F}_1, \mathcal{F}_2\}$.

The RkNNT query has been introduced in [13] recently. Though this work made an important contribution towards trajectory based reverse query processing, it has the following major limitations: (i) They have assumed that user trajectories (i.e. passenger transitions) contain only source and destination locations of the user, and provided a point-based solution where a user trajectory is considered as two separate points, (ii) They have used a simple distance function to measure the nearest neighbor from a source (or a destination) location to the

---

[1] In this paper we use the terms k-NN trajectories and top-k facilities interchangeably as we use different types of distances or weighted distances as a scoring function to find the best k facilities.

facility trajectory. Thus, their approach is not applicable for applications that require handling other optimizations such as travel distance, priorities, etc. in the distance measure between two multi-point trajectories (user and facility).

In this paper, we first propose a class of similarity scoring functions between a multi-point user trajectory and multi-point facility trajectory that cover a wide range of practical applications. Then we propose several optimizations to compute the k nearest (top-k) facility trajectory for a given user trajectory. After that, we propose an efficient pruning technique to compute the RkNNT for all given facility queries, and return the facility that results in the maximum cardinality of RkNNT result set as the answer to the MaxRkNNT query.

In summary, the contributions of this paper are as follows.

- We define a new class of scoring functions to measure the proximity (similarity) between a user and a facility trajectory according to user preference.
- We introduce a robust algorithm to compute top-k facilities for multi-point user trajectories.
- We proposed a pruning technique to efficiently compute RkNNT, which forms the basis to answer the MaxRkNNT query.
- We conduct detailed experimental study on real datasets to show the efficiency and efficacy of the proposed solution.

2   Related Works

In this section we review some of the previous works of trajectory search and classic RkNN search.

Trajectory Search. There are several studies on single-point based query which looks for the nearest trajectories for only one static [4] or continuously moving location point [10]. Frentzos *et al.* [5] solved Nearest Neighbor Search query over the trajectories of moving object from a stationary query point. Chen *et al.* [3] proposed k Best-Connected Trajectory(k-BCT) query which searches nearest trajectory from multiple location. The similarity function used in k-BCT query does not solve our problem, because exponential function assigns larger contribution to the closer matched query point and trajectories. Shang et al. [9] proposed a Reverse Path Nearest Neighbor (R-PNN) query which finds nearest point of a given moving object dataset. There are also some studies on trajectory search for point based optimal route finding [8] and region based travel path finding [7].

The initial step in *Trajectory Search* studies is to define similarity/distance function between trajectory points. Several kinds of distance function have been defined in considerable amount of related works of trajectory search. Dynamic Time Warping (DTW) [15], Longest Common Subsequence (LCSS) [12], Edit Distance with Real Penalty (ERP) [1] and Edit Distance on Real Sequences (EDR) [2] are some of the typical distance function studied in previous works of trajectory search. However, none of these distance functions can be extended to solve our problem scenarios, where user preference is also considered along with spatial distance.

Reverse kNN. Most of existing MaxRkNN search are based on static location points that apply various pruning-refinement frameworks to avoid scanning the entire dataset. Wong et al. [14] introduced the MaxOverlap algorithm to solve MaxRkNN problem for spatial points. The algorithm iteratively finds the intersection point of the Nearest Location Circles (NLCs) that are covered by the largest number of NLCs. However, the scalability of MaxOverlap is an issue and the computation of the intersection points is also expensive. Some other existing works like MaxFirst algorithm by Zhou et al. [16], MaxSegment algorithm by Liu et al. [6] overcome the limitations of MaxOverlap. They use a variant of plane sweep to find the optimal interval. These works solely focus on static point based intersection of geometric shapes, space partitioning or sweep line techniques, and thus cannot be applied or extended to find MaxRkNN query for multi-point trajectories of variable length.

3   Problem Formulation

Formally, we define the Maximizing Reverse k-Nearest Neighbors for Trajectories (MaxRkNNT) as follows.

Definition 1 (MaxRkNNT). *Let $\mathcal{D}$ be a trajectory dataset, where $\mathcal{D}_\mathcal{U}$ is a set of user trajectories, and $\mathcal{D}_\mathcal{F}$ is a set of existing facility trajectories. $\mathcal{Q}_\mathcal{F}$ is a set of query trajectories on a shared data space. Each trajectory $\mathcal{T} \in \mathcal{D}$ and $\mathcal{Q}_\mathcal{F}$ is a sequence of locations $\mathcal{T} = \{t_1, t_2, \ldots, t_n\}$; $n \geq 2$. Each $\mathcal{U} \in \mathcal{D}_\mathcal{U}$ represents a user's travel route and each $\mathcal{F} \in \mathcal{D}_\mathcal{F}$ represents stoppage locations of a facility trajectory. The RkNNT($\mathcal{T}$) finds a subset of $\mathcal{D}_\mathcal{U}$ that take $\mathcal{T}$ as one of their top-k (k nearest) trajectories. A MaxRkNNT query finds a $\mathcal{Q} \in \mathcal{Q}_\mathcal{F}$ for which $|RkNNT(\mathcal{Q})| \geq |RkNNT(\mathcal{Q}')|$, $\forall \mathcal{Q}' \in \mathcal{Q}_\mathcal{F} \setminus \mathcal{Q}$.*

In the context of Fig. 1 MaxRkNNT would output $\mathcal{Q}_2$ since it has the maximal RkNNT set cardinality. To find the top-k facility trajectories for a user trajectory, we need to first define a scoring function (or a distance function) that gives a ranking score between a user trajectory and facility trajectory. To define the distance function $d_t(\mathcal{U}, \mathcal{F})$ between a user trajectory $\mathcal{U}$ and a facility trajectory $\mathcal{F}$, we consider three separate factors that affects the scoring: (i) the distance between $\mathcal{U}$ and the nearest pick-up (or drop-off) point of $\mathcal{F}$, (ii) the travel length of user trajectory $\mathcal{U}$ through facility trajectory $\mathcal{F}$ (iii) user's preference (or weights w) for each point $u_i \in \mathcal{U}$.

Definition 2 (Distance Function). *Let $\mathcal{U}_s$ and $\mathcal{U}_e$ be the start and end locations of a user trajectory $\mathcal{U}$. Function $\eta(p, \mathcal{F})$ returns the nearest pick-up or drop-off point of facility trajectory $\mathcal{F}$ from a location point p of user trajectory $\mathcal{U}$, $l_t(\mathcal{U}, \mathcal{F})$ returns the travel length of a user through trajectory $\mathcal{F}$, and $d_e(a, b)$ is the euclidean distance between any two location points a and b.*

(i) When a user is only interested about her distance from source (destination) to pick-up (drop-off) point, then we can define the distance between a user trajectory $\mathcal{U}$ and facility trajectory $\mathcal{F}$ as follows.

$$d_t(\mathcal{U}, \mathcal{F}) = d_e(\mathcal{U}_s, \eta(\mathcal{U}_s, \mathcal{F})) + d_e(\mathcal{U}_e, \eta(\mathcal{U}_e, \mathcal{F})) \tag{1}$$

(ii) A user may also consider the travel length with the facility. For such as a case, we define the distance function as a combination of travel distance with the facility and the travel distance from source (destination) to pick-up (drop-off) point:

$$d_t(\mathcal{U}, \mathcal{F}) = d_e(\mathcal{U}_s, \eta(\mathcal{U}_s, \mathcal{F})) + d_e(\mathcal{U}_e, \eta(\mathcal{U}_e, \mathcal{F})) + l_t(\mathcal{U}, \mathcal{F})) \qquad (2)$$

(iii) A user may have different priorities for different locations on her travel route. Let us assume, each location $u_i \in \mathcal{U}$ has an associated $u_i.w$. Then we can define the distance function for this case as follows.

$$d_t(\mathcal{U}, \mathcal{F}) = \sum_{i=1}^{n} d_e(u_i, \eta(u_i, \mathcal{F})) * u_i.w \qquad (3)$$

Since trajectories $\mathcal{U}$ and $\mathcal{F}$ may not have the same number points, we normalize it in the above equation. Table 1 summarizes the notations used throughout this paper.

Table 1. Notation

Symbol	Description
$\mathcal{D}_\mathcal{U}$	The set of user trajectories
$\mathcal{D}_\mathcal{F}$	The set of facility trajectories
$\mathcal{Q}_\mathcal{F}$	The set of query trajectories
$d_t(\mathcal{U}, \mathcal{F})$	Distance of a facility trajectory from user trajectory
$l_t(\mathcal{U}, \mathcal{F})$	Travel length of user through facility $\mathcal{F}$
$d_e(p, q)$	Eulclidean distance between two points p and q
$d_{min}(p, \mathcal{N})$	Min distance of Quad-tree node $\mathcal{N}$ from point p
$min_e(u, \mathcal{S})$	Min euclidean distance between u_i and set of points $\mathcal{S}$
$\eta(p, \mathcal{F})$	Nearest point of $\mathcal{F}$ from a location point $p \in \mathcal{U}$

4   Processing of Top-k (k-NN)

In this section we describe methodologies to determine the top-k nearest facilities of a user trajectory. We first adopt the best-first approach from Tang et al. [11] to incrementally find the next nearest facility w.r.t. a user trajectory. We index all facility points of facility trajectory dataset using a hierarchical index (e.g., Quad-tree/R-tree). Then we incrementally retrieve nearest facility trajectories from a given user trajectory until we find the top-k trajectories for the user. A major challenge in this process is to derive an early termination strategy that avoids the computation of similarities between the user and a large number of trajectories. We propose a lower bound distance, *lbd*, based on the knowledge of the already explored data space and propose an early termination of search based on the computed *lbd*, which reduces the computation overhead significantly.

Lower Bound Distance. The lower bound distance, *lbd*, can be expressed as follows: Let $\mathcal{U} = \{u_1, u_2, \cdots, u_{|\mathcal{U}|}\}$ be a user trajectory. For each u_i, let $fmax_i$ be the farthest retrieved facility point. Thus an unknown facility trajectory will have at least $\sum_i^{|\mathcal{U}|} d_e(u_i, fmax_i)$ distance from $\mathcal{U}$. Then, $\sum_i^{|\mathcal{U}|} d_e(u_i, fmax_i)$ will be the lower bound distance, *lbd*. Based on this lower bound distance, we can describe the top-k processing steps as follows.

First, for a given user trajectory $\mathcal{U}$, we incrementally fetch the nearest facility points with respect to every point $u_i \in \mathcal{U}$. This facility point set $\mathcal{FP}$ contains $|\mathcal{U}|$ number of facility points each representing the NN for each $u_i \in \mathcal{U}$. Now, from the fetched facility point set $\mathcal{FP}$, we retrieve all the facility trajectories $\mathcal{FS}'$ that contain a facility point $f \in \mathcal{FP}$. Let $|\mathcal{FS}'| = n'$ be the number of facilities retrieved in the first phase. We compute the distance, between $\mathcal{U}$ and each facility $\mathcal{F} \in \mathcal{FS}'$. We continue the above process by retrieving more facility points, i.e., 2nd NN, 3rd NN, until we find k distinct facility trajectories. Then, we update the best known distance, λ_k to the kth facility trajectories in terms of distance rank according to our distance function. At this stage, we compute the lower bound distance, *lbd* as described above. If the *lbd* is greater than the distance, λ_k, to kth facility trajectory the search terminates. Otherwise, we repeat the above steps of retrieving more facilities w.r.t. user trajectories.

Delayed Retrieval. A major drawback of the above approach is that the algorithm processes a facility trajectory immediately after fetching any of its facility point w.r.t. any point location $u_i \in \mathcal{U}$. As a result, it may process many unnecessary facility trajectories which cannot be part of the result. Thus, we propose a delayed retrieval approach. In this approach, we process a facility if at least τ location points are fetched during the search process.

Similar to the above approach, we search for next nearest facility location point f_i from each user location point $u_i \in \mathcal{U}$, and add the corresponding facility in a candidate set $\mathcal{C}$. Now, candidates in $\mathcal{C}$ can be divided into two sets. First set $\mathcal{C}_\tau$ contains the candidates for which at least τ points have been found during the process and second set $\mathcal{C}_\tau'$ contains the candidates of $\mathcal{C} \setminus \mathcal{C}_\tau$. We process the candidate $c \in \mathcal{C}_\tau$ by computing corresponding distance $d_t(\mathcal{U}, c)$. We also update the top-k result list $\mathcal{R}$ and λ_k accordingly. On the other hand, we compute *expected distance* for the candidates in $\mathcal{C}_\tau'$, for which less than τ process have been found. Algorithm terminates when λ_k is less than *lbd* or the minimum *expected distance* of the potential candidates in $\mathcal{C}_\tau'$.

Expected Distance. Suppose that at some point during the search process for a user trajectory $\mathcal{U} = \{u_1, u_2, \cdots, u_n\}$, $\mathcal{F}_c$ is a potential candidate for which less than τ points have been retrieved (i.e., $\mathcal{F}_c \in \mathcal{C}_\tau'$). For each u_i, if $p_i \in \mathcal{F}_c$ be the nearest retrieved point, then $d_e(u_i, p_i)$ contributes to the *expected distance*. Otherwise, $d_e(u_i, fmax_i)$ contributes to the *expected distance* value, where $fmax_i$ is the farthest retrieved point from u_i. Finally, we normalize the distance. We notice that expected distance value must be less than the actual distance between $\mathcal{U}$ and $\mathcal{F}_c$. Figure 1 illustrates the computation of Expected

Distance for user trajectory U_2 and potential facility candidate $\mathcal{F}_2$ during the top-k facility search for U_2, where each circle represents the distance $d_e(u_i, fmax_i)$.

5 Computing RkNNT

In this section, we describe our algorithm to find the RkNNT set for a query trajectory based on the precomputed k-NN (or top-k) facilities for each user trajectory.

5.1 Algorithm

For a given set of query trajectories $\mathcal{Q}_\mathcal{F}$, a straightforward approach requires to compute the distance $d_t(\mathcal{U}, \mathcal{Q})$ of each $\mathcal{Q} \in \mathcal{Q}_\mathcal{F}$ from each user trajectory $\mathcal{U} \in \mathcal{D}_\mathcal{U}$. If the distance $d_t(\mathcal{U}, \mathcal{Q})$ is less than the distance of kth facility of user $\mathcal{U}$, $\mathcal{U}$ is included as one of the RkNNT of $\mathcal{Q}$.

Baseline Approach. Let $\varLambda_k$ be the maximum value among the distances of kth facility (λ_k) for all user trajectory $\mathcal{U} \in \mathcal{D}_\mathcal{U}$. Also assume that MBR($\mathcal{U}$) and MBR($\mathcal{Q}$) are *minimum bounding rectangles* containing user trajectory $\mathcal{U}$ and query trajectory $\mathcal{Q} \in \mathcal{Q}_\mathcal{F}$, respectively. Now for each $\mathcal{Q}$, we search for the user trajectories $\mathcal{U} \in \mathcal{D}_\mathcal{U}$ for which the minimum distance between MBR($\mathcal{U}$) and MBR($\mathcal{Q}$) is less than $\varLambda_k$. If $d_t(\mathcal{U}, \mathcal{Q})$ is less than $\mathcal{U}.\lambda_k$, we include $\mathcal{U}$ as one of the results of RkNNT for $\mathcal{Q}$.

An R*-Tree Based Approach. As a part of the pre-processing step, we maintain the distance of kth facility (λ_k) of each user trajectory $\mathcal{U}$. Now, to find the result of the RkNNT for a given set of query trajectories $\mathcal{Q}_\mathcal{F}$, we construct MBRs containing the points of each $\mathcal{U}$ and we denote the MBR as UMBR. However, a query cannot be considered as a k-NN of a user trajectory if it doesn't contain any point within the λ_k distance of the corresponding user trajectory points. Hence, we extend each UMBR by $\mathcal{U}.\lambda_k$ on each side and denote the extended MBR as E-UMBR. Finally, we build an R*-Tree using the E-UMBR for each user trajectory.

For each query trajectory $\mathcal{Q} \in \mathcal{Q}_\mathcal{F}$, we construct MBRs (QMBR) using the points of each $\mathcal{Q}$. If E-UMBR of a user $\mathcal{U}$ does not intersect with the QMBR of a query trajectory $\mathcal{Q}$, then no point of $\mathcal{Q}$ is located within the λ_k distance of the points of user trajectory $\mathcal{U}$. Thus, we can exclude $\mathcal{U}$ from the RkNNT candidate set of $\mathcal{Q}$. On the other hand, If QMBR of a query trajectory $\mathcal{Q}$ intersects E-UMBR of user trajectory $\mathcal{U}$, we consider $\mathcal{U}$ as a potential candidate of RkNNT of $\mathcal{Q}$. If $d_t(\mathcal{U}, \mathcal{Q})$ is less than $\mathcal{U}.\lambda_k$, we include $\mathcal{U}$ as one of the results of RkNNT for $\mathcal{Q}$. Finally we output the $\mathcal{Q}$ with maximum cardinality of RkNNT set to answer MaxRkNNT query. Figure 2 illustrates the RkNNT candidate selection strategy for a query trajectory $\mathcal{Q}_1$. QMBR of $\mathcal{Q}_1$ does not intersect the E-UMBR for user trajectory $\mathcal{U}_2$, which excludes $\mathcal{U}_2$ from the candidate set for RkNNT of $\mathcal{Q}_1$. On the other hand, QMBR of $\mathcal{Q}_1$ intersects E-UMBR of $\mathcal{U}_1$ and thus, included as a candidate of for RkNNT of $\mathcal{Q}_1$.

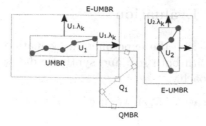

Fig. 2. Candidate trajectory selection using MBR of top-k results of users

5.2 Updates

Candidate trajectory selection depends on precomputed data i.e. on top-k processing of each user trajectory. A major drawback of using precomputed data is that any update in dataset may invalidate the data and trigger a complete recomputation. However, the algorithms presented in this paper are designed such that any update in dataset are handled without repeating the precomputation step. We may wish to add new user and/or facility trajectories to the existing dataset and run MaxRkNNT query. We may also want to change the value of k at some point. While we make these changes we do not want to recompute for the whole dataset, allowing a user the flexibility to tune parameters and get the query results in run-time. In this section we discuss how the algorithm handles these updates.

Update k. If k is increased to k', $k' - k$ facility trajectories must be added to top-k list of each user trajectory. Since at this point we have λ_k of each $\mathcal{U}$ and any further facility must be at a distance $\geq \lambda_k$, we only need to consider next nearest facility locations that is at least λ_k distance away from a user point. While traversing the quad tree for next nearest neighbor, nodes at distance $< \lambda_k$ can be safely pruned. No computation is required if k is decreased.

Add/Remove Facility Trajectory. Addition of facility trajectory $\mathcal{F}$ to $\mathcal{D}_{\mathcal{F}}$ may update top-k list of one or more user trajectories $\mathcal{U}$. We use R*-Tree Based algorithm RkNNT query to efficiently find the set of user trajectories that now takes $\mathcal{F}$ as one of their top-k nearest facilities. If some $\mathcal{F}$ is removed from dataset, we search RkNNT of $\mathcal{F}$. It is then removed from top-k facilities of these user trajectories. This creates an empty slot in top-k and a next nearest facility trajectory is added using the process of updating k described above.

Add/Remove User Trajectory. Adding a user trajectory $\mathcal{U}$ to $\mathcal{D}_{\mathcal{U}}$ requires finding top-k nearest facilities. We use Delayed Retrieval based top-k search algorithm for this since top-k search for $\mathcal{U}$ is independent of searches for $\mathcal{U}' \in \mathcal{D}_{\mathcal{U}} \setminus \mathcal{U}$. Removing $\mathcal{U}$ would not have any effect on the precomputed data of other user trajectories.

6   Experimental Evaluation

In this section, we describe the experimental evaluation of the algorithms for processing the query with both real and synthetic datasets and compare them with the baseline approach.

User Trajectory Dataset ($\mathcal{D}_\mathcal{U}$). We use T-Drive dataset[2] for real user trajectories. The dataset contains one-week trajectories of $10,357$ taxis from Beijing. Total number of points in the dataset is about 15 million and total distance covered by the trajectories is 9 million kilometers. For our experiments, we do periodic sampling for larger trajectories so that no user trajectory contains more than 10 points. Thus, our final dataset contains $165,736$ user trajectories.

Facility Trajectory Dataset ($\mathcal{D}_\mathcal{F}$). We download the OpenStreetMap[3] data within the same *latitude* and *longitude* range (Beijing city) of T-drive dataset. Then, we parse the location points of the nodes under the $<way>$ tags to construct the facility trajectories. We ignore the tags that contain less than 10 points. After final processing, our dataset contains $27,876$ facility trajectories.

Query Trajectory Dataset ($\mathcal{Q}_\mathcal{F}$). We prepared our query dataset by randomly generating trajectory locations within the same region as users and facilities. We randomly chose points located within the region and appended new points one by one with a limited rotation angle and step size.

Synthetic Dataset. We also evaluate our algorithm on synthetic dataset where trajectories are generated randomly within a specified area. We randomly select the start point for each trajectory and append new points one by one, while selecting the rotation angle randomly within $90°$ to avoid zigzag trajectories.

All experiments were performed on an Intel Core i5-6200U CPU with 8 GB RAM running Ubuntu 16.04 LTS, implemented in python 2.7. Table 2 shows the parameter setting used in the experimental evaluation.

Table 2. Parameter setting

Parameter	Range	Default
Number of query, ($|\mathcal{Q}_\mathcal{F}|$)	10, 20, 30, 40, 50, 60, 70	20
Number of facility point	10, 20, 30, 40, 50, 60	30
Retrieval threshold, (τ)	1, 3, 5, 7, 9, 11, 13, 15, 17	9
k	5, 10, 15, 20, 25	5

---

[2] https://www.microsoft.com/en-us/research/publication/t-drive-trajectory-data-sample/.

[3] http://www.openstreetmap.org.

6.1 Top-k Processing

We compare delayed retrieval approach for top-k processing with baseline approach since the brute-force approach is not scalable. Delayed retrieval clearly outperforms the baseline approach by 25–30% as expected since it reduces unnecessary trajectory distance computations. Table 3 shows the time in seconds (s) for both approaches for default values of parameters. It takes 5.1 h to perform Top-k processing for the entire T-drive dataset and 6.5 h for synthetic dataset. We vary several parameters for better insights of the top-k processing approaches. For the following experiments of top-k processing we use a subset of $\mathcal{D_U}$ and $\mathcal{D_F}$ to focus more on the graph trend than dataset size.

Table 3. Top-k processing time in seconds (s) for both delayed retrieval and baseline approach using Beijing dataset.

$\mathcal{D_U}$	Delayed retrieval	Baseline	$\mathcal{D_F}$	Delayed retrieval	Baseline
20,000	3,043 s	4,126 s	500	1,365 s	1,784 s
40,000	7,801 s	9,872 s	1,000	1,820 s	2,324 s
60,000	16,203 s	21,147 s	1,500	2,231 s	3,031 s
$k=5$, $\mathcal{D_F}=5{,}500$			$k=5$, $\mathcal{D_U}=20{,}000$		

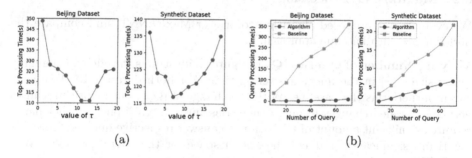

(a)   (b)

Fig. 3. (a) Effect on top-k processing time with the increase of retrieval threshold τ (b) Effect on MaxRkNNT query processing time with the increasing number of queries $|\mathcal{Q_F}|$

Varying τ. Figure 3a shows the effect of varying τ, the threshold amount of points for delayed retrieval in top-k processing time. For both datasets, the run-time starts to decrease with increasing value of τ and starts increasing after a certain point. This is because with a small τ, distance to a facility trajectory $\mathcal{F}$ is computed as soon as a small amount of points of $\mathcal{F}$ are found. This results in a large number of distance computation for trajectories that finally may not be in top-k. For a large τ, the algorithm has to delay computation until a large number of points of $\mathcal{F}$ are found.

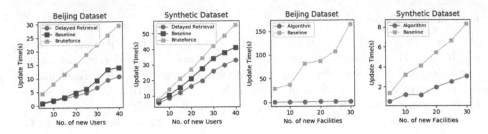

Fig. 4. Update time with the increasing number of new user and facility trajectories for Beijing dataset and synthetic dataset.

Varying No. of Facility Trajectory Points. We compute the top-k processing time by changing the number of facility points from 10 points to 60 points. To alter the facility point, we drop extra points while reading the trajectory from dataset file. Even though increasing the number of facility points yields increased amount of time during trajectory distance computation, it does not have significant effect on overall top-k processing time, as our algorithm reduces the number of unnecessary distance computation. For each dataset, delayed retrieval approach gives 25–30% improvement over the computation time for baseline approach.

6.2 MaxRkNNT Processing

We evaluate our proposed algorithm to answer MaxRkNNT, and compare the performance with baseline approach.

Varying Number of Queries $|\mathcal{Q}_\mathcal{F}|$. Figure 3b illustrates the effect of changing query size $|\mathcal{Q}_\mathcal{F}|$ in the query answering time. For both datasets R*-Tree approach outperforms the baseline. With the change of $|\mathcal{Q}_\mathcal{F}|$, our algorithm causes very small-scaled changes in query time. Baseline approach on the other hand, requires significant amount of CPU time to answer respective queries. Since our algorithm significantly reduces the search space for the queries, it takes very small CPU time in answering even a larger query set.

6.3 Update Processing

Updating Trajectories. Figure 4 illustrates the computation time required for updating new user and facility trajectories. To update new user trajectories, we only compute top-k for each new trajectory. Since baseline approach requires computing larger number of trajectory distance than Delayed Retrieval approach, it takes increased amount of CPU time to update new user trajectory. On the other hand, brute-force approach computes distance from the new user trajectories to all existing facilities, it gives poor performance during update. When new facility arrives, we need to find whether those facilities belong to the top-k facilities of any of the existing users. We use RkNNT query to find the users who has the new facility trajectories as one of their k-nearest neighbors trajectories. Finally, we update the top-k facilities of the corresponding users.

Updating k. When the value of k is increased, we avoid recomputing top-k facilities for each user by storing the state of the previous search for old value of k. We restore the priority queues of each users to resume the search to find the further top-k facilities.

7 Conclusion

In this paper, we have proposed efficient solution for Maximizing Reverse k-Nearest Neighbors for Trajectories (**MaxRkNNT**) query. We first introduced a generic similarity measure between a multi-point query trajectory and a multi-point facility trajectory that helps us to define the nearest neighbors according to user requirements. Then, we have proposed pruning strategies that can quickly compute k-NNs (or top-k) facility trajectories for a given user trajectory. Finally, we have developed a filter and refinement technique to compute the MaxRkNNT. Our experimental results show that our proposed approach significantly outperforms the baseline for both real and synthetic datasets.

References

1. Chen, L., Ng, R.T.: On the marriage of Lp-norms and edit distance. In: VLDB, pp. 792–803 (2004)
2. Chen, L., Tamer Özsu, M., Oria, V.: Robust and fast similarity search for moving object trajectories. In: ACM SIGMOD, pp. 491–502 (2005)
3. Chen, Z., Shen, H.T., Zhou, X., Zheng, Y., Xie, X.: Searching trajectories by locations: an efficiency study. In: ACM SIGMOD, pp. 255–266 (2010)
4. Cheung, K.L., Fu, A.W.-C.: Enhanced nearest neighbour search on the r-tree. SIGMOD Rec. **27**(3), 16–21 (1998)
5. Frentzos, E., Gratsias, K., Pelekis, N., Theodoridis, Y.: Algorithms for nearest neighbor search on moving object trajectories. GeoInformatica **11**(2), 159–193 (2007)
6. Liu, Y., Wong, R.C.-W., Wang, K., Li, Z., Chen, C., Chen, Z.: A new approach for maximizing bichromatic reverse nearest neighbor search. Knowl. Inf. Syst. **36**(1), 23–58 (2013)
7. Reza, R.M., Ali, M.E., Cheema, M.A.: The optimal route and stops for a group of users in a road network. In: SIGSPATIAL/GIS, pp. 4:1–4:10. ACM (2017)
8. Shafique, S., Ali, M.E.: Recommending most popular travel path within a region of interest from historical trajectory data. In: MobiGIS, pp. 2–11. ACM (2016)
9. Shang, S., Yuan, B., Deng, K., Xie, K., Zhou, X.: Finding the most accessible locations: reverse path nearest neighbor query in road networks. In: GIS, pp. 181–190. ACM (2011)
10. Song, Z., Roussopoulos, N.: K-nearest neighbor search for moving query point. In: Jensen, C.S., Schneider, M., Seeger, B., Tsotras, V.J. (eds.) SSTD 2001. LNCS, vol. 2121, pp. 79–96. Springer, Heidelberg (2001). https://doi.org/10.1007/3-540-47724-1_5

11. Tang, L.-A., Zheng, Y., Xie, X., Yuan, J., Yu, X., Han, J.: Retrieving k-nearest neighboring trajectories by a set of point locations. In: Pfoser, D., Tao, Y., Mouratidis, K., Nascimento, M.A., Mokbel, M., Shekhar, S., Huang, Y. (eds.) SSTD 2011. LNCS, vol. 6849, pp. 223–241. Springer, Heidelberg (2011). https://doi.org/10.1007/978-3-642-22922-0_14
12. Vlachos, M., Gunopulos, D., Kollios, G.: Discovering similar multidimensional trajectories. In: ICDE, pp. 673–684 (2002)
13. Wang, S., Bao, Z., Shane Culpepper, J., Sellis, T.K., Cong, G.: Reverse k nearest neighbor search over trajectories. CoRR, abs/1704.03978 (2017)
14. Wong, R.C.-W., Tamer Özsu, M., Yu, P.S., Fu, A.W.-C., Liu, L.: Efficient method for maximizing bichromatic reverse nearest neighbor. PVLDB $\mathbf{2}$(1), 1126–1137 (2009)
15. Yi, B.-K., Jagadish, H.V., Faloutsos, C.: Efficient retrieval of similar time sequences under time warping. In: ICDE, pp. 201–208 (1998)
16. Zhou, Z., Wu, W., Li, X., Lee, M.-L., Hsu, W.: MaxFirst for MaxBRkNN. In: ICDE, pp. 828–839. IEEE Computer Society (2011)

Auto-CES: An Automatic Pruning Method Through Clustering Ensemble Selection

Mojtaba Amiri Maskouni[1(✉)], Saeid Hosseini[1,2],
Hadi Mohammadzadeh Abachi[1], Mohammadreza Kangavari[1],
and Xiaofang Zhou[2]

[1] Iran University of Science and Technology, Tehran, Iran
{amiri_m,hadi_mohammadzadeh,kangavari}@comp.iust.ac.ir
[2] The University of Queensland, Brisbane, Australia
saeid.hosseini@uq.net.au, zxf@itee.uq.edu.au

Abstract. Ensemble learning is a machine learning approach where multiple learners are trained to solve a particular problem. Random Forest is an ensemble learning algorithm which comprises numerous decision trees and nominates a class through majority voting for classification and averaging approach for regression. The prior research affirms that the learning time of the Random Forest algorithm linearly increases when the number of trees in the forest augments. This large number of decision trees in the Random Forest can cause certain challenges. Firstly, it can enlarge the model complexity, and secondly, it can negatively affect the efficiency of large-scale datasets. Hence, ensemble pruning methods (e.g. Clustering Ensemble Selection (CES)) are devised to select a subset of decision trees out of the forest. The main challenge is that the prior CES models require the number of clusters as input. To solve the problem, we devise an Automatic CES pruning model (*Auto-CES*) for Random Forest which can automatically find the proper number of clusters. Our proposed model is able to obtain an optimal subset of trees that can provide the same or even better effectiveness compared to the original set. *Auto-CES* has two components: clustering and selection. First, our algorithm utilizes a new clustering technique to classify homogeneous trees. In selection part, it takes both accuracy and diversity of the trees into consideration to choose the best tree.

Extensive experiments are conducted on five datasets. The results show that our algorithm can perform the classification task more effectively than the state-of-the-art rivals.

Keywords: Machine learning · Ensemble method · Random Forest
Decision tree · Clustering Ensemble Selection
Pruning of Random Forest

© Springer International Publishing AG, part of Springer Nature 2018
J. Wang et al. (Eds.): ADC 2018, LNCS 10837, pp. 275–287, 2018.
https://doi.org/10.1007/978-3-319-92013-9_22

1   Introduction

Machine learning techniques have widespread applications in Data Mining field. Ensemble methods are machine learning algorithms that construct a set of trained classifiers whose individual decisions are combined to classify new examples. Ensemble methods have various types such as bagging [4], boosting [22], random subspace [15], and random forests [5].

Augmenting the *diversity* among individual classifiers, on the one hand, can improve the efficiency through combining the classifiers, and on the other hand, it can promote the generalization performance [18]. However, the definition of diversity is ambiguous. One can define diversity as the capability to maximize prediction correctness for a set of classifiers that are categorized into a unique ensemble. Nevertheless, not necessarily a good diversity can always assure an accurate estimation outcome, but it can achieve a fitting *stability*. To maximize the stability, bagging and random subspace, are two models which employ *randomization* to originate a collection of diverse classifiers. Randomization is done in two ways: First, random sub-sampling for bootstrap samples as proposed by Breiman [4], Second, random selection of input features for generating individual base decision trees [15].

Breiman [5] has made a significant modification on bagging to develop a new model named as *Random Forest* (*RF*). The RF model initiates a set of individual decision trees through randomization. The generalization error of the *RF* model is computed through two metrics. Firstly, the strength of comprising decision trees, and Secondly, the level of correlation among them. Since RF model effectively takes advantage of the randomization techniques. The prior research [5] with regard to the existing ensemble algorithms shows that the RF approach can foster diversity among the classifiers and consequently provide a better decision-making results.

In this work, our algorithm is implemented for the RF model, however, it can also work for other ensemble methods.

Previous experimental results [19] demonstrate that adding excessive classifiers in the forest does not improve the accuracy. The main challenge here is to find an optimum subset of the RF classifiers that keeps or enhances the generalization accuracy. To address the challenge, pruning of the Random Forest classifiers is the model that has been widely [1,2,8,9,24,25] studied recently.

In this paper, we propose an **Auto**matic pruning algorithm based on **C**lustering **E**nsemble **S**election (**Auto-CES**). Moreover, the prior works require the user to specify the input parameters (the number of clusters or the fixed number of iteration). Suggesting a number for each of parameters is challenging. Our method differentiates itself from existing methods through exploiting the appropriate number of clusters that can ensure a reasonable accuracy. The proposed method in this paper especially presents the following new contributions:

- We present a new clustering algorithm to group RF trees that does not need to the number of clusters to be specified.

- Our method resembles the mean-shift clustering. It finds the clustering threshold dynamically.
- We propose the cohesiveness measure based on accuracy and diversity. This measure aimed at discovering the best tree in each cluster.

The rest of this paper is structured as follows: The related work is surveyed in Sect. 2. In Sect. 3, we elucidate essential concepts. Subsequently, in Sect. 4, we explain our pruning algorithm. Moreover, as reported in Sect. 5, we perform evaluations and compare our method with another baseline using multiple datasets. Finally, we conclude this paper in Sect. 6 and include promising future directions.

2 Related Work

In recent years, several methods on pruning of Random Forest (RF) have been proposed. Zhang and Wang [25] believe that two properties of the accuracy and correlation are significant in the pruning procedure. From one perspective, a tree in the forest can be pruned if it has the minimum impact on the overall prediction accuracy (minimal accuracy). From another perspective, a tree which is less correlated/similar to others should not be eliminated. On the other hand, a tree in the forest can be pruned if the mean correlation of the tree is higher than others. Some pruning models monitor how the trees are added to the forest. For example, [24] determines the number of decision trees in the forest dynamically through two thresholds. Firstly, the difference between data and the fitted curve. Secondly, the number of continuous points satisfying the later threshold. This iterative model requires the fitted value and the accuracy curve as inputs to determine the termination step. The trade-off between diversity and accuracy is another feature which can be used to perform CES process. Accordingly, Elghazel et al. [8] utilize the fitness function [11,20] to develop the fit-select method to benchmark the output based on diversity and accuracy. Similarly, ERF [2] originates a set of clusters containing the most accurate trees and subsequently chooses the best tree from each cluster. The inputs required by this method are the top P number of trees with the highest accuracy and the Q as the number of clusters. While, CLUB-DRF [9] employs the K-modes algorithm [13] to cluster the similar trees in the forest, it require the k number of clusters. Even if in the selection module it aggregates the trees based on the AUC measure. to k number clusters base on their vector of prediction outcomes. Then it aggregates the trees with the highest AUC from the clusters. Similarly, our proposed method in this paper utilizes a mean-shift like clustering model which takes advantage of the double-fault measure to compute the dissimilarities.

Our *Auto-CES* approach distinguishes itself from previous similar works [2,8,9] in one main aspect. All aforementioned methods require input parameter adjustments. However, rather than requesting the input values such as the number of clusters or the dissimilarity thresholds, our model in a distance-aware approach finalizes the optimum set of clusters dynamically.

3   Problem Statement

In this section, we concisely introduce some definitions and concepts employed in the paper.

3.1   Preliminary Concepts

Definition 1. *(Learning data) Let learning data be $D = \{(X_1, Y_1), \ldots, (X_M, Y_M)\}$, where each data instance (X_i, Y_i), comprises a vector of features $X_i \in \mathcal{X} = \{\mathcal{X}_1, \mathcal{X}_2, \ldots, \mathcal{X}_d\}$ and a class label $Y_i \in \mathcal{Y} = \{1, 2, \ldots, l\}$.*

Definition 2. *(Decision tree) is a non-linear learning model for the classification and regression* [6].

Definition 3. *(Random Forest) RF is an Ensemble of classifier consisting of a collection of decision trees ($\{T_i \in \mathcal{R} | i = 1, \ldots, n\}$), where each tree T_i casts a unit vote $\mathcal{V}_i$ to select the most popular class $\mathcal{Y}^j$ with regard to the random feature vector of the input (X_i)* [5].

To produce every single tree T_i in the forest $\mathcal{R}$, the following steps have been utilized: If the number of instances in the training set is M_{train}, then m ($m \ll M_{train}$) instances are sampled with a random and replacement strategy. This is so-called bootstrapping. These m instances will be the training set for growing the tree. If there are d input features, a number of features d' ($d' \ll d$) at each node is selected at random to find the best split for the node. The value of d' is held constant during the growth of trees in $\mathcal{R}$ where the maximum of depth of the trees and the number of trees in $\mathcal{R}$ are predefined by the user.

Definition 4. *(Diversity) among the ensemble of classifiers is considered as a key issue in combining of classifiers. Measuring the diversity is challenging because this concept does not have a generally accepted definition.*

One way to obtain the diversification metric among a pair of classifiers is to compare the predictions on the same data samples. The methods for calculating the diversification metric are two-fold: pairwise and non-pairwise [23].

With regard to *data clustering*, the aim is to find groups of samples that are *homogeneous* with each other and demonstrate diversity toward the members of other clusters. Many clustering algorithms have been proposed, each utilizing different distance/similarity measures [7,12].

Definition 5. *Cluster Ensemble Selection (CES) methods are two-fold. First, those methods which categorize homogeneous classifiers. Secondly, the models which select a subset of clusters to maximize diversity between chosen classifiers.*

A CES approach is a joint process that produces a small ensemble that can perform classification as effective, or even better than the original ensemble [10]. In fact, a smaller set can perform more efficient than the complete ensemble.

3.2   Problem Definition

Given a full set of trained RF trees $\mathcal{R} = \{\mathcal{T}_1, \dots, \mathcal{T}_n\}$, our aim is to prune $\mathcal{R}$ by choosing a subset of the trees in $\mathcal{R}$. we achieve this goal by devising an Automatic Clustering Ensemble Selection model named as *Auto-CES*.

The *Auto-CES* framework performs three sub-tasks as described below:

1. *Clustering:* Given the set of trees in $\mathcal{R}$, *Auto-CES* clusters the homogeneous trees based on predefined similarities.
2. *Selection:* From each cluster $\{g_c | g_c \in \mathcal{G}\}$, *Auto-CES* selects the tree which firstly, gains the best average accuracy both in training and validation, and secondly has the highest diversity among the trees of the same cluster.
3. *Creation of the new RF:* The Auto-ECS then collects the selected trees and produces the new RF.

4   Proposed Algorithm

In this article, we propose an automatic *pruning* method so called as *Auto-CES* for Random Forest through employing the *clustering ensemble selection* approach. As illustrated in Fig. 1, our framework takes the complete list of *RF* trees as input, and accomplishes the pruning procedure in two steps of *Clustering* and *Selection*. Firstly, in the clustering step, we utilize the diversity feature to categorize the trees into a set of independent groups. For the selection component, from each group, we choose the most cohesive tree that gains the highest average accuracy and has the most diversification compared to the other members of the same cluster. Eventually, the returned subset from RF trees can achieve a better effectiveness and efficiency for the classification task. The Pseudo code of our implementation of *Auto-CES* is depicted in Algorithm 1.

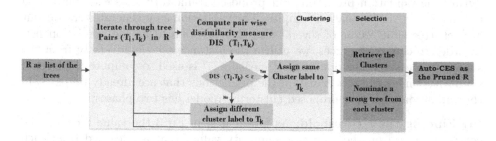

Fig. 1. Proposed framework

Question: Why no necessity for any input parameter? As we mentioned in Sect. 1, our proposed method adapts a mean-shift-like approach [7] that doesn't necessitate the final number of clusters as an input parameter. Moreover, the assignment condition for the cluster labels for each tree in the list ($\mathcal{R}$) can be found dynamically via the pair-wise average of all diversities (Eq. 3).

Algorithm 1. pseudo-code for *Auto-CES*

1: **Input:** $\mathcal{R}$, $New_{RF} = \emptyset$, $\mathcal{G} = \emptyset$
2: **Output:** *Auto-CES as the RF pruned*
3: $\epsilon \leftarrow$ *calculate all DIS values*
4: **for** each pair of trees$(\mathcal{T}_i, \mathcal{T}_k)$ in $\mathcal{R}$ **do**
5:     **if** $\mathcal{T}_i$ has not a class label **then**
6:         assign a new cluster label to $\mathcal{T}_i$
7:     **end if**
8:     **if** $\mathcal{T}_k$ has not a class label **then**
9:         $DIS_{\mathcal{T}_i, \mathcal{T}_k} = 1 - DF_{\mathcal{T}_i, \mathcal{T}_k}$
10:         **if** $DIS(\mathcal{T}_i, \mathcal{T}_k) < \epsilon$ **then**
11:             Update $\mathcal{G}$ by assigning $\mathcal{T}_i$ cluster label to $\mathcal{T}_k$
12:         **else**
13:             Update $\mathcal{G}$ by assigning a new cluster label to $\mathcal{T}_k$
14:         **end if**
15:     **end if**
16: **end for**
17: **for** each $cluster g_c \in \mathcal{G}$ **do**
18:     **for** each tree $t_{i'} \in g_c$ **do**
19:         Cohesiveness$(t_{i'}) = \tilde{\theta}_{i'} * DIV_{i'}$
20:     **end for**
21:     select $\mathcal{T}_{i'}$ which have higher Cohesiveness.
22:     $New_{RF}.\text{add}(\mathcal{T}_{i'})$
23: **end for**
24: **Return:** *Auto-CES* $= New_{RF}$

4.1   Clustering Step

Let $\mathcal{R}$ be the list of the trained trees. Where the training stage is finished, during the validation procedure, our proposed framework tests each individual tree in $\mathcal{R}$ over the evaluation samples. The validation step generates the output of each tree as a vector of several class labels - named as the prediction list. In order to cluster the trees, we utilize the distance metric adversely from the similarity measure. The double fault measure [7] is used to compute the level of similarity among the tree based on the predictions that are already prepared in the validation step. Our proposed clustering model has two phases:

(a) **Finding the ϵ threshold:** As formulated in Eq. 3 the value for ϵ can be computed based on the pair-wise similarity values that are learned from each pair of the trees in $\mathcal{R}$.

$$DF_{\mathcal{T}_i, \mathcal{T}_k} = \frac{\mathcal{N}^{00}}{\mathcal{N}} \tag{1}$$

Equation 1 elucidates that we utilize the double fault criterion to find the level of similarity $DF_{\mathcal{T}_i, \mathcal{T}_k}$ among each pair of the trees $(\mathcal{T}_i, \mathcal{T}_k)$. Accordingly, we divide the number of joint misclassified samples of the tree pair $(\mathcal{N}^{00})$ by the total number of validation samples $\mathcal{N}$. Equation 2 states how we can determine the dissimilarity value from the contrary likeness measure.

$$DIS_{T_i, T_k} = 1 - DF_{T_i, T_k} \tag{2}$$

Then all of these dissimilarity values will be averaged (Eq. 3) to obtain the value of the ϵ threshold.

$$\epsilon = \frac{2}{n * (n-1)} * \sum_{i=1}^{n-1} \sum_{k=i+1}^{n} DIS_{T_i, T_k} \tag{3}$$

(b) Grouping the trees: The algorithm starts with the first tree T_1 and allocates the first cluster label (e.g: No. 1) to it. Subsequently, the pairwise dissimilarity DIS among the first tree with others $T_k \in \mathcal{R}$ will be calculated. For instance, if DIS_{T_1, T_2}, as the value of dissimilarity between the first tree T_1 and the second tree T_2, is less than ϵ, T_2 will obtain the T_1's label. Otherwise, a new label (e.g: No. 2) will be granted to T_2. To continue, for each tree T_i, if it misses the cluster label, our model firstly assigns a new label to it, and afterwards, the pairwise DIS values of T_i with other trees $T_k \in \mathcal{R}$ will be recomputed. When all the trees possess a label, they will be grouped based the labels. When the grouping procedure is finished, those clusters comprising of an at least one shared tree will be further combined into a new cluster.

4.2 Selection Step

The clustering step provides the total number of $\mathcal{G}$ tree clusters for the *selection step*. In the selection stage, we choose the best tree from each cluster based on the cohesiveness feature (ζ). To compute the cohesiveness measure associated with each tree T_i, we first calculate the impact of the tree on accuracy in both of training($\theta_{T_i}^{train}$) and validation($\theta_{T_i}^{validation}$). In order to find out the general accuracy of T_i, we employ the average of both accuracy features ($\tilde{\theta_{T_i}}$) as denoted by Eq. 4. Secondly, for each tree T_i, we take advantage of the diversification mean between T_i and other trees in the forest (Eq. 5).

$$\tilde{\theta_{T_i}} = \frac{1}{2}(\theta_{T_i}^{train} + \theta_{T_i}^{validation}) \tag{4}$$

$$DIV_{T_i} = \frac{\sum_{k=1, i \neq k}^{n} DIS(T_i, T_k)}{n-1} \tag{5}$$

Note that the accuracy ($\tilde{\theta_{T_i}}$) and diversity (DIV_{T_i}) have the joint impact on the cohesiveness (ζ_{T_i}) feature (Eq. 6). The $\tilde{\theta_{T_i}}$ is a tree specific factor ($0 \leq \tilde{\theta_{T_i}} \leq 1$). Also DIV_{T_i} is collectively computed among T_i and other trees where is a tree universal factor ($0 \leq DIV_{T_i} \leq 1$). Therefore, the outcome of the cohesiveness ($0 \leq \zeta \leq 1$) of a tree T_i is very sensitive to both DIV_{T_i} and $\tilde{\theta_{T_i}}$ values.

$$\zeta_{T_i} = \tilde{\theta_{T_i}} * DIV_{T_i} \tag{6}$$

Subsequently, from each cluster $\{g_c | g_c \in \mathcal{G}\}$ we choose the tree with the highest cohesiveness that can represent the cluster more effectively. Finally, the chosen set of trees will mutually characterize the output pruned random forest.

5   Experiments

In this section, we release a comprehensive set of experiments to compare our proposed solution (*Auto-CES*) with two state-of-the-art models, CART-based RF [5] and CLUB-DRF [9]. We have implemented the CART-based RF algorithm [5], CLUB-DRF [9] as the rival and Auto-ECS as our method in the Python programing language [21]. All the experiments have been conducted on a system with Intel(R)Core(TM) i7-3770, CPU with 3.40 GHz and 8 GB for RAM. In each experiment, we have incorporated various noise levels in datasets, through unsupervised add-noise component in WEKA [16]: (1) No added noise, (2) 10% in class labels and (3) 20% noise in class labels. We have employed two evaluation metrics of *F-measure* and *Accuracy* to compare the performance of the competitors. we also investigated the efficiency through the time test for examination (*latency*) of the competitors. To perform the good experiments, we divide each datasets into three parts $\{training(0.6), validation(0.2) and test(0.2)\}$. In training step, we build the initial Random Forest. Then we continue with the pruning process through using the validation samples. In order to maximize the performance of the rivals, we have accomplished the parameter setting. The random sub-sampling is the bootstrap parameter m is set to $(0.6 * M_{train})$, Where M_{train} is the total number of the instances in the training set. The d' is the metric for random feature selection which is set to $\sqrt{d}$, where d represents the total number of features. Finally, the maximum depth at each tree is 100.

5.1   Dataset

For our experiments, we have used four real datasets (Soybean, Wilt, Breast Cancer, Sonar) from the UCI repository [3] and an additional Enrol email dataset which was provided by *Herman* [14]. Table 1 depicts characteristics of datasets.

Table 1. Description of the data sets

Dataset	#instances	#features	#classes
Soybean	307	35	4
Breast cancer	699	10	2
Herman's	306	3	2
Wilt	4838	5	2
Sonar	208	60	2

5.2   Competing Methods

The methods that have participated in the experiments are explained below:

- **B**reiman's as **CART**-based **RF** [5] (*BC-RF*), which employs the CART algorithm as the base-learner.

- *CLUB-DRF* applies the K-MODES clustering model to group the trees and collect the most accurate trees based on the Area Under the Curve.
- Automatic Clustering Ensemble Selection *Auto-CES* is our proposed pruning approach which dynamically computes the final number of trees in the forest and does not require any input parameter. To discover impact of the cohesiveness measure, we study three cases in the selection: 1- **B**ased on the **A**ccuracy and **D**iversity (B-A-D). 2- **B**ased on the **A**ccuracy alone (B-A). 3- **B**ased on the **D**iversity alone (B-D).

5.3   Evaluation Metrics

There are various approaches to evaluate a classifier algorithm. We apply multiple measures in comparison to discern distinctive aspects of the algorithms. The accuracy metric as the most frequently used performance measure for classification deems to create incorrect outcomes when classes are strongly unbalanced. Therefore, we further measure the effectiveness of the competitors through ***F-measure*** [17] which is defined as the weighted harmonic mean for the precision and recall (Eq. 8).

$$Fmeasure = 2 * \frac{Precision * Recall}{Precision + Recall} \tag{7}$$

$$Precision = \frac{1}{l} \sum_{j=1}^{l} \frac{\wp_j}{\mathcal{PC}_j}, \quad Recall = \frac{1}{l} \sum_{j=1}^{l} \frac{\wp_j}{\mathcal{C}_j} \tag{8}$$

In this paper, the final *precision* and *recall* of the classifiers are respectively computed through the average of the metrics in all l classes in the test set. The *precision* for the sample class j is the fraction of the events where the classifier correctly predicts the class label ($\wp_j$) out of all the instances that truly or falsely are predicted for the class ($\mathcal{PC}_j$). Also, *recall* for class j is the number of the events that are correctly associated with class j ($\wp_j$) divided by the total number of the cases where the ground truth is j ($\mathcal{C}_j$).

   Accuracy is used to study how effectively each of the methods can classify the test instances.

$$Accuracy = \frac{\mathcal{CP}}{\mathcal{P}} \tag{9}$$

In Eq. 9, $\mathcal{CP}$ is the number of correct predictions provided by the classifier. Also, $\mathcal{P}$ is the total number of predictions.

5.4   Performance Comparison

With regard to the current pruning approaches, our model (Auto-CES) aims to further reduce the size of the random forest and at the same time achieve a better accuracy. Intuitively, the fewer number of trees in a forest will demand fewer time requirements to the test step. Hence, Auto-CES can outperform the

Table 2. Impact of the number of tree on the accuracy

Data	BC-RF		CLUB-DRF		Auto-CES		
					B-A-D	B-A	B-D
	#T	ACC	#T	ACC	ACC	ACC	ACC
Breast cancer	400	%97	129	%95/9	%96/5	%95/9	%97
Soybean	100	%90	41	%70	**%100**	%98	%90
Herman's	300	%68/8	10	%71	%69/6	%68/9	**%71/2**
Wilt	300	%98/7	14	%98/2	%98/7	%98/6	%98/6
Sonar	200	%88/5	20	%86/4	%88/5	**%89/5**	**%89/5**

Table 3. Impact of the number of tree on the test time

Data	BC-RF		CLUB-DRF		Auto-CES
	#T	Latency (msec)	#T	Latency (msec)	Latency (msec)
Breast cancer	400	73/337	129	24/445	**23/891**
Soybean	100	0/991	41	0/361	**0/322**
Herman's	300	20/87	10	**0/883**	0/936
Wilt	300	890/913	14	32/034	**29.468**
Sonar	200	17/238	20	1/532	**1/412**

original model (e.g. BC-RF) in efficiency and effectiveness. Moreover, in order to verify the comparison results, we utilize both the Accuracy and F-measure.

Table 2 depicts the accuracy with regard to the number of trees for the competitors. The results obtained over the Breast cancer dataset indicate that while the number of trees decreases from 400 to 129, our B-D method, reaches the same accuracy of the BC-RF. Also, rather than rival pruning model where effectiveness is extremely decreased over the Soybean dataset, our method improves the accuracy through pruning. Nevertheless, the highest pruning level has been acquired over Herman's data set and all of the pruned models have improved the accuracy. Wilt and Sonar gain the second and third highest pruning levels where no significant improvement is achieved based on the accuracy.

The Table 3 shows the impact of the number of trees over the test time (milliseconds). Except the results shown for Herman's dataset, Auto-CES gains the best efficiency.

We continue the next experiments with the F-measure metrics that jointly study the precision and recall of the models. we incorporate the noise in each dataset in three levels of 0%, 10%, and 20%. We initially compare the effectiveness of our model against BC-RF and CLUB-DRF where no noise is added to the datasets (Fig. 2). As depicted in Fig. 2c, where the pruned models do not excel in all the datasets, Auto-CES-B-A-D has achieved the same or better results than BC-RF.

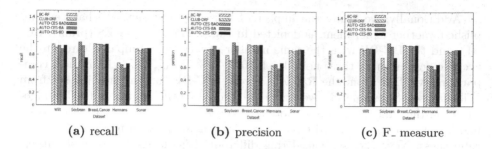

(a) recall   **(b)** precision   **(c)** F_ measure

Fig. 2. Comparing without noise

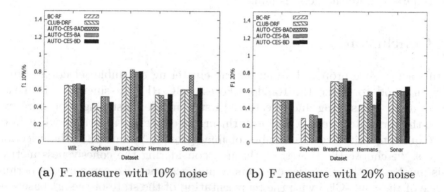

(a) F_ measure with 10% noise   **(b)** F_ measure with 20% noise

Fig. 3. Noisy comparison

Furthermore, Fig. 3a and b illustrate the results through f-measure where the respective amount of 10 and 20% of the noise have been added to the datasets. Nevertheless, both figures demonstrate that outperforms both BC-RF and CLUB-DRF baselines. Two reasons support these results. First, as indicated in Eq. 6, an essential component in calculating of the cohesiveness for each tree is the average accuracy $\tilde{\theta}$ that is computed during both training and validation. Hence, the trees that are selected have the highest *stability* among other trees. Second, the effect of $\tilde{\theta}$ (Eq. 4) and DIV (Eq. 5) are simultaneously employed to compute the cohesiveness metric (ζ). As a result, the selected trees create the ensembles that achieve higher robustness.

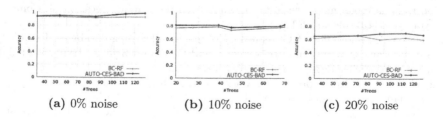

(a) 0% noise   **(b)** 10% noise   **(c)** 20% noise

Fig. 4. Impact of noise on Wilt dataset

Additionally, we study the impact of noise on accuracy. We have accomplished another experiment as depicted in Fig. 4. Both Auto-CES (pruned BC-RF) and the BC-RF with the same number of trees are compared through the accuracy criterion on three noise levels (0%, 10%, 20%). To perform these comparisons, we first train the Random Forest (BC-RF) on the training set from Wilt dataset. Subsequently, we prune the forest by utilizing the Auto-CES algorithm on the validation subset. Note that the Auto-CES is a subset of the original forest, but the retrieved trees chosen by our model gain more stability and robustness. Nevertheless, considering different noise levels, our model outperforms the baseline in terms of accuracy. However, the accuracy of both models is correlated where the noise is null.

6   Conclusion

In this article, we proposed an automatic clustering ensemble selection (Auto-CES) method to prune the Random Forest (BC-RF) classifier based on two major steps - clustering and selection. Firstly, in the clustering procedure, we group the correlated trees in the forest through a clustering algorithm which does not require to initialize the number of final groups. Secondly, in the selection process, we choose the best trees through considering the cohesiveness metric. This involves both properties of diversity and accuracy. To compare the performance of the Auto-CES with the representation of the state-of-the-art baselines (BC-RF, CLUB-DRF), we conduct three sets of experiments on five real-world datasets. We also study the impact of the noise in pruning procedure. The results demonstrate that Auto-CES can effectively and efficiently prune the forest trees.

As a future work, we aim to extend our algorithm in a large-scale environment including the multi-cluster spark platforms. Hence, we are going to deal with the important challenge of huge data size and accordingly design smaller ensembles to speed up the classification process.

References

1. Bernard, S., Heutte, L., Adam, S.: On the selection of decision trees in random forests. In: International Joint Conference on Neural Networks, IJCNN 2009, pp. 302–307. IEEE (2009)
2. Bharathidason, S., Venkataeswaran, C.J.: Improving classification accuracy based on random forest model with uncorrelated high performing trees. Int. J. Comput. Appl. **101**(13), 26–30 (2014)
3. Blake, C.L., Merz, C.J.: UCI repository of machine learning databases. University of California, Department of Information and Computer Science, Irvine 55 (1998). http://www.ics.uci.edu/mlearn/mlrepository.html
4. Breiman, L.: Bagging predictors. Mach. Learn. **24**(2), 123–140 (1996)
5. Breiman, L.: Random forests. Mach. Learn. **45**(1), 5–32 (2001)
6. Breiman, L., Friedman, J., Stone, C.J., Olshen, R.A.: Classification and Regression Trees. CRC Press, Boca Raton (1984)

7. Comaniciu, D., Meer, P.: Mean shift: a robust approach toward feature space analysis. IEEE Trans. Pattern Anal. Mach. Intell. **24**(5), 603–619 (2002)
8. Elghazel, H., Aussem, A., Perraud, F.: Trading-off diversity and accuracy for optimal ensemble tree selection in random forests. In: Okun, O., Valentini, G., Re, M. (eds.) Ensembles in Machine Learning Applications. SCI, vol. 373, pp. 169–179. Springer, Heidelberg (2011). https://doi.org/10.1007/978-3-642-22910-7_10
9. Fawagreh, K., Gaber, M.M., Elyan, E.: CLUB-DRF: a clustering approach to extreme pruning of random forests. In: Bramer, M., Petridis, M. (eds.) Research and Development in Intelligent Systems XXXII, pp. 59–73. Springer, Cham (2015). https://doi.org/10.1007/978-3-319-25032-8_4
10. Fern, X.Z., Lin, W.: Cluster ensemble selection. Stat. Anal. Data Min.: ASA Data Sci. J. **1**(3), 128–141 (2008)
11. Gacquer, D., Delcroix, V., Delmotte, F., Piechowiak, S.: On the effectiveness of diversity when training multiple classifier systems. In: Sossai, C., Chemello, G. (eds.) ECSQARU 2009. LNCS (LNAI), vol. 5590, pp. 493–504. Springer, Heidelberg (2009). https://doi.org/10.1007/978-3-642-02906-6_43
12. Hartigan, J.A., Wong, M.A.: Algorithm as 136: a k-means clustering algorithm. J. Roy. Stat. Soc.: Ser. C (Appl. Stat.) **28**(1), 100–108 (1979)
13. He, X.G., Hou, W.S., Huang, C.S.: Implications for B→ ηk and B→ glueball+ K modes from observed large B→ η' K+ x. Phys. Lett. B **429**(1–2), 99–105 (1998)
14. Hermans, F., Murphy-Hill, E.: Enron's spreadsheets and related emails: a dataset and analysis. In: Proceedings of the 37th International Conference on Software Engineering, vol. 2, pp. 7–16. IEEE Press (2015)
15. Ho, T.K.: The random subspace method for constructing decision forests. IEEE Trans. Pattern Anal. Mach. Intell. **20**(8), 832–844 (1998)
16. Holmes, G., Donkin, A., Witten, I.H.: WEKA: a machine learning workbench. In: Proceedings of the 1994 Second Australian and New Zealand Conference on Intelligent Information Systems, pp. 357–361. IEEE (1994)
17. Hripcsak, G., Rothschild, A.S.: Agreement, the f-measure, and reliability in information retrieval. J. Am. Med. Inform. Assoc. **12**(3), 296–298 (2005)
18. Kuncheva, L.I., Whitaker, C.J.: Measures of diversity in classifier ensembles and their relationship with the ensemble accuracy. Mach. Learn. **51**(2), 181–207 (2003)
19. Latinne, P., Debeir, O., Decaestecker, C.: Limiting the number of trees in random forests. In: Kittler, J., Roli, F. (eds.) MCS 2001. LNCS, vol. 2096, pp. 178–187. Springer, Heidelberg (2001). https://doi.org/10.1007/3-540-48219-9_18
20. Opitz, D.W., Maclin, R.: Popular ensemble methods: an empirical study. J. Artif. Intell. Res. (JAIR) **11**, 169–198 (1999)
21. Pedregosa, F., Varoquaux, G., Gramfort, A., Michel, V., Thirion, B., Grisel, O., Blondel, M., Prettenhofer, P., Weiss, R., Dubourg, V.: Scikit-learn: machine learning in python. J. Mach. Learn. Res. **12**(Oct), 2825–2830 (2011)
22. Schapire, R.E.: The strength of weak learnability. Mach. Learn. **5**(2), 197–227 (1990)
23. Tang, E.K., Suganthan, P.N., Yao, X.: An analysis of diversity measures. Mach. Learn. **65**(1), 247–271 (2006)
24. Tripoliti, E.E., Fotiadis, D.I., Manis, G.: Dynamic construction of random forests: evaluation using biomedical engineering problems. In: 2010 10th IEEE International Conference on Information Technology and Applications in Biomedicine (ITAB), pp. 1–4. IEEE (2010)
25. Zhang, H., Wang, M.: Search for the smallest random forest. Stat. Interface **2**(3), 381 (2009)

DistClusTree: A Framework for Distributed Stream Clustering

Zhinoos Razavi Hesabi[1]([✉]), Timos Sellis[2], and Kewen Liao[2]

[1] School of Computer Science and IT, RMIT University, Melbourne, Australia
zhinoos.razavi@rmit.edu.au
[2] Department of Computer Science and Software Engineering,
Swinburne University, Hawthorn, VIC, Australia
{tsellis,kliao}@swin.edu.au

Abstract. In this paper, we investigate the problem of clustering distributed multidimensional data streams. We devise a distributed clustering framework DistClusTree that extends the centralized ClusTree approach. The main difficulty in distributed clustering is balancing communication cost and clustering quality. We tackle this in DistClusTree through combining spatial index summaries and online tracking for efficient local and global incremental clustering. We demonstrate through extensive experiments the efficacy of the framework in terms of communication cost and approximate clustering quality.

1 Introduction

Classical clustering algorithms are mainly designed for static datasets while anytime clustering of massive data streams is highly demanded in modern distributed data acquisition systems. Continuously changing data distributions raises a challenge: new data should be able to efficiently locate its cluster, and the clustering structure should be updated incrementally in a continuous online manner, that is, the structure is reorganized once the distribution with new data significantly invalidates the older organization. Further, in the setting of distributed clustering, updating master clustering via communications and its entire reorganization become far more challenging.

Hence, the problem we target to solve is on optimizing the *lifecycle* of distributed stream clustering – how can we build, organize, track, and update high quality summaries/approximations of clusters in an effective and efficient manner?

ClusTree [8] is one state-of-the-art centralized multidimensional stream clustering approach that leverages spatial index and microclusters together as hierarchical summaries of clusters. It achieves effective and efficient anytime clustering. However, for a distributed framework, communication cost is often the main bottleneck and the quality of global clustering is paramount. Hence, the focus of the study is to track and balance these criteria in our proposed DistClusTree framework while in terms of the clustering quality performing no worse than

© Springer International Publishing AG, part of Springer Nature 2018
J. Wang et al. (Eds.): ADC 2018, LNCS 10837, pp. 288–299, 2018.
https://doi.org/10.1007/978-3-319-92013-9_23

ClusTree. Specifically, the new framework DistClusTree defines the effectiveness of global clustering at a central site as a cost function of communication and degree of cluster approximation. This means the framework is able to monitor changes in local sites and strategically send updates to the central site. In this way, communication is only triggered between local sites and the central site whenever the quality of clustering degrades beyond a threshold.

To the best of our knowledge, this is the *first attempt* of a distributed multidimensional stream clustering framework that combines index data structure for summarizing and maintaining local microclusters, and online tracking for the monitoring and maintenance of global clustering.

As a summary, our main contributions of the paper are as follows:

- We extend ClusTree into a distributed framework DistClusTree.
- We propose adaptable solutions to select local microcluster summaries to be sent to the central site. The central site then refines the quality of clustering according to real-time network traffic and degree of privacy.
- We model the monitoring and maintenance of distributed clustering as online tracking and extend a 1-to-1 multidimensional online tracking scheme into m-to-1 (m local sites with one central site).
- We demonstrate through extensive experiments the performance of our framework in balancing communication cost and clustering quality.

2   Related Work

Due to space limit, here we only briefly review the typical distributed clustering algorithms related to our work. In [2], two types of continuous distributed clustering algorithms were proposed: local and global. The algorithm is formulated based on k-center clustering algorithm. The main objective in k-center is to minimize the maximum radius/diameter of the clusters. In their local solutions, each local site builds and keeps its local model, and only updates are sent to the central site. In their global algorithm, a global model is created iteratively in a central site by message passing between local sites and the global site. Then the global model is sent to all local sites and in this way all sites have the same view of the clustering model. Local sites insert their data points into the global clustering and continuously send their updates to the central site. The central site decides whether it needs to recompute the global model and sends the new clusters to the local sites. As in most of the distributed clustering settings, distributed clustering results are compared with their centralized counterpart.

A distributed extension of the Expectation Maximization (EM) algorithm called CluDistream is proposed in [12]. The authors introduced a framework for clustering distributed data streams in the presence of noisy and incomplete data. The underlying distribution of data has been learnt by maximizing the likelihood of the data clusters. Local sites monitor the current model till they could not describe a new chunk of data. Then a clustering is performed to account for the changing data distribution. In this way, they reduced communication cost by just sending updates from local sites to the central site. In [5], centralized density based clusterings algorithm (DBSCAN) [3] was extended to the distributed model. Each local site performs a clustering on its own data and sends its representatives to the central site. Local representatives are grouped into each other to represent the final clustering in the global site. The work shows that the results of clustering in centralized and distributed model are significantly close to each other. There are some other works that have addressed clustering distributed data streams such as [6,7] and there is a recent survey [9] on distributed clustering of ubiquitous data streams.

3   Preliminaries

In this section we explain in more detail: (i) the ClusTree approach adopted for local clustering in DistClusTree; (ii) the underlying R-tree data structure in which local cluster summaries are stored and maintained.

ClusTree- ClusTree is introduced in [8] as a stream clustering algorithm with the ability of anytime clustering. ClusTree consists of two phases: online and offline. In the online phase, it collects summary of data in the form of a vector of number of data points (N), linear sum (LS), and Squared Sum (SS) of data points – the *Cluster Feature Vector (CFV)* considered as a microcluster. Storing these summaries instead of raw data helps to save space. Also, these summaries are sufficient to compute statistical parameters such as mean, variance, centroid, radius, diameter for further off-line clustering. Updating *CFVs* is easy and computationally fast because of their additivity and subtractive properties. ClusTree uses an index tree data structure, essentially an R-tree, to maintain collected summary statistics (i.e. the microclusters). The idea is to build a hierarchy of microclusters at different levels of granularity. This data structure accelerates the process of searching the right microclusters for inserting new data points as they arrive. When a new data point arrives, it descends the index tree till arriving the leaf node which contains a microcluster that has the minimum distance to the inserted data point. From time to time microclusters are transfered to a disk to be kept for further offline processing. For example a data partition clustering like k-means or DBSCAN is performed on microclusters to form final clusters in an offline phase. The outputs of the offline phase are macroclusters whose size is relatively small compared to the entire data stream.

R-tree- ClusTree leverages an R-tree [4] data structure to maintain the collected summary statistics of data (i.e., *CFVs*) online. R-tree is a tree data structure used as a spatial index. R-tree clusters multidimensional data based on their proximity. It represents nearby data objects with their minimum bounding boxes in different levels of the tree. The main goal of this data structure is to group adjacent data objects and represent them with their Minimum Bounding Rectangle (MBR) in the next higher level of the tree. Since all data objects fall within this MBR, a query can be answered if it intersects any bounding rectangle. Aggregation/Summarization of objects occurs at the higher levels of the tree while the root represents aggregation of all data objects. From a clustering point of view, descending the tree reduces within-cluster sum of squares error. The within-cluster sum of squares measures the variability of the data points within each cluster. Usually a cluster with a small sum of squares is more compact than a cluster that has a large sum of squares. This translates to an increased granularity of clustering at the leaf level of the tree where data objects are indexed. This can also be seen as an increasingly coarser approximation of data distribution as we move up in the tree.

4   DistClusTree

In the framework, m local sites are distributed in a network and each of them receives and incrementally clusters a continuous stream of data, possibly with an infinite length. A master/central site instead clusters and maintains the union of the local site data to produce the final global clustering result. We are particularly interested in devising mechanisms that allow local sites to communicate with the central site efficiently. Leveraging summarized but still informative data to be sent to the central site for global clustering instead of sending the actual massive data points is a key approach to reduce communication cost and preserve privacy. Moreover, a communication can be triggered between local sites and the central site every time a new data object arrives at each local site so as to update clusters maintained at the central site. This poses an expensive communication rounds of $O(n)$, where n is the total number of arrived data points. Therefore, a plausible way to balance the communicate cost and clustering quality is to trigger communication periodically and only send the selected updated summaries/representatives to the central site. Our studies shows the choice of proper local representatives has a significant impact on communication cost and central clustering result. The representatives form a summary of local models at a given time snapshot. The summary is sent to the central site and kept being locally updated as new data points (stream snapshots) arrive.

In essence, DistClusTree consists of four stages: (1) Continuous local clustering; (2) Extracting local representatives; (3) Distributed microcluster tracking; and (4) Maintaining global clusters. These are described in detail in the following.

1- Continuous Local Clustering. Every local site clusters its data incrementally with the ClusTree approach. Summaries of data are collected as CFVs and maintained dynamically in an R tree. In this way micro-clusters are maintained in various levels of the tree and in different resolutions (i.e. coarser microclusters are located in higher levels of the tree). Therefore, the root node in the ClusTree contains the broadest view of all microclusters at the current snapshot, while the leaf nodes include all of the fine-grained micro-clusters. Such hierarchically summarized organization is shown in Fig. 1.

2- Extracting Local Representatives. To extract local representatives, we propose two simple but effective and adaptable approaches: Naive-DistClust and DistClust.

Naive-DistClust- Local representatives from different levels of the tree are extracted regularly (i.e. at every ΔT time period) to be communicated to the

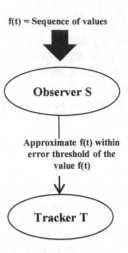

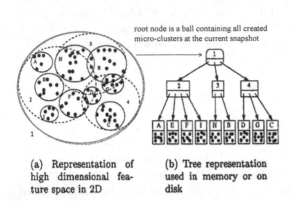

(a) Representation of high dimensional feature space in 2D

(b) Tree representation used in memory or on disk

Fig. 1. The local ClusTree summary in DistClusTree (source [10]).

Fig. 2. One-to-one online tracking.

central/global site. This approach is adjustable based on the network traffic (i.e. the frequency of data arrivals), degree of privacy, and required quality of central clustering. Depending on traffic and required quality of clustering, local sites can send created micro-clusters at different levels of the tree to the central site. For maximum quality, local sites should send all created micro-clusters at their leaf level. While in a heavily loaded network (e.g., peak hours), more compressed trees (i.e. at most the root level) with some sacrifice of clustering quality can be sent to the central site. This translates to reducing the overall communication cost by sending more coarse local micro-clusters from higher levels of the tree to the central site.

DistClust- A further way to reduce communication cost is for every tree node only sending statistical summaries of its contained microclusters to the central site. For example, in an R-tree only with 3-fan outs (i.e. the number of entries in each node where each entry represents one summarized micro-cluster), at level 1 (considering level 0 as the root level), we have 3 subtrees each containing 3 micro-clusters. This means we have 9 micro-clusters in total at level 1. Instead of sending all these 9 entries to the central site, we could choose to send only the median of the entries from each node, thereby reducing communication cost to one-third. Next, we discuss in detail how local representatives (i.e. the selected microclusters) are tracked and sent with an on-line tracking algorithm.

3- Distributed Microcluster Tracking. We first give a brief introduction on online tracking and then illustrate how we formulate the global clustering in DistClusTree as an online tracking problem. In the conventional online tracking, a pair of observer and tracker communicates with each other. Observer observes values of a function f over time and keeps inform the tracker these values time to time as shown in Fig. 2. However, determination of a strategy that minimizes communication cost is the main issue in online tracking problems. A naive solution is that observer sends every observed value to the tracker. This leads to a heavy communication. To minimize the communication cost, an error threshold is generally introduced. This means observers only communicate with the tracker whenever a value of $f(t_{now})$ exceeds a predefined error threshold Δ from the last communicated value $f(t_{last})$. We extend the multidimensional one-to-one online tracking framework presented in [11] that only works when there is an observer and a tracker. It is not designed for the distributed m-to-one communication where there are multiple observers and a central tracker. The one-to-one online tracking algorithm divides the entire tracking period into rounds and denotes A_{opt} as the offline optimal algorithm. A round is started by initializing a set $S = S_0$ which contains all possible points that might be sent by A_{opt} in its last communication. In a while loop, a median of S is calculated and sent to the tracker. If $\|f(t_{now}) - f(t_{last})\| \geq \beta\Delta$, where $\beta = 1/(1 + \epsilon)$ and Δ represents the threshold error, then S is updated as $S \leftarrow S \cap Ball(f(t_{now}), \Delta)$, where $f(t_{now})$ is the center of Ball and Δ is its radius in d-dimensional space. A round is terminated when S becomes empty. The online tracking algorithm is represented in Algorithm 1.

1. Let $P = Ball(f(t_{now}), \beta\Delta)$;
2. **while** $(\omega_{max}(p)) \geq \epsilon\Delta$ **do**
   Let $g(t_{now})$ be the centroid of P;
   send $g(t_{now})$ to tracker;
   wait until $\|f(t_{now}) - g(t_{last})\| \geq \beta\Delta$
   $S \leftarrow S \cap Ball(f(t_{now}), \Delta)$
   end

Algorithm 1. *One round of d-dimensional tracking*

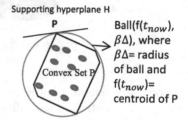

Fig. 3. Convex set P is covered by $Ball(f(t_{now}, \beta\Delta)$.

We model our clustering algorithm based on the above online tracking algorithm. First we show how we can keep track of micro-clusters assuming there is one local site and one central site, and then we extend our algorithm from one local site to multiple local sites as shown in Fig. 4 (i.e., distributed) that they communicate with a central site in a synchronous mode. We explain with the Definition 2 and Lemma 4 from [11] below to illustrate our tracking model.

Definition 2 *(Directional Width).* For a set P of points in R^d, and a unit direction μ, the directional widths of P in direction μ is $\omega_\mu(P) = max_{p \in P} \langle \mu, p \rangle - min_{p \in P} \langle \mu, p \rangle$, where $\langle \mu, p \rangle$ is the standard inner product.

For simplicity, suppose a given set of points form a convex set P, and the centroid of P is the intersection of hyperplanes that divide P into two equal parts. This convex set has minimum and maximum directional width as $\omega_{min}(p)$, $\omega_{max}(p)$, respectively.

Lemma 4. For any convex set P, if H is any supporting hyperplane of P at $p \in \partial P$, that is, H contains p and P is contained in one of the two halfspaces bounded by H. Then there is a ball B with radius $\beta\Delta$ such that H is tangent to B at p and B contains P as shown in Fig. 3.

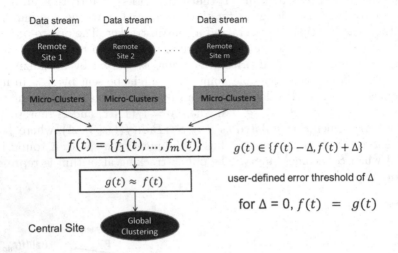

Fig. 4. The global DistClusTree framework.

Local site acts as an observer that sends an approximation of created microclusters to a central site at different time snapshots. Assume that error threshold Δ is determined based on the maximum distance between centroids of two clusters at two consecutive snapshots of t_i and t_{i+1}, where $C_{t_i} = f(t_{last})$ and $C_{t_{i+1}} = f(t_{now})$ are the centroids of previous and current root node. According to [11], a convex set P in our local ClusTree is a set of microclusters taken at snapshot t_{now}. Based on Lemma 4, a ball containing P is the root node at snapshot t_{now}. Following this, we initialize P with the root node, and then centroid of the current root (i.e. as a representative of all microclusters) is computed as $g(t_{now})$ and sent to the tracker. In the next snapshot, if the absolute euclidean distance between the centroid of the previous root node and the current root node is within the predefined error threshold, then there is no communication. Otherwise, the intersection of two roots (two balls) is computed. If the maximal directional width of this intersection is greater than $\beta\Delta$, then a communication between local site and the central site is triggered and the centroid of the intersection is sent to the central site. Otherwise, this round is finished and the next new round is triggered. Different scenarios that may happen between the last communicated root node and the new root node at two different snapshots of t_1 and t_2 are presented in Fig. 5 (a–c).

4- Maintaining Global Clusters. For simplicity, we only enhance the tracking framework from 1-to-1 to m-to-1 sites in a synchronous manner. Each local site

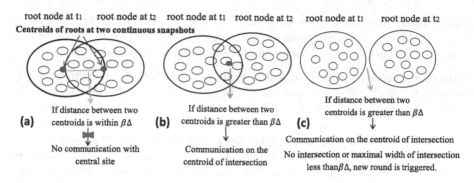

Fig. 5. Different scenarios to trigger a communication between a local site and a central site to update the global clustering.

keeps track of its local representatives in periodical time snapshots and if any threshold breaking occurs at a local site, then this site simply sends its updates to the central site along with all other updates from other local sites. As depicted in Fig. 4, local sites communicate with a central site if $f_1(t_1) - f_1(t_2)$ are within some error threshold. After sending updates to the central site, central site does a global clustering using k-means over the union of all received microclusters from local sites. Local sites incrementally send their updates to the central site to keep global clusters updated. By receiving regular updates, the central site incrementally keep global clusters updated.

5   Experiments

We implement DistClusTree under Massive Online Analysis (MOA) [1] and evaluated the distributed algorithms based on a synthetic dataset. The dataset is generated using Gaussian distribution with varying number of attributes and classes. Data points are randomly and equally divided among sites and for the central clustering, we use the union of the local points. Our experiments focus on clustering quality and the communication cost of distributed clustering considering their dependency on different parameters such as number of sites, the accuracy ϵ, granularity of local representatives and runtime of distributed clustering in comparison with centralized clustering. To assess our framework, we ran ClusTree on each local site and then collected all representatives of local sites w.r.t the demanded granularity of local clusterings (i.e., different levels of local trees) and then performed a global clustering on these representatives. We executed all the experiments on the same machine and reported all the results as average of 10 runs of our algorithms. We compare clustering quality of our distributed clustering (i.e., DistClusTree) against its centralized counterpart, i.e. ClusTree. As mentioned in [5], different studies have evaluated their algorithms based on characteristics of their distributed clustering algorithm in variety of ways and the majority of studies compares their proposed distributed clustering algorithm against their centralized counterpart [9]. Therefore, we compared the result of our distributed clustering algorithms to a central clustering of the n data points when all n data points are clustered using ClusTree in local sites and applying k-means on top of the microclusters created at leaf level of the tree.

Clustering quality - We measure quality of clustering by defining Mean Squared Error (MSE), and also using within-cluster sum of squares error. As the baseline, firstly we sent all microclusters created at the leaf level to the central site and applied k-means to calculate cluster centroids. Secondly we sent microclusters of each level of the local trees and find cluster centroids for each level using k-means. To calculate MSE, we take the average of euclidean distances between cluster centroids obtained from the last level of tree in ClusTree (i.e., centralized model) and every level of the local trees (DistClust/Naive-DistClust). As it can be seen in Fig. 6(A), MSE is reduced by descending tree since microclusters with smaller within cluster sum squared error are located at the lower level of the tree which impacts on quality of clustering in the central site. We compared MSE of $k = 5$ centroids at different levels of the tree for both DistClust and Naive-DistClust. In the latter, we send all created microclusters from different levels of trees while in DistClust we only send a mean of microclusters of each node of tree. That is the reason MSE between ClusTree and NaiveClust is less than MSE between ClusTree and DistClust. The MSE difference between both distributed algorithms is getting higher at the lower levels of tree since granularity increases at the bottom levels and sending less microclusters impacts on calculating right centroids and consequently on clustering quality. We ran the experiments with 3 number of fans out at each node of R-tree as referring to [8], 3 fans out is the best number of entries (#microclusters at each node) in terms of space and distance computation.

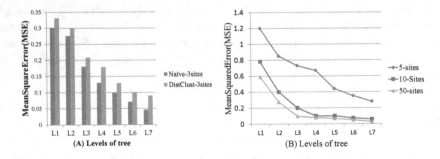

Fig. 6. (A) Comparison of clustering quality of Naive-DistClust and DisClust with ClusTree on different levels of tree, when number of sites = 6 and number of entries = 3; (B) MSE comparison of varying number of sites: 5, 10, 50.

On the other hand, as you can see in Fig. 6, MSE is reduced by descending the tree. The reason is that purity of microclusters at lower levels of tree is increased which causes to reduce MSE between cluster centroids obtained from upper and lower levels of the tree. We test our framework for different numbers of sites 5,

10, and 50. Although in all plots in Fig. 6(B) MSE is reduced by descending the tree, reducing number of sites reduces quality of clustering because we send less micro-clusters which impacts on final quality of clustering at the central site.

Communication cost - We calculated communication cost in terms of number of transfered microclusters from each level of the tree as *communication ratio* $= (compressed tree/uncompressed tree) \times number of sites$.

In our formula, communication ratio is calculated as the ratio of compressed tree to uncompressed tree. Uncompressed tree is a full multi-way tree with maximum number of levels. Maximum number of level is predefined by the user or local memory limit. Compressed tree is a full multi-way tree with less number of levels compared to the uncompressed one. The lowest communication ratio is the ratio of the minimum number of levels (maximum compression, i.e., root level of tree) to the maximum number of levels. Communication ratio also depends on the number of entries in each node. For instance, in a 3-way full tree, level 0 which is root level has 1 node, level 1 has 3 nodes, level 2 has 9 nodes and in general for n-multi-way tree, the number of node in level n is calculated as m^n, where m represents number of ways in the tree.

We compare communication cost of different levels of the tree for different number of entries at each node of the R-tree. In Fig. 7, we compare the communication cost for two different number of entries, 3 and 4 in our two proposed distributed clustering algorithms. By sending median of microclusters at each node in DistClust, we reduce communication cost to $1/k$, where k is the number of entries. We reduce communication cost to one third with Distclust for the choice of three entries in all levels of tree. This reduction is obvious in the lower levels of the tree where more granular microclusters are required.

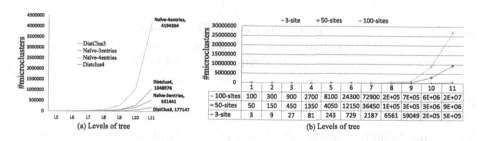

Fig. 7. (a) Effect of number of entries on communication cost; (b) Communication cost of DistClust for different number of sites when number of entries $= 3$.

Figure 7(b) represents the communication cost in terms of number of microclusters for 3,50 and 100 sites. The number of entries in all 3 experiments has been set to 3 and the height of tree is 11. As it can be clearly seen that communication cost depends on the number of sites and different levels of the tree. To have more granular clusters we need to send microclusters at the lower level of tree causing to increase communication cost exponentially. While by sending representatives from upper levels of trees we reduce communication cost significantly and still have good quality clustering as demonstrated in the above experiments.

Effect of error threshold Δ - We evaluated the effect of varying error threshold on communication cost. Error threshold is the difference between centroid of the new microcluster at snapshot t_i and the previous transmitted at snapshot t_{i-1}. As error threshold is increased the communication cost is decreased since we send less number of updates to the central site by increasing euclidean difference between centroids of previous and current snapshots. The communication cost at the lower levels of the tree is higher than the upper levels of tree as shown in Fig. 8 for L1 as root level and level 6. However, increasing error threshold reduces quality of clustering.

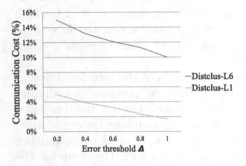

Fig. 8. Effect of different Δ values on communication cost, level 1 and 6, 10 sites.

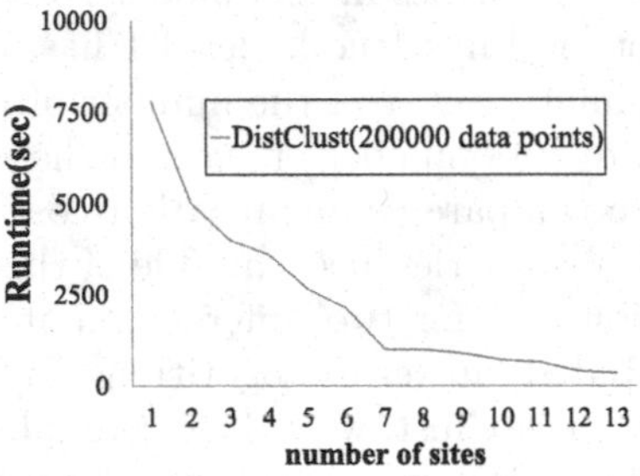

Fig. 9. Runtime for central and distributed clustering with varying number of sites.

Runtime - In Fig. 9, the runtime of DistClusTree is shown. As number of sites are increasing, the distributed approach performs much better than a single clustering algorithm applied to the complete data set of 200k data points.

6   Conclusion

We extended ClusTree into DistClusTree, a comprehensive distributed framework for stream clustering. The framework leverages both spatial index summaries and online tracking for balancing communication cost and clustering quality. We demonstrated in experiments that DistClusTree efficiently produces clusters as good as its centralized version. DistClusTree is able to reduce communication cost significantly and it is easily configurable in practice according to the requested clustering quality. For future work, we plan to carry out more insightful theoretical analysis and justification of DistClusTree.

References

1. Bifet, A., Holmes, G., Kirkby, R., Pfahringer, B.: MOA: massive online analysis. J. Mach. Learn. Res. **11**, 1601–1604 (2010)
2. Cormode, G., Muthukrishnan, S., Zhuang, W.: Conquering the divide: continuous clustering of distributed data streams. In: 2007 IEEE 23rd International Conference on Data Engineering, pp. 1036–1045, April 2007
3. Ester, M., Kriegel, H.-P., Sander, J., Xu, X.: A density-based algorithm for discovering clusters a density-based algorithm for discovering clusters in large spatial databases with noise. In: Proceedings of the Second International Conference on Knowledge Discovery and Data Mining, KDD 1996, pp. 226–231. AAAI Press (1996)
4. Guttman, A.: R-trees: a dynamic index structure for spatial searching, vol. 14. ACM (1984)
5. Januzaj, E., Kriegel, H.-P., Pfeifle, M.: Towards effective and efficient distributed clustering. In: Workshop on Clustering Large Data Sets ICDM, pp. 49–58 (2003)
6. Kargupta, H., Huang, W., Sivakumar, K., Johnson, E.: Distributed clustering using collective principal component analysis. Knowl. Inf. Syst. **3**, 2001 (1999)
7. Klusch, M., Lodi, S., Moro, G.: Distributed clustering based on sampling local density estimates. In: Proceedings of the 18th International Joint Conference on Artificial Intelligence, IJCAI 2003, pp. 485–490. Morgan Kaufmann Publishers Inc., San Francisco (2003)
8. Kranen, P., Assent, I., Baldauf, C., Seidl, T.: The clustree: indexing micro-clusters for anytime stream mining. Knowl. Inf. Syst. **29**(2), 249–272 (2011)
9. Rodrigues, P.P., Gama, J.: Distributed clustering of ubiquitous data streams. Wiley Interdisc. Rev. Data Mining Knowl. Disc. **4**(01), 38–54 (2014)
10. White, D.A., Jain, R.: Similarity indexing with the SS-tree. In: Proceedings of the Twelfth International Conference on Data Engineering, pp. 516–523, February 1996
11. Yi, K., Zhang, Q.: Multidimensional online tracking. ACM Trans. Algorithms (TALG) **8**(2), 12 (2012)
12. Zhou, A., Cao, F., Yan, Y., Sha, C., He, X.: Distributed data stream clustering: a fast EM-based approach. In: 2007 IEEE 23rd International Conference on Data Engineering, pp. 736–745, April 2007

Short Research Papers

Mobile Application Based Heavy Vehicle Fatigue Compliance in Australian Operations

Luke Mirowski[✉] and Joel Scanlan

School of Technology, Engineering and Design,
University of Tasmania (UTAS), Hobart, Australia
{Luke.Mirowski, Joel.Scanlan}@utas.edu.au

Abstract. The Australian National Heavy Vehicle Regulator (NHVR) defines the rules for fatigue management in heavy haulage trucking operations. The rules place restrictions on total work and minimum rest hours, and are aimed at regulating the potential for fatigue risk amongst drivers. This paper presents a performance-based fatigue management system based on driver fatigue data stored in simple mobile databases and deployed via Android smart phones. The system funded by WorkSafe Tasmania and entitled, Logistics Fatigue Manager (LFM), was evaluated with a cohort of heavy haulage drivers in Australian forestry. The correlation between driver fatigue estimates and actual sleep hours (recorded using FitBits) is confirmed, and is also supported through driver interviews. The benefit is that management of fatigue risk could be more tailored to individual drivers opening up efficiency gains across supply chains.

Keywords: Data entry · Mobile databases · Data heuristics

1 Introduction

This research project funded by WorkSafe Tasmania aligns with compliance requirements of the Australian Heavy Vehicle Driver Fatigue laws from the National Heavy Vehicle Regulator (NHVR) [1], which stipulates all stakeholders in a supply chain which uses heavy haulage trucks must comply with standard, basic and advanced fatigue management rules.

There are two elements to the legislation: regulated work and rest hours, and work diary reporting; and secondly, a general duty element. Firstly, the laws regulate work and rest hours for heavy vehicle drivers. All parties in the supply chain are legally responsible for preventing drivers from becoming fatigued (i.e. tired through lack of rest). Secondly, all reasonable steps must be taken to enable drivers to manage and recover from fatigue, which means: drivers must stop if fatigued; operators and schedulers planning a driver's rest breaks; loading managers ensuring queuing is managed to allow for efficient truck movement; and contracts requiring drivers to break the law are illegal. The current approaches are paper based with data residing in paper based and offline storage.

The aim of this research project is to trial and evaluate a performance-based approach to heavy haulage driver fatigue management that evaluates individual driver fatigue, and improves safety standards by integrating heavy vehicle fatigue

© Springer International Publishing AG, part of Springer Nature 2018
J. Wang et al. (Eds.): ADC 2018, LNCS 10837, pp. 303–308, 2018.
https://doi.org/10.1007/978-3-319-92013-9_24

management regulations, transport scheduling requirements and driver rostering principles in an electronic system based on simple mobile databases, apps and fatigue risk models.

The system developed in the project has been primarily developed for and deployed within Tasmania's forestry industry heavy haulage operations to test the feasibility of the technology and the accuracy. The objective has been to first build a technologically innovative fatigue risk management system that is capable of assisting drivers to comply and exceed safety standards within the Australian forestry industry and transportation sector. The software, Logistics Fatigue Manager (LFM), and all the tools it comprises of, are available online at www.logisticsfatiguemanager.com.au.

2 Background

Heavy vehicles are the predominant transport mode in use in Australia for land based freight tasks [2]. Sustainability of these transport operations, from a supply chain management and logistics perspective, relies on finding appropriate levels and combinations of many operational factors, all of which impact on safety and cost. The optimal combination of factors is difficult to achieve as factors are selected to minimise cost in preference to fatigue risk management which often requires stoppages and breaks in driving.

Australian fatigue laws now include all the personnel and all the parties involved in the chain of responsibility to be made liable for fatigue if they influence the driver's activities. This challenging when data resides in paper based and offline storage.

'Standard Hours' guidelines focuses on having a minimum rest (driver must take a break for at least 30 min in 5 h interval during their work, for example) and having a maximum upper-limit on work hours, they also provide basic record keeping requirements which are suitable for the most of the businesses but which are paper based [3, 4].

Under the current paper based system, for productivity of heavy vehicle truck drivers, one of the major challenges is the truck driver's hours of work are reduced which will lead to significantly less payment for a truck driver. Whereas the truck driver may be capable of driving 14 h, the regulations mean the truck driver, under a standard hour's operation, can only drive 12 h in a day. This means the truck driver is working 2 h less per day, 14 h less per week [5].

To resolve these challenges, this research applies a performance based approach to fatigue assessment by way of an electronic system supported by a mobile apps, databases and applications. It leverages data captured through a mobile app and data stored on the phone to calculate a driver's individual fatigue risk score.

3 Method

The research consists of two parts: development of the performance-based fatigue system, and a trial/evaluation period spanning two phases.

3.1 Software Development

The software tool, an android mobile application (the 'LFM for the Driver' mobile application), was installed on driver electronic tablet devices. The software eliminates identified deficiencies in the physical work-diary formats being used currently by drivers by providing a more efficient method to capture, collect and distribute data:

- Driver reading/writing deficiencies: the software enables drivers to record work and rest periods on their tablets using a simple button interface.
- Cost of specialised equipment: the software is capable of operating on any standard Android mobile phone or tablet, utilising its inbuilt GPS, Wi-Fi.
- Fatigue assessment: the software runs a fatigue score calculator in the background, which keeps a history of the driver's fatigue level based on data captured.

The simple mobile database underpinning the system enables low-cost localised monitoring, management and support for drivers whilst an online dashboard and database allows data to be shared with supervisors and managers. Options in the software allow for mediation of access to database data across the organisation and supply chain.

3.2 Data Collection

Heavy haulage truck drivers from Australian forestry volunteered from several companies to be part of the trial and evaluation of the LFM system.

Phase One
The drivers used an Android tablet to record estimates of their sleep periods in 24 and 48-h periods before commencing a working shift with data stored locally and remotely. They also recorded the periods and time of rest along with then vehicle's odometer readings in the 'LFM for the Driver' app.

Phase Two
The methodology conducted for collating data remained largely the same. However, it was supplemented by the use of the FitBit device as secondary option of verifying driver sleep information.

4 Results and Discussion

Both quantitative and qualitative data was collected from the drivers involved in the trial and evaluation of the system across the phases. These are now reported.

4.1 Quantitative Results

Estimation of Previous Sleep Before Work
The graph in Fig. 1 represents information from the LFM app that correlates the drivers' estimated sleep hours and the start of shift fatigue score, confirming drivers are good at estimating their prior sleep hours through the app.

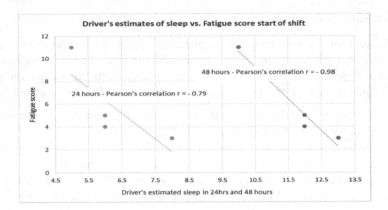

Fig. 1. Driver's 24-h & 48-h sleep estimation vs. fatigue scores before work.

The findings confirmed through correlation that the driver's sleep estimates and the sleep hours recorded on the FitBit device were similar. The data confirmed that the individual drivers estimated their time spent asleep with a fair amount of accuracy, proving the reliability of a fatigue score rating collected through the app.

Managing Fatigue During Work Periods
Figure 2 confirms the relationship between the drivers' work and rest activity and dynamic fatigue score calculated throughout day 1 (as an example). Dynamic fatigue levels increase when mandated rest periods are not taken during a working shift. Driving for five and a half hours continuously without a rest period increases the dynamic fatigue score. The driver then worked for an additional 4½ h without rest. The graph registers a significant increase in the dynamic fatigue score. This confirms the electronic system can model work and rest from the drivers' data, with a fatigue risk model score, reflecting driver accumulation and recovery from fatigue.

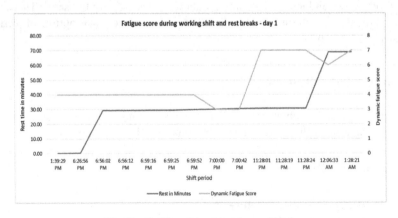

Fig. 2. Fatigue & rest breaks – shift 1.

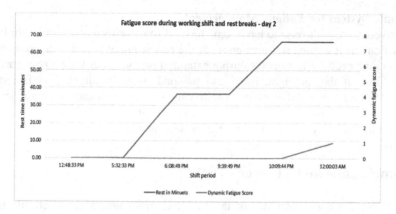

Fig. 3. Fatigue & rest breaks – shift 2.

Figure 3 demonstrates the relationship between the drivers' work and rest activity and dynamic fatigue score throughout the working of day 2. The dynamic fatigue score at the start of the working shift was low. At the end of the working shift the fatigue score began to increase because (a) the shift was 12 h and hence longer, and (b) the rest taken at the end of a shift did not compensate for the extended hours. Again, this confirms that the electronic system can model fatigue risk interrelationships.

The data for day three (not shown) was similar to day two, at the start of the working shift the dynamic fatigue score is low. This low fatigue score is maintained throughout the day by (a) taking the mandated rest periods and, (b) taking the rest in the stipulated intervals. The data for the fourth day (not shown) shows that the driver is set into a routine and which continues to confirm the above relationships.

For the trial and evaluation periods, most of the data from across all the days again confirms correlation of fatigue scores with work and rest hours in the electronic system. Hence a simple mobile app and collected data combined with a fatigue risk model is an effective approach to capturing performance based fatigue risk information.

4.2   Qualitative Results

Trial participants were also interviewed during the project to establish qualitative factors to successfully managing fatigue risk through the LFM system and these are now reported.

Self-management of Fatigue
Most drivers considered themselves to be the best judge of when they felt fatigued during the work shift. This misconception of self-regulating their rest breaks arose from their personal interest and that of the principal contractors. Though drivers complied with mandated rest breaks to a fair extent, they did take the liberty of self-managing fatigue during a shift. The system was confirmed as helpful to this process by the drivers as distinct from a paper diary through localized fatigue risk management via their smart phones (and the data stored locally to them).

Electronic System for Fatigue Management

Most drivers were not averse to have some form of monitoring and reporting for fatigue management, as it created self-awareness of the rest required and also demonstrated to employers the need for rest breaks during extended periods of driving. Other variables, such as time of day or night, route and payload, were highlighted as factors that impacted fatigue levels and essential to achieving accurate estimates of fatigue levels in any assessment period. As these factors were collected using the LFM system, drivers perceived the LFM system to be robust at collecting fatigue data.

5   Conclusions and Further Work

In this paper the main outcomes of the trial and evaluation of an electronic fatigue management system, entitled Logistics Fatigue Manager (LFM), were reported. This project was funded by WorkSafe Tasmania.

During the project, quantitative data was collated on heavy vehicle driver fatigue in a forestry supply chain, using the Logistics Fatigue Manager (LFM) system. Correlated results from the LFM system and FitBits confirmed that drivers could make reliable estimates of their sleep hours from which fatigue risk scores could be calculated.

Qualitative interviews were conducted to contextualize and support the findings. There were unanimously favorable response to the electronic system and active participation in feedback for future improvements to the electronic system.

The results suggest that simple mobile-deployed databases and apps combined with fatigue risk models could generate effective data collection opportunities to shift fatigue risk management in Australian heavy haulage operations from compliance-based to performance based modes of operation.

This in turn could increase accuracy and speed of reporting, as well as create opportunities to focus on managing individual 'customised' driver risk profiles.

Further work may consider options for the widespread collection and collation of heavy haulage driver data through smart phones and mobile databases for low-cost and performance-based management of heavy haulage driver fatigue risks.

References

1. NHVR: Basic Fatigue Management (2016). https://www.nhvr.gov.au/safety-accreditation-compliance/fatigue-management/work-and-rest-requirements/standard-hours
2. Department of Infrastructure and Regional Development-Australian Government: Freightline 1—Australia freight transport overview (2014)
3. NHVR: Electronic Work Diary (2016). https://www.nhvr.gov.au/safety-accreditation-compliance/fatigue-management/electronic-work-diaries-ewds
4. NHVR: Chain of Responsibility (2015). https://www.nhvr.gov.au/safety-accreditation-compliance/chain-of-responsibility
5. Goel, A., et al.: Truck driver scheduling in Australia. Comput. Oper. Res. **39**, 1122–1132 (2012)

Statistical Discretization of Continuous Attributes Using Kolmogorov-Smirnov Test

Hadi Mohammadzadeh Abachi[1]([✉]), Saeid Hosseini[1,2],
Mojtaba Amiri Maskouni[1], Mohammadreza Kangavari[1],
and Ngai-Man Cheung[2]

[1] Iran University of Science and Technology, Tehran, Iran
{hadi_mohammadzadeh,amiri_m,kangavari}@comp.iust.ac.ir
saeid.hosseini@uq.net.au
[2] Singapore University of Technology and Design, Singapore, Singapore
ngaiman_cheung@sutd.edu.sg

Abstract. Unlike unsupervised discretization methods that use simple rules to discretize continuous attributes through a low time complexity which mostly depends on sorting procedure, supervised discretization algorithms take the class label of attributes into consideration to achieve high accuracy. Supervised discretization process on continuous features encounters two significant challenges. Firstly, noisy class labels affect the effectiveness of discretization. Secondly, due to the high computational time of supervised algorithms in large-scale datasets, time complexity would rely on discretizing stage rather than sorting procedure. Accordingly, to address the challenges, we devise a statistical unsupervised method named as SUFDA. The SUFDA aims to produce discrete intervals through decreasing differential entropy of the normal distribution with a low temporal complexity and high accuracy. The results show that our unsupervised system obtains a better effectiveness compared to other discretization baselines in large-scale datasets.

Keywords: Discretization · Kolmogorov-Smirnov · Data mining
Data reduction · Naïve Bayes

1 Introduction

Data preprocessing as a main stage in knowledge extraction and data mining, includes components such as data transformation, cleaning, and data reduction. Discretization, as one of the basic data reduction procedures, maps the data from a huge range of continuous values to a greatly shrunk subset of discrete values. A discretization scheme partitions a sorted numerical attribute into k discrete and disjoint intervals denoted as $\eta = \{[s_0, s_1], (s_1, s_2), \cdots (s_{k-1}, s_k]\}$; where s_0 and s_k are respectively the minimum and the maximum values of the numerical attribute. Subject to different applications, the discretization methods can be classified into various twin categories including global vs. local, top-down vs. bottom-up, direct vs. incremental, static vs. dynamic, and finally supervised vs. unsupervised [3].

As a matter of fact, prior supervised as well as unsupervised approaches face certain challenges. Most unsupervised methods are so naïve that may not lead to effective results. Additionally, where the irrelevant data exist, outliers may not be handled in an appropriate manner and consequently can affect the accuracy negatively. To address these challenges, supervised models employ class information. However, required class information is at times noisy and even inaccessible. Moreover, due to the high computational complexity and additional statistical criterions, the efficiency of supervised algorithms in large-scale datasets and complex environments is significantly flattened. To this end, in this paper, we devise a new unsupervised approach that not only promotes the effectiveness, but also reduces the complexities involved in supervised approaches.

2   Related Work

Discretization. Many discretization techniques have been proposed in the literature that can be used in several applications such as: association mining algorithms, induction rules, clinical datasets and recommendation systems [4]. Equal width (EWD) and frequency discretization(EFD) are *Unsupervised Methods* that divide the observed samples between s_{min} and s_{max} into k equally sized intervals or into k intervals so that each interval includes approximately the same number of instances. Here k is a user predefined value. The complexity of such methods is $O(n * log(n))$, that only relies on the sorting algorithm.

Entropy minimization discretization (Fayyad) [2], is the essential *Supervised Method.* This greedy algorithm uses the class information entropy of possible intervals to select the boundaries for discretization. Considering all possible cut points, it starts finding a single cut point that minimizes the entropy of intervals. The complexity of the Fayyad's method, assuming m as the number of classes, is $O(m * n * log(n))$ which dominates the sorting complexity. The supervised algorithms require a high computational time to discretize numerical attributes which is tangible in large scale datasets. Our work relates itself to the literature through proposing a non-parametric unsupervised discretization algorithm which provides accurate and effective results.

3   Problem Statement

3.1   Preliminary Concepts

Definition 1. *In statistics, the Kolmogorov_ Smirnov a non-parametric test is used to compare a group of samples with a reference probability distribution (one-sample KS test). The Kolmogorov_ Smirnov statistic test calculates the distance between the empirical distribution function of the sample and the cumulative distribution function of the reference distribution.*

$$D_n = \sup_x |F_n(x) - F(x)| \tag{1}$$

3.2 Problem Definition

Given a dataset S consisting N examples and M attributes (features), where the attributes can be either numerical (M_c) or nominal (M_d), we try to discretize numerical attributes (M_c) based on one-sample Kolmogorov-Smirnov.

Assuming that numerical attributes are distributed normally, we define an initial normal distribution as a reference for every feature and set the related parameters such as mean and standard deviation. The next step is to define a null hypothesis and try to reject it by comparing the calculated $pValue$ to a predefined threshold. Note that, the $pValue$ is the probability of getting a test statistic result at least as high as the one that was actually spotted, assuming that the null hypothesis is true. In discretization procedure, splitting a feature as an interval to sub intervals is associated with rejecting or accepting the null hypothesis.

4 Proposed Algorithm

In this section, we further elucidate our proposed **Statistical Unsupervised Feature Discretization Algorithm (SUFDA)**. The proposed model in this paper is local, top-down, static, incremental, and unsupervised. Our model independently considers each individual feature as an initial interval and subject to the statistical analysis, splits it into sub-intervals recursively until it meets the stopping criterion. Aiming to reduce the algorithm complexity on large-scale datasets, our algorithm utilizes an optimized and approximate approach for the Kolmogorov-Smirnov (KS) assessment. This can lead to a linear temporal complexity [7,9]. Additionally, unlike other unsupervised algorithms, the number of intervals can be inferred through the distribution as well as the frequency of feature samples. At times, the discretization of the numerical attributes can negatively affect the accuracy. Therefore, during the splitting stage, our model categorizes the samples with high frequencies into distinguished intervals. Where a numerical instance is repeated in more than half of the interval size, it will be recorded as having a high frequency. The significant factors of our model are twofold. First, the distribution of samples matters as they may follow a non-normal distribution(e.g. skewed or uniform) or Gaussian (normal) distribution. Second, samples belonging to the same interval during discretization, should follow the interval's normal distribution with a low deviation from the mean. Regarding low standard deviation, if samples are normally distributed we should adjust a compactness level (φ) through further restrictions. In this paper, we utilize the KS assessment on numerical features to find the discretized intervals through compacted samples. The KS statistics can be rewritten as formulated in Eq. 2:

$$D_n = \max_{i=1}^{n}(\phi(Z_i) - \frac{i-1}{n}, \frac{i}{n} - \phi(Z_i)) \tag{2}$$

Here, n is the size of samples, Z is the sorted samples, and ϕ represents the Cumulative Distribution Function (CDF) of the theoretical distribution used for assessment. Intuitively, the CDF value for normal distribution can be calculated as follows (Eq. 3):

$$\phi(x|\mu_{s_k}, \delta_{s_k}) = \frac{1}{2}[1 + erf(\frac{x - \mu_{s_k}}{\delta_{s_k}\sqrt{2}})] \tag{3}$$

The mean and standard deviations are formulated in Eq. 4. Note that the μ_{s_k} and δ_{s_k} are the mean and standard deviation of each interval k that is being processed at the time.

$$\mu_{s_k} = \frac{\sum_i^k x_i}{N_k}; \delta_{s_k} = \sqrt{\frac{1}{N_k}\sum_i^k (x_i - \mu_{s_k})^2} \tag{4}$$

The error function (erf) in Eq. 3 is the probability that a number drawn at random from the Standard Normal Distribution (mean $= 0$, standard deviation $= 1$), will be no greater than given x. The error function is defined in Eq. 5.

We can approximate the integral as a partial sum of an alternating infinite series.

$$erf(x) = \frac{2}{\sqrt{\pi}}\int_0^x e^{-t^2} dt \tag{5}$$

The null hypothesis (H_0) states that the interval samples follow the normal distribution $(N(\mu, \delta))$, which is a reference to every numerical feature. The mean and standard deviation parameters of the current interval, which is being scanned, can be denoted by $\mu = \mu_s$ and $\delta = \varphi * \delta_s$ respectively. Note that the initial interval represents the whole samples of the numerical features. Also, the $0 < \varphi <= 1$ is a constant compactness factor that defines the tuning deviation of the compression. This parameter is defined in according to decrease the differential entropy of normal distribution: $\frac{1}{2}\log(2\pi e\sigma^2)$, where entropy is corresponding to standard deviation.

The $pValue$ (observed significance level) can be calculated using Eq. 6. In Eq. 6, the parameter c is a threshold that determines the significance level. Also $k_0(m)$ is CDF of the KS distribution (formulated in Eq. 7) that can be approximated with a maximum number of partial sums or a tolerance by Cauchy criterion [8,9]. The pseudo code of the proposed method is represented in Algorithm 1.

$$pValue = p(\lambda \neq H_0 \mid H_0) = p(D_n \geq c \mid H_0) \approx 1 - k_0(D_n) \tag{6}$$

$$k_0(m) = 1 + 2\sum_{l=1}^{\infty}(-1)^l \exp(-2l^2 m^2) \tag{7}$$

5   Experimental Evaluation

We have employed the Naïve Bayes classifier on discretized features followed by the $K - fold$ (e.g. $K = 10$) cross-validation to verify the performance of the classifier. All the algorithms were implemented through the Spark MLlib and the WEKA libraries. Table 1 shows the information with regard to each dataset. All the experiments have been conducted on a system with Intel(R)Core(TM)i7-5500U CPU @2.40 GHz with 8 GB of RAM.

Algorithm 1. pseudo code of SUFDA

```
Input: ε, φ, numerical-features
Output: A = ∅;
for feature_i in numerical-features do
    SrtFeat_i ←Sort(feature_i)
    DISCRETIZE(SrtFeat_i)
end for
function DISCRETIZE(Interval)
    mean ← Calculate-mean(Interval)
    stdev ← Calculate-stdev(Interval)
    pValue ← KS-test ('normal', mean, φ* stdev)
    if pValue ≤ ε then
        newIntv ← SplitIntoTwoIntervals(Interval)
        for Intv in newIntv do
            DISCRETIZE(Intv)
        end for
    else
        A_i = A_i∪[Interval]
    end if
end function
```

5.1   Evaluation Metrics

We apply multiple measures in comparison to perceive distinctive aspects of the algorithms. The accuracy metric as the most frequently used performance measure for classification deems to create incorrect outcomes when classes are strongly unbalanced. Hence, we further employ the Kappa [6] and F-measure [5] models to strengthen the experimental results.

Table 1. Description of datasets

Datasets	#Instances	#Attributes	#Class
Magic	19020	10	2
Skin-segmentation	245057	3	2
Wine-quality	4898	11	7
Abalone	4177	8	28

5.2   Baseline Methods

The models participated in the experiments are explained below:

- **Fayyad (MDLP):** This is a classic top-down, supervised approach which considers a tradeoff between the loss of information and the number of intervals [2].
- **ur-CAIM:** This model is an extension of CAIM model that maximizes the class-attribute interdependency with a minimal number of discrete intervals on balanced and unbalanced data [1].
- **Equal Frequency Discretization:** An unsupervised algorithm that divides a continuous field into m intervals. Each interval contains approximately N/m samples, where N is the total number of samples.

5.3   Performance Comparison

Table 2 depicts the accuracy of Naïve Bayes classifier on various discretization models. To evaluate performance, the significance level (ϵ) and compactness factor (φ) parameters of SUFDA are set to 0.1 and 0.75 respectively. In comparison to continuous state, employing our discretization algorithm as a preprocessing step leads to an improvement in classification accuracy with Naïve Bayes. Accordingly, we conduct an experiment on unbalanced data to study the performance of our model. As Fig. 1a illustrates, our proposed solution (SUFDA) not only completes the discretization task appropriately but also can outperform the models such as ur-CAIM that have been specifically devised to deal with unbalanced data. Furthermore, as depicted in Fig. 1b, according to the F-measure our model can excel other baselines including Fayyad. The discretization is regarded as a preprocessing task for data mining applications. These applications usually need to handle large-scale datasets. Discretization as a data reduction component is employed to improve the speed of learning stage. Hence, we examine the time complexity of our framework. According to Sect. 4, the time complexity of our approach is $T(n) = 2 * T(n/2) + O(n)$ where $O(n)$ is the complexity of *pValue* calculations. Nevertheless, while we maintain the simplicity as well as the low time complexity, SUFDA can outperform other efficient unsupervised algorithms (e.g. EFD). In short, from one perspective SUFDA can adopt the low complexity of the unsupervised algorithm. From another perspective, it can achieve the same or even better effectiveness compared to the supervised discretization approaches.

Table 2. Accuracy of NB classifier

Datasets	Naïve Bayes				
	Continuous	Fayyad	ur-CAIM	EFD	SUFDA
Magic	72.68%	78.29%	73.88%	74.76%	78.61%
Skin-segmentation	92.38%	94.33%	92.17%	93.26%	94.61%
Wine-quality	44.26%	48.91%	47.91%	47.75%	54.28%
Abalone	23.84%	26.19%	26.16%	25.66%	26.83%

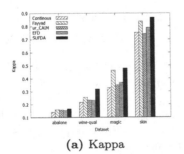

(a) Kappa

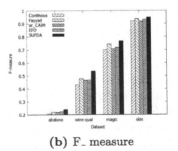

(b) F_ measure

Fig. 1. Performance metrics

The time complexity of the devised model is $O(n * d + nlog(n))$ where d denotes the depth of the binary splitting stage $(d \in O(log(n)))$. Therefore, from an efficiency perspective, our algorithm maintains a minimum time complexity suchlike other unsupervised discretization algorithms that merely rely on the sorting procedure.

6   Conclusion

In this paper, we formulate the new discretization algorithm as an important component in preprocessing stage to maintain the high accuracy of supervised models and improve the complexity of discretizaton at the same time. The experimental results demonstrate that our proposed method outperforms the state-of-art approaches in the field of discretization.

References

1. Cano, A., Nguyen, D.T., Ventura, S., Cios, K.J.: ur-CAIM: improved CAIM discretization for unbalanced and balanced data. Soft Comput. **20**(1), 173–188 (2016)
2. Fayyad, U., Irani, K.: Multi-interval discretization of continuous-valued attributes for classification learning (1993)
3. Garcia, S., Luengo, J., Sez, J.A., Lopez, V., Herrera, F.: A survey of discretization techniques: taxonomy and empirical analysis in supervised learning. IEEE Trans. Knowl. Data Eng. **25**(4), 734–750 (2013)
4. Hosseini, S., Li, L.T.: Point-of-interest recommendation using temporal orientations of users and locations. In: Navathe, S.B., Wu, W., Shekhar, S., Du, X., Wang, X.S., Xiong, H. (eds.) DASFAA 2016. LNCS, vol. 9642, pp. 330–347. Springer, Cham (2016). https://doi.org/10.1007/978-3-319-32025-0_21
5. Hripcsak, G., Rothschild, A.S.: Agreement, the f-measure, and reliability in information retrieval. J. Am. Med. Inform. Assoc. **12**(3), 296–298 (2005)
6. Landis, J.R., Koch, G.G.: The measurement of observer agreement for categorical data. Biometrics **33**(1), 159–174 (1977)
7. Massey Jr., F.J.: The Kolmogorov-Smirnov test for goodness of fit. J. Am. Stat. Assoc. **46**(253), 68–78 (1951)
8. Pelz, W., Good, I.J.: Approximating the lower tail-areas of the Kolmogorov-Smirnov one-sample statistic. J. Roy. Stat. Soc. Ser. B (Methodol.) **38**(2), 152–156 (1976)
9. Simard, R., L'Ecuyer, P.: Computing the two-sided Kolmogorov-Smirnov distribution. J. Stat. Softw. **39**(11), 1–18 (2011)

Econometric Analysis of the Industrial Growth Determinants in Colombia

Carolina Henao-Rodríguez[1](✉), Jenny-Paola Lis-Gutiérrez[2],
Mercedes Gaitán-Angulo[2], Luz Elena Malagón[3], and Amelec Viloria[4]

[1] Corporación Universitaria Minuto de Dios, Bogotá, Colombia
linda.henao@uniminuto.edu
[2] Fundación Universitaria Konrad Lorenz, Bogotá, Colombia
{jenny.lis,mercedes.gaitana}@konradlorenz.edu.co
[3] Corporación Universitaria del Meta, Villavicencio, Colombia
viceacademica@unimeta.edu.co
[4] Universidad de la Costa, Barranquilla, Colombia
aviloria7@cuc.edu.co

Abstract. An econometric study is carried out using a panel data model with fixed effects to identify the industrial development determinants in Colombia during the term 2005–2015. The database used in the study corresponds to World Bank and the Colombian state. The determinants of industrial growth identified at the theoretical level that allow the enhancement of productive capacities to face foreign competition in Colombia are: innovation; networks of innovations and knowledge among companies and organizations; the interest rate; the capital-product ratio, the unit labor cost; and the exchange rate. The amount invested in scientific, technological and innovation activities by industrial group is the only variable that is not significant in the model.

Keywords: Economic growth · Industry · Panel data · Industrial structure
Colombia · Database World Bank

1 Introduction

Economic development of in country is related to the expansion of tradable activities such as industry, and knowledge-intensive services, since the development of these sectors generates a series of positive externalities to accelerate the growth of the economy [1]. The development of the industrial sector is framed in processes of endogenous development, where the determinants of capital accumulation create an environment conducive to the transformation processes and development of the local economies [2, 3]. Therefore, local and regional governments must create or improve competitive capabilities to transform their productive systems. Since these are endogenous processes, it is imperative to detect the potentialities of the region [2]. In this context, it is important to identify the determinants of industrial development, which allow to enhance the productive capacities of the industry and, thus, generate productive chains that impulse the economic growth. In this sense, this study develops an econometric study using a panel data model with fixed effects to identify the determinants of industrial development in Colombia during the term 2005–2015. Among the studies conducted at an econometric level for the industrial structure in Colombia, we can see: [4–6].

2 Methodology

The data used in the study correspond to permanent remunerated personnel, salaries, social benefits, value added, amount invested in scientific, technological and innovation activities, employed personnel with postgraduate studies, and industrial company external sources where the ideas of technological innovation come from. For the industrial groups analyzed, the statistics published by the National Administrative Department of Statistics of Colombia (Dane) were taken from the Annual Manufacturing Survey and the Survey on Development and Technological Innovation. For the purposes of the study, the splicing of the data was performed using the Classification of Economic Activities CIIU Review 4 adapted for Colombia. The data of the real exchange rate index and the real interest rate were based on statistics published by the World Bank. Based on the data, an econometric exercise was carried out to analyze the national determinants of industrial growth in the period 2005–2015. To avoid the bias due to the heterogeneity of the industrial groups, econometric panel data techniques were used to reduce the problems related to the identification of the models.

The individuals analyzed were the industrial groups that contributed most to the national industrial production in Colombia [7], for example: Processing and preservation of meat, fish, crustaceans, and mollusks; Preparation of coffee products; Manufacture of clothing, except fur garments; among others. The dependent variable used for the measurement of industrial growth is the value added by industrial group (va). The explanatory variables are:

- Clup. Unitary labor cost; taken as a representation of the labor productivity, defined as the ratio of the labor cost required for the manufacture of a product, because it measures the relationship between production and remuneration [8], therefore, a negative sign is expected.
- i. Real interest rate; a negative impact of this variable on industrial value added is expected. Since an increase in the interest rate decreases, the consumption is stimulated, and the financing of the productive activity becomes more difficult.
- Tc. Effective real exchange rate index 2010 = 100; a positive relationship of this variable is expected with industrial growth, however, not always a devaluation of the currency has a positive effect on the industry since a boom in resources could have a positive effect on manufacturing. If the influence of appreciation increases, the production of manufactures could be maintained with a greater national demand associated with the resource boom. Therefore, the losses of competitiveness would be compensated by the increase in national demand [9].
- fe. Participation of the companies that use external sources where the ideas of technological innovation come from, in the total of innovative companies of the industrial group. It is used as a proxy for networks of innovations and knowledge between companies and organizations because the dissemination of knowledge and skills to structure the local economy is essential to generate goods with high value

added, better quality, and innovators [8]. Therefore, a positive correlation between this variable and industrial growth is expected.

- pp. Personnel employed in industrial companies, by postgraduate educational level by industrial group; it is taken as a proxy of human capital. Since human resources are key for the competitiveness of the industry, properly trained personnel cannot be replaced by any technology [10]. The years of education have a positive impact on the creation of new products and services [11]. So, it is expected that the industrial value added will increase as the employment of trained personnel increases.
- tmi. Amount invested in scientific, technological and innovation activities by industrial group, serves as a proxy for innovation. A positive sign is expected since the adoption of innovations allows companies a wider range of products and work in plants of smaller economic dimension but more efficient, which strengthens the internal economies of scale [12, 13].
- ta. Total assets. It is used as a proxy for the product capital ratio since the consolidation of the industry is related to the advance in sectoral investment and is shown when the productive sector of a region is exposed to external competition, where a greater domestic investment is needed to achieve processes of technological adaptation and develop dynamic competitive advantages [14]. A positive relationship between industrial growth and this variable is expected.

The model is specified as follows:

$$Inva_{jt} = \beta_0 + \beta_1 lnclup_{jt} + \beta_2 \ln i_{ct} + \beta_3 \ln tc_{ct} + \beta_4 \ln fe_{jt} + \beta_5 \ln pp_{jt}$$
$$+ \beta_6 \ln tmi_{jt} + \beta_7 \ln ta_{jt} + \eta_j + \varepsilon_{jt} \tag{1}$$

$Inva_{jt}$ is the natural logarithm of the value added of the industrial group j in the year t, $lnclup_{jt}$ is the natural logarithm of the unit labor cost of the industrial group j in the year t, $\beta_2 \ln i_{ct}$ is the natural logarithm of Colombia's real interest rate in the year t, $\beta_3 \log tc_{ct}$ is the natural logarithm of the effective real exchange rate index in Colombia in the year t, $\beta_4 \ln fe_{jt}$ is the natural logarithm of the participation of the companies that use from external sources, where the ideas of technological innovation come from in the total of innovative companies of the industrial group j in the year t, ln_{jt} is the natural logarithm of the personnel employed in the industrial companies, by the postgraduate educational level of the industrial group j in the year t, $\ln tmi_{jt}$ is the natural logarithm of the amount invested in scientific, technological and innovation activities of the industrial group j in the year t, $\beta_7 \ln ta_{jt}$ is the natural logarithm of the total assets of the industrial group j in the year t, ηj is the effects that vary with time not observed, δt captures a common deterministic trend; ε_{jt} is a random disturbance that is supposed $\varepsilon_{jt} \sim N(0, \sigma^2)$.

3   Results

The Hausman test (Table 1) determines a chi^2 of 0.87 and a Prob > chi^2 equal to 0.000, which leads to reject the null hypothesis, that is the estimator must be selected for fixed effects, which confirms that there are previous conditions that are constant in time.

Table 1. Test statistics conducted to the model

Hausman test	Test: Ho: difference in coefficients not systematic chi2(7) = (b − B)'[(V_b − V_B)^(−1)](b − B) = 180.87 Prob > chi^2 = 0.0000
Wooldridge test	Wooldridge test for autocorrelation in panel data H0: no first-order autocorrelation F(1, 16) = 34.126 Prob > F = 0.0000
The Wald test	Modified Wald test for groupwise heteroskedasticity in fixed effect regression model H0: sigma(i)^2 = sigma^2 for all i chi2(20) = 3325.67 Prob > chi2 = 0.0000
Friedman test	Friedman's test of cross sectional independence = 0.800, Pr = 1.0000 Average absolute value of the off-diagonal elements = 1.000
Test for the joint significance test of the temporary dichotomous variables	chi^2(7) = 6.87 Prob > chi2 = 0.4421

When applying tests of Wald for homoscedasticity of Wooldridge for autocorrelation, and Friedman for e transversal dependence on panel data models, it was determined that there were problems of heteroscedasticity and autocorrelation in the proposed model. To correct these problems, standard error estimators corrected for panel were used, although fixed effects were not calculated directly, dichotomous variables of time were not introduced since, when performing the test F for the joint significance of these variables, it was not possible to reject the null hypothesis $\eta_1 = \eta_2 = \ldots = \eta_t = 0$. Therefore, it is not possible to affirm that the temporary dichotomous variables are jointly significant and belong to the model (Fig. 1).

The unit labor cost is significant in the model at a level of significance of 1%. However, it did not show the expected sign, which indicates that the empirical evidence does not prove that the unit labor cost has a negative relationship with the industrial value added. The effective real exchange rate index is significant in the model at a level of significance of 5% and has a negative relationship with the industrial value added, which confirms that not always a devaluation of the currency has a positive effect on the industry since a boom in resources could have a positive effect on manufacturing.

The participation of companies that use external sources where the ideas of technological innovation come from, in the total of innovative companies of the industrial group is significant in the model at a level of significance of 6%. But, the sign is negative, therefore, there is no empirical evidence that the networks of innovations and knowledge among companies and organizations increase the industrial value added in Colombia.

The personnel employed in the industrial companies, by postgraduate educational level and by industrial group is significant in the model at a level of significance of 5%, and presents a positive relationship with the industrial value added. Therefore, it can be confirmed that human resources are key in the competitiveness of the industry [10, 11].

```
. xtpcse va clup i tc fe pp tmi ta,  het c(ar1)

Number of gaps in sample:  3
(note:  computations for rho restarted at each gap)
(note:  estimates of rho outside [-1,1] bounded to be in the range [-1,1])

Prais-Winsten regression, heteroskedastic panels corrected standard errors

Group variable:      gp                          Number of obs        -      142
Time variable:       ao                          Number of groups     -       20
Panels:              heteroskedastic (unbalanced) Obs per group: min  -        2
Autocorrelation:     common AR(1)                               avg   -      7.1
                                                                 max   -        8

Estimated covariances      -         20           R-squared            -   0.9969
Estimated autocorrelations -          1           Wald chi2(7)         -   346.66
Estimated coefficients     -          8           Prob > chi2          -   0.0000
```

va	Coef.	Het-corrected Std. Err.	z	P>|z|	[95% Conf. Interval]	
clup	1.406393	.2279935	6.17	0.000	.9595343	1.853252
i	-1.119475	.2197403	-5.09	0.000	-1.550158	-.6887923
tc	-.6328382	.3175354	-1.99	0.046	-1.255196	-.0104804
fe	-.0839665	.0434932	-1.93	0.054	-.1692116	.0012785
pp	.0350522	.0175449	2.00	0.046	.0006648	.0694396
tmi	.0133613	.0235228	0.57	0.570	-.0327425	.0594652
ta	.7609874	.0499586	15.23	0.000	.6630703	.8589046
_cons	3.576541	1.925457	1.86	0.063	-.197285	7.350366
rho	.6808316					

Fig. 1. Model for identifying the determinants of industrial growth in Colombia 2005–2015

Finally, the total of assets is significant in the model at a level of significance of 1%, and presents the expected sign which confirms that the consolidation of the industry is related to the advance in the sector investment [13].

4   Conclusions

When performing the econometric analysis for the determinants of national industrial growth in the period 2005–2015 in Colombia for the industrial groups that contributed more to the national industrial production, it was found that: the unit labor cost is significant in the model and there is no empirical evidence to verify that there is a negative relationship with the industrial value added. This may be because the domestic demand that stimulates industrial growth is determined by the income of workers. Regarding the real interest rate, the interest rate decreases, industrial value-added increases because consumption is stimulated, and, in addition, financing of productive activity is facilitated, as predicted by the economic theory. The effective real exchange rate index is significant in the model and presents a negative relationship with the industrial value added, which shows that not always a devaluation of the currency has a positive effect on the industry, since a boom in resources could have a positive effect on the production of manufactures because it can be boosted through greater national demand. Therefore, the empirical evidence does not show that there is a loss of competitiveness of the industry derived from several years of appreciation of the real exchange rate.

References

1. Frenkel, R., Rapetti, M.: Fragilidad externa o desindustrialización: ¿Cuál es la principal amenaza para América Latina en la próxima década? CEPAL Serie Macroeconomía del Desarrollo, no. 116. Cepal, Santiago de Chile (2011)
2. Akoorie, M.E.M., Salcedo-Claramunt, C.: The impact of foreign direct investment on local industry in Chile. Suma de Negoc. 1(2), 7–23 (2010)
3. Vargas-Hernández, J., Martínez, M., Palos, G.: Análisis del enfoque de las competencias técnicas en las pequeñas empresas del sector industrial en la ciudad de San Luis Potosí, México. Suma de Negoc. 3(2), 25–35 (2012)
4. Clavijo, S., Fandiño, A., Vera, A.: La Desindustrialización En Colombia. ANIF, Bogotá (2012)
5. Duana, D., Vázquez, A.: Modelo econométrico para determinar el impacto de la industria maquiladora en la generación de empleos. Suma de Negoc. 3(2), 9–24 (2012)
6. Henao-Rodríguez, C., Lis-Gutiérrez, J.P., Viloria, A., Ariza-Salazar, J.: Application of a gravity model in the evaluation of the determinants of intraindustrial trade in Colombia. Int. J. Control Theory Appl. 10(18), 1–6 (2016)
7. Zambrano, A.G.: Baja competitividad en Colombia, ¿un efecto cepalino? Divergencia (22) (2017)
8. Cardona, M., Cano, C.: Dinámica industrial, crecimiento económico y Pymes: un análisis de Datos de Panel para el caso colombiano 1980–2000. Observatorio de la Economía Latinoamericana, vol. 50. Departamento Nacional de Planeación, Bogotá (2005)
9. Sierra, L., Manrique, K.: Impacto del tipo de cambio real en los sectores industriales de Colombia: una primera aproximación. Rev. de la CEPAL 114, 127–143 (2014)
10. Estrada, R., García, D., Sánchez, V.: Factores determinantes del éxito competitivo en la Pyme: Estudio Empírico en México. Rev. Venez. de Gerenc. 14(46), 169–182 (2009)
11. Subramanian, A.: A longitudinal study of the influence of intellectual human capital on firm exploratory innovation. IEEE Trans. Eng. Manag. 59(4), 540–550 (2012)
12. Vázquez, A.: Desarrollo endógeno y globalización. EURE 26(79), 47–65 (2000)
13. Vázquez, A.: Desarrollo endógeno. Teorías y políticas de desarrollo territorial. Investig. Reg. 11, 183–210 (2007)
14. Kshetri, N.: The evolution of the offshore outsourcing industry: Brazil versus other BRIC economies. Suma de Negoc. 3(3), 33–46 (2012)

Parallelizing String Similarity Join Algorithms

Ling-Chih Yao and Lipyeow Lim[✉]

University of Hawai'i at Mānoa, Honolulu, HI 96822, USA
{lingchih,lipyeow}@hawaii.edu

Abstract. A key operation in data cleaning and integration is the use of string similarity join (SSJ) algorithms to identify and remove duplicates or similar records within data sets. With the advent of big data, a natural question is how to parallelize SSJ algorithms. There is a large body of existing work on SSJ algorithms and parallelizing each one of them may not be the most feasible solution. In this paper, we propose a parallelization framework for string similarity joins that utilizes existing SSJ algorithms. Our framework partitions the data using a variety of partitioning strategies and then executes the SSJ algorithms on the partitions in parallel. Some of the partitioning strategies that we investigate trade accuracy for speed. We implemented and validated our framework on several SSJ algorithms and data sets. Our experiments show that our framework results in significant speedup with little loss in accuracy.

1 Introduction

Given a string-based data collection and a similarity measure, the *string similarity join (SSJ)* problem takes as input two sets of strings and returns all pairs of strings from the two data sets where their similarity value are above a user-specified threshold. Many real-world applications apply SSJ for data cleaning, duplicate detection, data integration and entity resolution. Other less obvious applications include nearest-neighbor-like queries in web search, social media, and even recommender systems. The SSJ problem is well studied in the literature with a plethora of algorithms proposed [3,5,8,9,15].

With the advent of big data, a modern challenge in SSJ processing is the rapid growth of the size of the data sets. For example, in 2010, the size of the Google N-gram dataset has exceeded 1 trillion data items [13], and the amount of log data that Facebook receives each day exceeds 6 TB [2]. A natural question is how to parallelize SSJ processing to handle the large data sets we have today. Two recent studies [12,13] have utilized MapReduce and Spark for parallel SSJ processing. Nevertheless, there is a large body of work on sequential SSJ algorithms with new ones added every year. Parallelizing any complex algorithm is hard in general and parallelizing each of those sequential SSJ algorithms is clearly a challenge with or without using frameworks like MapReduce and/or Spark.

© Springer International Publishing AG, part of Springer Nature 2018
J. Wang et al. (Eds.): ADC 2018, LNCS 10837, pp. 322–327, 2018.
https://doi.org/10.1007/978-3-319-92013-9_27

In this paper, we investigate a parallelization approach for existing SSJ algorithms that first partitions the data, run the existing (in-memory) SSJ algorithms on each partition in parallel, and finally merge the results. In particular, we propose a variety of data partitioning strategies and investigate their impact on parallelizing existing SSJ algorithms. The contribution of this paper are as follows.

- We reduce the unnecessary computation by partitioning dissimilar data into different partitions.
- We show that partitioning strategies can achieve significant speedup with little loss in accuracy.
- We can parallelize any sequential string similarity algorithm without modifications on the original algorithms with our data partitioning strategies.
- Our experimental evaluation shows that our partitioning strategies achieve excellent performance on several real-world data sets.

The rest of paper is organized as follows. We give a problem definition and related work in Sects. 2 and 3. We describe our parallelization framework and the different strategies of data partitioning in Sect. 4. We present the experiment results in Sect. 5. And we conclude the paper in Sect. 6.

2 Preliminaries

Given two data sets R and S, similarity function sim, and threshold δ, the **string similarity join** operator returns all similar pairs (x, y), where $x \in R$, $y \in S$, and $sim(x, y) > \delta$. We define a string-based record as a set of tokens by mapping each unique string in the data sets to a unique token. We use **token-based similarity functions** to compute the similarity of two records. The popular token-based functions are Jaccard, Cosine, Dice, and Overlap (where x and y denote the input sets of string tokens):

Overlap: $\mathrm{Olp}(x, y) = |x \cap y|$ Jaccard: $\mathrm{Jac}(x, y) = \frac{|x \cap y|}{|x \cup y|}$

Dice: $\mathrm{Dice}(x, y) = \frac{2|x \cap y|}{|x|+|y|}$ Cosine: $\mathrm{Cos}(x, y) = \frac{|x \cap y|}{\sqrt{|x||y|}}$

For example, consider the strings 'Yesterday rained during the afternoon' and 'Yesterday it rained during the afternoon'. We first break them into string tokens x: {Yesterday, rained, during, the, afternoon} and y: {Yesterday, it, rained, during, the, afternoon}, respectively, then we can measure their similarity by similarity functions: $Olp(x, y) = 5$, $Jac(x, y) = \frac{5}{6}$, $Dice(x, y) = \frac{10}{11}$, and $Cos(x, y) = \frac{5}{5.477}$.

3 Related Work

There are many SSJ algorithms proposed due to the inefficiency of determining the similar pairs by examining every string pair. The proposed algorithms are classified into two categories: approximate SSJ and exact SSJ.

Approximate SSJ algorithms trade the accuracy for the efficiency by reducing the dimensionality of the input vectors. *Local-Sensitive Hashing (LSH)* is a common technique for reducing the input's dimensionality by hashing input data. In 2012, Satuluri and Parthasarathy [10] utilize a Bayesian approach to optimize a LSH-based SSJ algorithm. In 2017, Sohrabi and Azgomi proposed a parallel SSJ algorithm based on the LHS techniques [11].

Exact SSJ, which output the exact result pairs, has received more attention partly because approximate SSJ algorithms often produce non-trivial errors in practical applications. The common technique is generating signatures and then using inverted index to filter dissimilar pairs. AllPair [1], PPJoin+ [16], and AdaptJoin [14] are popular prefix-filtering algorithms that generate signatures based on the prefix of strings. Partition-based algorithms generate signatures by partitioning strings into non-overlapping subsets [6,9].

Sequential SSJ algorithms are inadequate for very large data sets such as data from network monitoring, internet of things, internet-scale applications. Vernica et al. proposed an efficient parallel exact SSJ algorithm based on Hadoop MapReduce [13] in 2010. It partitions data by their prefix and process the partitions in parallel. Sun et al. proposed Dima, a similarity-based query system on Spark, in [12]. It partitions data by global and local index, so the target range and data transmission can be decreased.

There are currently many (sequential) SSJ algorithms with new algorithms invented almost every year. Parallelization of the sequential string similarity algorithms remains a very challenging task – many of them do not fit nicely onto the Map-Reduce framework utilized by Hadoop and Spark. Instead of parallelizing each existing sequential SSJ algorithm or inventing a new parallel SSJ algorithm, our work investigate data partitioning (and hence parallelization) strategies for parallel processing of the SSJ problem using *any existing* sequential SSJ algorithm as a sub-routine.

4   Parallelizing String Similarity Join

In this paper, we propose to parallellize the SSJ operation by first partitioning the data into partitions or buckets in a one-time offline phase. Each partition is stored locally in a compute node. In the online SSJ processing phase, we execute the SSJ algorithm at each compute node in parallel. We then consolidate the results from the compute nodes to be returned to the user. A key idea of our framework is to avoid doing cross-partition joins by leveraging a suitable partitioning strategy to partition the data so that similar records will be co-located in the same partition. Hence, there will be some loss of accuracy and our framework will trade-off accuracy for speed. In general we only need to partition data once and the same partitions are reused for multiple queries. Next, we describe the partitioning strategies that are the thrust of this paper.

4.1   Partitioning by the First Token

For this partitioning method, we determine the partition identifier (ID) of a record by using the first token of each record. The assumption is that similar record pairs are very likely to have same first token. Since the number of distinct first tokens can be quite large, we use a variety of techniques to limit the number of partitions: (1) compute a hash value of the first token, (2) use the first letter of the first token, and (3) use the first k letters of the first token. In our experiment, we use the first letter (strategy *First*), and the first two letters of the first token (strategy *Second*).

4.2   Partitioning by Keyword

Previous research [1,6,16] have shown that low frequency tokens have higher power to filter dissimilar data. In this partitioning strategy we use the token with least frequency in each record to determine the partition ID. We first build a dictionary containing all tokens in the data set and their occurrence frequency. For each record, we use the dictionary to find the token with the smallest frequency and use that token to compute the partition ID.

4.3   Partitioning by the Prefix

Prefix filtering is a popular method to filter dissimilar data [1,6,14,16] in SSH algorithms. It is proposed in SSJ algorithm SSJoin [4] and extended to prefix-based framework in ALLPair algorithm [1]. The key idea is to first sort the tokens in each record according to some predetermined order and then if a pair of records do not share any token in their prefix, they must be dissimilar. For this partitioning strategy, we first sort the tokens in each record, and then use a prefix of the record to compute the partition ID.

5   Experiments

For our experiments, we implemented our parallelization framework using the Message Passing Interface (MPI) [7] and Python. For the sequential string similarity algorithm to be executed on each compute node, we run the executable file of the original author's implementation of the algorithm for PPjoin+ [16] and AdaptJoin [14]. We conducted our experiments on a Cray CS300 high performance computing (HPC) clusters with 276 total nodes. Each node contains two 10-core Intel Ivy Bridge, 2.8 GHz processors and 118 GB usable RAM. We performed extensive experiments using three data sets, two existing SSJ algorithms, different numbers of cores and different thresholds. Due to the space limitation, we only show part of the results.

We use three real-world data sets in our experiments: DBLP, a collection of author names and titles from computer science bibliography; QueryLog, query strings randomly selected from AOL Query Log [14]; and Enron, a collection of the titles and bodies from Enron emails [14].

Table 1 shows the basic information of the data sets. Column Records shows the number of records; columns l_{avg}, l_{min} and l_{max} show the average, minimal, and maximal token size, respectively; columns PPJoin+ and AdaptJoin show the sequential running time of these two algorithms; and column Result Pairs show the similar pairs with Jaccard threshold 0.9. Note that PPjoin+ did not generate any results because it exited with a segmentation fault.

Table 2 shows the speedup and accuracy of our parallel SSJ framework. We can see *Keyword* worked best on average with different data sets, and the best speedup happened in *Second* on DBLP. *First* worked worse than *Keyword* but the data partitioning time is much faster. Prefix is slowest (because each record may partition to more than one partitions and cause duplicate computation) but the accuracy is the most stable.

First and *Second* worked well on DBLP and Enron with accuracy more than 97%; but they worked worse on QueryLog with accuracy around 66%. It is because DBLP starts with authors' name and Enron start with the titles of emails, so their first tokens have more filter power. *Keyword* worked worse on Enron as the average token size in Enron is 133.51, one keyword is not enough to filter dissimilar data. Note that accuracy of *Prefix* cannot reach 100% since we only retrieved two tokens instead of whole prefix (for reducing the data partitioning time.)

Table 1. Information on the data sets. The result pairs are for threshold $\delta = 0.9$.

	Records	l_{avg}	l_{min}	l_{max}	File size	PPJoin+	AdaptJoin	Result pairs
DBLP	3,422,478	16.48	6	233	370M	-	60.57 s	131,743
QueryLog	1,208,844	20.44	1	500	26M	-	6.44 s	20,603
Enron	517,431	133.57	1	3162	435M	-	65.62 s	1,332,622

Table 2. The speedup and accuracy in parenthesis of our parallel SSJ framework using different strategies on 11 processors. The AdaptJoin SSJ algorithm with Jaccard threshold 0.9 was used.

	First	Second	Keyword	Prefix
DBLP	7.1 (98.4%)	9.4 (98.4%)	8.2 (96.7%)	3.6 (98.1%)
QueryLog	6.4 (67.9%)	2.6 (66.5%)	8.1 (96.8%)	4.4 (98.9%)
Enron	2.5 (97.6%)	3.5 (97.6%)	5.5 (85.3%)	3.9 (93.0%)

6　Conclusion

In this paper, we studied data partitioning strategies for parallelizing existing sequential SSJ algorithms. We partitioned the data set into partitions using a variety of strategies based on the first k letters of the first token, the least frequent keyword, and the prefix of each record. These partitions were then processed in parallel with existing SSJ algorithms and the results merged together for the user. We performed extensive experimental validation and observed that different data sets achieve the best accuracy and performance with different strategies. Users can choose different strategies for different data sets depending on the filtering power of the partitioning strategies on that data set. The right strategy can result in significant speedup with little loss of accuracy.

References

1. Bayardo, R.J., Ma, Y., Srikant, R.: Scaling up all pairs similarity search. In: WWW, pp. 131–140. ACM (2007)
2. Blanas, S., Patel, J.M., Ercegovac, V., Rao, J., Shekita, E.J., Tian, Y.: A comparison of join algorithms for log processing in MapReduce. In: SIGMOD, pp. 975–986. ACM (2010)
3. Bocek, T., Hunt, E., Stiller, B., Hecht, F.: Fast similarity search in large dictionaries. University of Zurich (2007)
4. Chaudhuri, S., Ganti, V., Kaushik, R.: A primitive operator for similarity joins in data cleaning. In: ICDE, p. 5. IEEE (2006)
5. Ciaccia, P., Patella, M., Zezula, P.: M-tree: an efficient access method for similarity search in metric spaces. In: VLDB, vol. 23, pp. 426–435 (1997)
6. Deng, D., Li, G., Wen, H., Feng, J.: An efficient partition based method for exact set similarity joins. VLDB 9(4), 360–371 (2015)
7. Gabriel, E., et al.: Open MPI: goals, concept, and design of a next generation MPI implementation. In: Kranzlmüller, D., Kacsuk, P., Dongarra, J. (eds.) EuroPVM/MPI 2004. LNCS, vol. 3241, pp. 97–104. Springer, Heidelberg (2004). https://doi.org/10.1007/978-3-540-30218-6_19
8. Gravano, L., Ipeirotis, P.G., Jagadish, H.V., Koudas, N., Muthukrishnan, S., Srivastava, D., et al.: Approximate string joins in a database (almost) for free. In: VLDB, vol. 1, pp. 491–500 (2001)
9. Li, G., Deng, D., Wang, J., Feng, J.: Pass-join: a partition-based method for similarity joins. VLDB 5(3), 253–264 (2011)
10. Satuluri, V., Parthasarathy, S.: Bayesian locality sensitive hashing for fast similarity search. VLDB 5(5), 430–441 (2012)
11. Sohrabi, M.K., Azgomi, H.: Parallel set similarity join on big data based on locality-sensitive hashing. Sci. Comput. Program. 145, 1–12 (2017)
12. Sun, J., Shang, Z., Li, G., Deng, D., Bao, Z.: Dima: a distributed in-memory similarity-based query processing system. VLDB 10(12), 1925–1928 (2017)
13. Vernica, R., Carey, M.J., Li, C.: Efficient parallel set-similarity joins using MapReduce. In: SIGMOD, pp. 495–506. ACM (2010)
14. Wang, J., Li, G., Feng, J.: Can we beat the prefix filtering? An adaptive framework for similarity join and search. In: SIGMOD, pp. 85–96. ACM (2012)
15. Xiao, C., Wang, W., Lin, X.: Ed-Join: an efficient algorithm for similarity joins with edit distance constraints. VLDB 1(1), 933–944 (2008)
16. Xiao, C., Wang, W., Lin, X., Yu, J.X.: Efficient similarity joins for near duplicate detection. In: WWW, pp. 131–140. ACM (2008)

Exploring Human Mobility Patterns in Melbourne Using Social Media Data

Ravinder Singh[(✉)], Yanchun Zhang, and Hua Wang

Victoria University, Footscray Park, Footscray, Melbourne, VIC 3011, Australia
ravinder.singh24@live.vu.edu.au

Abstract. Location based social networks such as Swarm provide a rich source of information on urban functions and city dynamics. Users voluntarily check-in at places they visit using a mobile application. Analysis of data created by check-ins can give insight into user's mobility patterns. This study uses location-sharing data from Swarm to explore spatio-temporal and geo-temporal patterns within Melbourne city. Descriptive statistical analyses using SPSS on check-in data were performed to reveal meaningful trends and to attain a deeper understanding of human mobility patterns in the city. The results showed that mobility patterns vary based on gender and venue category. Furthermore, the patterns are different during different days of a week as well as at different times of a day but are not necessarily influenced by weather.

Keywords: Swarm · Mobility patterns · Social media data
Location-based social network (LBSN) · Spatio-temporal · Geo-temporal
Check-in data

1 Introduction

The aim of this study is to explore new ways to investigate human mobility patterns by utilizing user-generated location based social network data (LBSN). Intra-urban mobility has always been a topic of interests across research communities, including urban planners, computer scientists, physicists and geographers [1]. Urban planners are interested in improving transport efficiency by investigating spatial and temporal differences of travel time and travel flow. Geographers are usually interested in spatial distribution of intra-urban mobility, and computer scientists & physicists are interested in modeling distribution of travel distance in mathematical ways [2]. These intra-urban mobility patterns can give insight into behavior traits for a group of people in a city or at a particular area in a city [3]. The type of places people visit and the time of the day they visit those places tells a lot about their mobility and behavior traits.

The use of social media sites is on the rise and people indulge into these for pleasure, education, business and many other reasons [4, 5]. All these activities generated data at an unprecedented rate that can be explored for research [6]. Social media data has not been fully explored in academia [7]. Traditional ways to obtain data for mobility patterns research have become inadequate to meet contemporary policy demands [8]. Data obtained via social media platforms and analyzed using various data mining techniques can make the process efficient and help us discover patterns that are

© Springer International Publishing AG, part of Springer Nature 2018
J. Wang et al. (Eds.): ADC 2018, LNCS 10837, pp. 328–335, 2018.
https://doi.org/10.1007/978-3-319-92013-9_28

otherwise improbable [9, 10]. In this study we have used data from Swarm, which is the most popular social-driven LBSN application, to explore human mobility patterns in Melbourne. The service has more than 60 million registered users and more than 50 million monthly active users. As of October 2017, the platform has surpassed 12 billion check-ins and has reached to an average of 8 million daily check-ins [11]. We analyzed user check-ins to discover various patterns, in particular, we were interested in finding these patterns based on gender. We also explored various categories of places people visited the most, busy times to check-in during a day and busy days of a week. The information obtained from the results of this study can be utilized by the local government authorities and businesses to plan travel and business activities in Melbourne City. The results can also be utilized to develop user mobility profiles, which can further lead to the development of a targeted recommendation system.

2 Methodology

2.1 Data

Data source for this research project is check-in data from Swarm (A Foursquare subsidiary). The app allows users to check-in when they are at a particular venue. Users launch Swarm app and log in a check-in. Once logged in, the check-in details are shared with user's connection on the platform. Check-in data is classified as a large-scale location-based data and contains username, message, time, day, date, venue category, check-in latitude and longitude coordinates and gender. Most users of Swarm broadcast their check-in via Twitter to followers. These tweets containing Swarm check-ins are the data source for this project. Data was collected during a summer (Feb 2017) and a winter (June 2017) month and was aggregated into one data set of 3332 tweets.

2.2 Data Processing

Each check-in that we collected was assigned to one of the twenty venue categories that we created for this study and these are - Airport, Bank, Bar, Education, Entertainment, Food, Grocery, Gym, Home, Hotel, Landmark, Medical, Neighborhood, Outdoor, Public Transport, Religious Place, Salon, Shopping Centre, Sports and Work. Each of the venue categories was assigned a number from 1 to 20. For example, 1 represented a check-in at an airport and 2 at a bank. Similarly, each day of the week was also assigned a number ranging from 1 to 7. For gender classification, males were assigned a value of 1, females 2. Days from both thirty-day periods were assigned values from 1 to 30 respectively. A day was divided into 4 time zones in which morning was represented by 1, afternoon by 2, evening by 3 and night by 4.

2.3 Data Analyses

Descriptive statistical analyses using SPSS were performed on the dataset to investigate how people move around in Melbourne based on the time of a day and the day of a week. Different venue categories were explored to see which ones were the busiest at different time frames. Mobility patterns based on gender were also analyzed to see the difference in places that were popular among males and females. The analyses looked into different times of a day and different days of a typical week to gauge difference in patterns. The results are discussed in the next section.

3   Results and Discussions

3.1   Spatio-Temporal User Activity Patterns

In this sub section, we present the results of our statistical analysis for spatio-temporal activity patterns. Our results suggest that activities in Melbourne differ during the course of day and also course of a week. There are more people active and moving around in the afternoon than in the morning and this activity increases in the evening before it starts slowing down after 9 pm. Evening 4 pm–9 pm is the busiest time in the city with 36.3% of the check-ins, followed by 28% in the afternoon, 24.3 in the morning and only 11.4% at night. Explanation for evening being the busiest time could be that most people finish work during 4 pm–9 pm time frame and visit places such as train stations, restaurants, bars, sports centers, movies, and airport etc. Most people sleep at night so there is not much activity in city. This may not have been the case if we had collected data from city such as New York, where people are active almost any time of a day. 12.5% of all check-ins at night are at home or at a hotel. These people are not really moving around in the city but are at home. The check-ins at hotels and homes are the highest at night as compared to other time frames indicating people returning back home after finishing their days. Most check-ins in the Mornings are at Café's, Airport and work; with café being the busiest. Twenty-four out of the total two hundred check-ins at work are at night, indicating that around 12% of the total workforce do some sort of night work/shift. Gym check-ins are the highest in the evening & morning and around 8.3% of gym goers prefer to exercise late at night. Most people visit banks or ATM in the afternoon. This resonates with people having quick visits to banks and ATMs during their lunch breaks from work. Visits at the doctor and hospitals and grocery stores are steady during the day. Public transport is busy in the morning when most people go to work and evening when they come back home. Airport is busiest in the Morning with 46% of total check-in taking place during this time. The activity indicates that most flights are schedule early in the morning (Fig. 1).

The findings also suggest that as the week passes, people indulge more in leisure activities. Check-ins are highest at venue such as bar, entertainment, food, Outdoors, shopping centres and sports centres during weekends. In contrast, activities at work are slowest on the weekends. Airport activities are similar throughout the week with Wednesdays and Sundays little busier than other days. Sunday is the busiest day for grocery shopping with all other six days showing similar sort of activity.

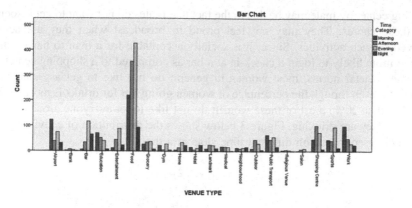

Fig. 1. Spatio-temporal user activity patterns.

3.2 Gender Based Activity Analysis

Based on the results males represent 58% and female 42% of all check-ins. Figure 2 below shows gender-based activity for all the 20 venue categories.

Males lead females in 16 out of the 20 categories when it comes to visiting a place and logging a check-in. It shows an interesting finding; 4 out of 5 check-ins made in bars are by males. On the contrary 4 in 5 check-in made in shopping centers are by females. One would imagine that even men need to go to shopping centers for buying clothes, shoes etc.; and then how come their check-in percentage is so low at shopping centers as compared to women's? Similarly one can argue that the percentage of women going to a bar or a pub for a drink has to be more than 20%. Why have we got such different results from our dataset? This can be explained as follows. Due to our societal norms, a female rather than a male has always been associated with household chores that include grocery and other type of shopping. Low percentage of check-in in

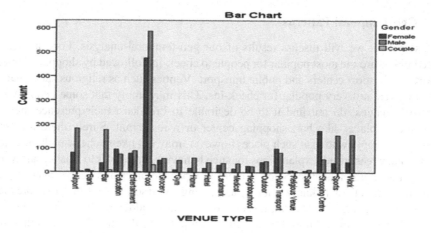

Fig. 2. Gender and venue based activity analysis.

shopping center by male may be due to the fact that males do not want to get associated with these chores. They may not feel proud to broadcast when they are actually involved in such activities. Since, it is socially acceptable for a man to have a drink, they are more likely to login a check-in at a bar as compared to a shopping center. For the same societal norms, most women in general do not like to get associated with alcohol. So even though the percentage of women going out for drinks is most likely to be higher than 20%, most of these women do not like to let everyone around them to know that they are drinking. Figure 3 below shows the distribution of activity by male and female users based on different time slots in a day.

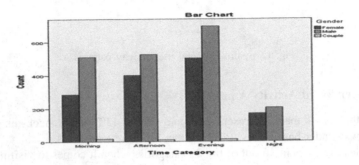

Fig. 3. Gender and time of a day based activity analysis.

As it can be seen that male activities are low and very similar during mornings and afternoons because that is when most people especially males (because male constitute 63.3% of all full time jobs in Australia) are at work. Activity increases for them as they finish work and visit places and eventually goes down for a night period. On the other hand female activity increases throughout a day and eventually falls down at night in line with overall activities by both genders. Fewer females participate in full time employments and that provides them more flexibility to visit places, they have to, even during the afternoon, when most men are at work.

3.3   Geo-Temporal Patterns

In this section, we will discuss results of our geo-temporal analysis. Food and drink related places are the most popular for people to check-in, followed by shopping centers, airport, work, sport centers and public transport. Venues such as religious spots, banks, and salons are not very popular for check-ins. This may imply that some people when visit such venues, do not find it to be desirable to broadcast their presence there as compared to places like bar, shopping center or a restaurant. Surely there are large numbers of people who visit such places however, may not like to check-in there. There may be many reason and explanations for such behavior. In regards to a bank, safety and security may the main cause. Salon is more of a private place and people may not like everyone around them to know that they are having some sort of treatment to make them look better. According to Swarm, most of its users are middle age individuals [11] and these individual may not find it to be cool to get associated with religion and that may explain why a lot of people do not check-in when they visit such venues.

Activity at each venue category varies depending on the time of a day. Most people go to work in the morning and check-in when they reach and most of them in Melbourne use public transport to get to work. This explains why morning is busy for these two types of venue categories. Higher number of check-ins at Airport indicates that most airline organize their flights early in the morning. Whether these are incoming or outgoing flights, airport is busy in the morning. Second busiest time at the airport is in the evening. This may be due to domestic flights because most people who fly into Melbourne in the mornings fly back in the evenings. Apart from work, public transport and airport, other categories that are also somewhat busy in the morning are education, food, gym, and hotel. Most education institutes are busy during morning and afternoon. Busy food places means a lot of people getting their coffees and breakfasts.

3.4   Check-In Dynamics

This section presents the results of Check-in (mobility activity) dynamics analysis. We studied all check-ins as whole representing human mobility patterns within Melbourne during different days of a week.

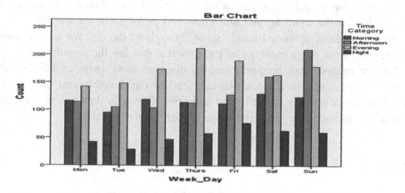

Fig. 4. Temporal patterns analysis.

As it can be seen by the results in Fig. 4 above, most of the check-ins, which represent mobility patterns, takes place during evenings. Evenings are busier than any other time period every day except on Sundays. On Sunday it's the afternoon activities that leads the charge. Explanation for this could be that since Monday is the first working day after the weekend, most people tend to take it easy and stay home for Sunday evenings and in some cases prepare for work on Monday. Most people also prefer to stay home and catch up with their favorite movies during Sunday evenings. However, afternoon on Sunday's are the busiest leading to relatively quieter evenings. From the graph above, we can also deduce that nighttime activity is the highest on Fridays followed by Saturday. Most people are in party mood on the weekend and they start it on Fridays leading to Saturdays. It can be seen from the chart that activity during nights is slow at the start of a week and picks up as the week passes with the exception of Monday night. A lot of young people, who work on the weekends, go out on

Monday nights and this may explain higher activity for that night. Morning activity is pretty stable throughout the week. So even though most people do not go to work on the weekend morning, they are still busy check-in at places such as café's, gyms, sports canter, airport, shopping center, and outdoors. The results also show a positive correlation between a number of afternoon activities and the day of the week. The number of afternoon activity increases as the week passes. Over all afternoon activity is higher during the weekend as compared to weekdays as most people are at work during weekday afternoons.

4 Conclusion and Future Work

In this paper, we performed descriptive statistical analysis using SPSS on location sharing check-in data from Swarm to explore human mobility pattern in Melbourne. The results showed that Restaurants, café's bars, shopping centers, gyms, and sports centers are some of the most visited places in the city and activity at these places increase as the week pass. Results revealed that mobility patterns changed during different times of a day and a week. Night activity is slow in Melbourne at the start of a week and picks up as the week passes and is highest on Fridays. Activities outside work were low in the morning and afternoon and picks up in the evening for males users and nevertheless remained nearly same throughout the day for female users.

The results show some meaningful patterns that can lay the foundation for future work. Deeper analysis can be performed to discover busy parts of the city during different times of a day or a week that can lead to the development of a predictive analytic framework on user mobility and activities. Check-in data can also be used to develop a new methodology to mine other human behavior traits.

References

1. van Zanten, B.T., Van Berkel, D.B., Meentemeyer, R.K., Smith, J.W., Tieskens, K.F., Verburg, P.H.: Continental-scale quantification of landscape values using social media data. In: Proceedings of the National Academy of Sciences, pp. 12974–12979 (2016)
2. Gonzalez, M.C., Hidalgo, C.A., Barabasi, A.-L.: Understanding individual human mobility patterns. arXiv preprint arXiv:0806.1256 (2008)
3. Colombo, G.B., Chorley, M.J., Williams, M.J., Allen, S.M., Whitaker, R.M.: You are where you eat: foursquare checkins as indicators of human mobility and behaviour. In: 2012 IEEE International Conference on Pervasive Computing and Communications Workshops (PERCOM Workshops), pp. 217–222. IEEE (2012)
4. Fossen, B.L., Schweidel, D.A.: Social TV: how social media activity interacts with TV advertising. GfK Mark. Intell. Rev. 9(2), 31–36 (2017)
5. Oh, C., Yergeau, S.: Social capital, social media, and TV ratings. Int. J. Bus. Inf. Syst. 24(2), 242–260 (2017)
6. Ruths, D., Pfeffer, J.: Social media for large studies of behavior. Science 346(6213), 1063–1064 (2014)

7. Weller, K., Strohmaier, M.: Social media in academia: how the social web is changing academic practice and becoming a new source for research data. IT-Inf. Technol. **56**(5), 203–206 (2014)
8. Zook, M.A., Graham, M.: Mapping DigiPlace: geocoded internet data and the representation of place. Environ. Plann. B: Plann. Des. **34**(3), 466–482 (2007)
9. Aggarwal, C.C.: Data Mining: The Textbook. Springer, Cham (2015). https://doi.org/10.1007/978-3-319-14142-8
10. Japkowicz, N., Stefanowski, J.: Big Data Analysis: New Algorithms for a New Society. Springer, Heidelberg (2016). https://doi.org/10.1007/978-3-319-26989-4
11. https://foursquare.com/about. Accessed 23 Oct 2017

Bootstrapping Uncertainty in Schema Covering

Nguyen Thanh Toan[1], Phan Thanh Cong[1], Duong Chi Thang[2],
Nguyen Quoc Viet Hung[3]([⊠]), and Bela Stantic[3]

[1] Bach Khoa University, Ho Chi Minh, Vietnam
[2] Ecole Polytechnique Federale de Lausanne, Lausanne, Switzerland
[3] Griffith University, Gold Coast, Australia
`quocviethung.nguyen@griffith.edu.au`

Abstract. Schema covering is the process of representing large and complex schemas by easily comprehensible common objects. This task is done by identifying a set of common concepts from a repository called concept repository and generating a cover to describe the schema by the concepts. Traditional schema covering approach has two shortcomings: it does not model the uncertainty in the covering process, and it requires user to state an ambiguity constraint which is hard to define. We remedy this problem by incorporating probabilistic model into schema covering to generate probabilistic schema cover. The integrated probabilities not only enhance the coverage of cover results but also eliminate the need of defining the ambiguity parameter. Experiments on real-datasets show the competitive performance of our approach.

Keywords: Schema matching · Schema covering · Probabilistic models

1 Introduction

Schema matching is the process of finding correspondences between attributes of schemas [1,2]. It is used extensively in many fields [3–5], especially data integration [6,7]. Schema matching traditionally performs matching on attribute-level to create attribute correspondences. This process is ineffective considering a large schema with thousands of attributes. Moreover, users tend to think schemas in terms of business object level when designing schema mappings. Therefore, describing the schemas at low-level structure such as attribute makes the manual matching process error-prone. This matching process would be easier if we could represent schemas in a higher level of abstraction.

Since schemas are used to capture everyday business activities and some of these business activities are the same among organizations, these schemas may contain many common parts. These common parts represent business objects that are comprised in the schemas which are called concepts. Some common concepts are "Address", which describes the location of an entity, or "Contact", which provides information about a person or an organization. Based on this

© Springer International Publishing AG, part of Springer Nature 2018
J. Wang et al. (Eds.): ADC 2018, LNCS 10837, pp. 336–342, 2018.
https://doi.org/10.1007/978-3-319-92013-9_29

observation, the process of describing schemas in terms of concepts can be made possible and it is called schema covering. Schema covering is a novel approach which has been studied carefully in [8,9].

In [8], the schema cover found by schema covering must satisfy a pre-defined ambiguity constraint which limits the number of times a schema attribute can be covered. However, this ambiguity constraint is hard to define since it must be stated beforehand and for each attribute in the schema. Traditional schema covering approach has another shortcoming that it does not support modeling uncertainty arisen in the covering process. As a result, these problems lead to the employment of probability to express uncertainty. We propose incorporating probabilistic model into schema covering to introduce *probabilistic schema covering*.

In short, our goal is to create a new schema covering mechanism that does not require a user-defined ambiguity constraint by incorporating probabilistic model. The paper is organized as follows. In Sect. 2, we model and formulate the problem of probabilistic schema cover. In Sect. 3, we present the probabilistic schema covering framework. In Sect. 4, we run various experiments on probabilistic schema covering, before Sect. 5 concludes the paper.

2   Model and Problem Statement

Let schema $s = \{a_1, a_2, \ldots, a_n\}$ be a finite set of attributes. Let s and s' be schemas with n and n' attributes, respectively. Let $S = s \times s'$ be the set of all possible *attribute correspondences* between s and s'. Each attribute correspondence (a pair of attributes) is associated with a confidence value $m_{i,j}(s, s') \in [0, 1]$ which represents the similarity between the i-th attribute of s and the j-th attribute of s' [10,11].

A concept c is also a set of attributes: $c = a_1, a_2, \ldots, a_m$ where a_i is an attribute. A concept and a schema is basically the same as they are both sets of attributes. However, a concept is more meaningful as it describes a business object and it also has a smaller size. Concepts have relations between them called *micromappings*. Each micromapping is actually a set of attribute correspondences. We also define the counterpart of concepts in the schema which are subschemas. A subschema t is also a set of attributes and it is a subset of schema s. Each concept and its subschema has an alignment score $f(t, c)$ which describes the similarity between them.

In general, the schema covering framework mentioned in [8] takes a schema and a prebuilt concept repository as input. The concept repository is a corpus of predefined concepts, which is built before-hand [8].

Definition 1. *Given a set of subschemas T_s of schema s, a set C of concepts, we define a set of valid matchings between subschemas and concepts:*

$$E(T_s, C) = \{(t, c) | t \in T_s, c \in C\}$$

where (t, c) is a set of attribute correspondences between subschema t and concept c. A cover of s by C, $v_{s,C} \subseteq E(T_s, C)$ is a subset of valid matchings between T_s and C.

The schema cover found by traditional schema covering approach must satisfy an ambiguity constraint which limits the number of times a schema attribute can be covered. Therefore, traditional schema covering approach is also called ambiguity-based schema covering, which is discussed in [8]. Having described the traditional schema covering approach, we can turn to the problem we want to solve.

Formally, our problem takes a set of $\langle subschema, concept \rangle$ pairs, $E(T_s, C) = \{(t, c) | t \in T_s, c \in C\}$, as input where T_s is a set of sub-schemas and C is a set of concepts in the repository. Each pair is attached with an alignment score $f(t, c)$ where f is a user-defined function. In this problem, we want to compute a probabilistic schema cover. It is a set of possible covers v_i and each cover is associated with a probability $Pr(v_i)$. The formal definition for probabilistic schema cover is described as follows.

Problem 1 (Probabilistic Schema Cover). *Let* E *be a set of* $\langle subschema, concept \rangle$ *pairs. The probabilistic schema cover built from* E *is a set* $V = \{(v_1, Pr(v_1)), \ldots, (v_n, Pr(v_n))\}$ *such that*

- *For each* $i \in [1, n]$, v_i *is a cover and for every* $i, j \in [1, n]$, $i \neq j \Rightarrow v_i \neq v_j$
- $Pr(v_i) \in [0, 1]$ *and* $\sum_{i=1}^{n} Pr(v_i) = 1$.

3   Probabilistic Schema Covering

The probabilistic schema covering framework has three steps as described in Fig. 1. It takes a set of pairs after decomposition E as input and return a probabilistic schema cover containing a set of covers with probabilities attached to each of them.

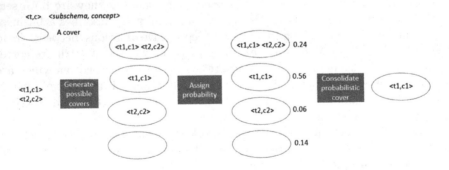

Fig. 1. The probabilistic schema covering framework

3.1   Generate All Possible Covers

From a set of pairs $E = \{(t, c) | t \in T_s, c \in C\}$ found after decomposing the schema, we generate all its subsets $\Omega = \{v_i | v_i \subset E\}$. Generating its subsets using all the pairs would lead to computational explosion since the size of Ω, $|\Omega| = 2^{|E|}$, is large. Therefore, we need some methods to reduce the computational space.

We introduce the alignment score threshold λ and the error window ϵ to decrease the size of the computational space. Using the threshold λ and the error window ϵ, we define two sets of pairs E_c and E_u:

- Certain set $E_c = \{(t,c) \in E | f(t,c) \geq \lambda + \epsilon\}$
- Uncertain set $E_u = \{(t,c) \in E | f(t,c) < \lambda + \epsilon \wedge f(t,c) \geq \lambda - \epsilon\}$.

By setting the alignment score threshold λ, we want to focus only on the promising pairs. Pairs with alignment scores higher than the threshold are more likely to be correct. On the other hand, the error window value ϵ represents pairs that we are unsure if they are correct or not. That means we need to assign probabilities to only these pairs in E_u to express uncertainty.

From the uncertain set of pairs E_u, we generate the possible covers $\Omega_u = v_i^* | v_i^* \subset E_u$. Therefore, the number of possible covers $|\Omega_u|$ is $2^{|E_u|}$. Since $2^{|E_u|} \ll 2^{|E|}$, we have reduced the computational space significantly. Finally, the probabilistic schema cover for E is computed based on Ω_u as follows: $\Omega = \{v_i | v_i = v_i^* \cup E_c, v_i^* \in \Omega_u\}$ and $Pr(v_i) = Pr(v_i^*)$.

3.2 Assign Probability to Each Cover

After the first step, we have generated a set of possible covers Ω_u from the uncertain set of pairs E_u. In this step, we assign probability to each cover $v_i^* \in \Omega_u$.

Consistency Constraint. Despite the fact that alignment scores express how similar between the subschemas and the concepts, they do not tell us which concept a subschema should align to.

Definition 2. *A probabilistic cover V is consistent with a pair (t,c) if the sum of probabilities of all covers that contain (t,c) equals the alignment score $f(t,c)$. A probabilistic cover V is consistent with a pair (t,c) if*

$$\sum_{(t,c) \in v_i} Pr(v_i) = f(t,c)$$

A probabilistic cover V is consistent with a set of pairs M if it is consistent with each pair in M.

This constraint is introduced to ensure that a cover containing a pair with low alignment score has low probability. Since a pair with low alignment score is more likely to be incorrect, the cover in which it participates is also less likely to be correct.

Entropy Maximization. The probability assignment problem can now be reformulated to a constraint optimization problem (OPT). That is, we need to assign the probabilities to the covers in a probabilistic cover such that both the consistency constraint is satisfied and the entropy is maximized. The optimization problem is described as follows.

Table 1. Statistics of the five schemas

	Apertum	CIDX	Excel	Noris	Paragon
#Nodes	140	40	54	65	77
#Internal nodes	25/115	7/33	12/42	11/54	12/65
Depth	4	3	3	3	5

Table 2. #Golden mappings between schemas

	Apertum	CIDX	Excel	Noris	Paragon
Apertum		54	79	85	66
CIDX	54		65	32	49
Excel	79	65		50	60
Noris	85	32	50		45
Paragon	66	49	60	45	

Definition 3. *Let* $Pr(v_1), \ldots, Pr(v_n)$ *be the probabilities of cover* $v_1, \ldots, v_n$ *respectively.* $Pr(v_i)$ *is found by solving the following OPT problem:*

$$maximize \sum_{i=1}^{n} -Pr(v_i) \log Pr(v_i), \ subject \ to:$$

1. $\forall i \in [1, n], 0 \leq Pr(v_i) \leq 1$
2. $\sum_{i=1..n} Pr(v_i) = 1$
3. $\forall (t, c) \in E_u : \sum_{j \in [1,n]:(t,c) \in v_j} Pr(v_j) = f(t, c).$

4   Experiments

Dataset. We start by introducing the dataset being used for evaluation. In fact, finding an appropriate dataset is a non-trivial task as the collected schemas must be relevant and belong to a same domain. We have collected 5 schemas from the Purchase Order domain. Their statistics are described in Table 1. From these schemas, we also create the golden mappings between them manually. The number of goldenmappings between pairs of schemas is described in Table 2.

Concept Repository. We build the concept repository by COMA++ [12] with default parameters, resulting in 45 concepts, 50 micromappings, 220 attributes, 5.089 attributes per concept in average, 1.11 micromappings per concept in average.

Metrics. Let R be the set of correct correspondences found manually. Let F denote the set of correspondences that we generate (or we consider them to be correct). Let $I = R \cap F$ denote the actual correct correspondences in F. In order

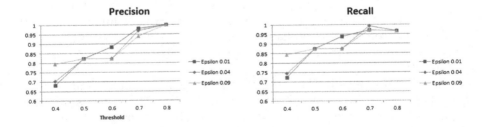

Fig. 2. Precision and recall of the cover of schema Excel

to evaluate the result, we use two typical metrics: precision, which is $|I|/|F|$ and recall, which is $|I|/|R|$. A high value of both precision and recall is desired. As it is hard to find the correct cover from such a large concept repository, we take a different approach to calculate the precision and recall. For each subschema and concept pair, we calculate its precision and recall value then we take the average to get the precision, recall of the whole cover.

Effects of Score Threshold and Error Window on Cover Result. In this experiment, we want to find the cover of schema Excel by the concept repository. We vary the threshold, error window to see their effects on the final cover. To consolidate cover, we select the cover with the highest probability. The result is shown in Fig. 2. In general, precision and recall are high, both of them are higher than 60%. This means that we can find a good cover. Intuitively, the precision and recall increase when the threshold are higher. This is reasonable that the higher the threshold is, we only consider the more likely-correct pairs.

A Comparison with Ambiguity-Based Schema Covering. In this experiment, we compare probabilistic schema covering with the ambiguity-based schema covering approach mentioned in [8]. Figure 3 shows the comparison of two approaches on the precision and recall value. With a low threshold, ambiguity-based covering has higher precision and recall. However, as we analyze the cover chosen by ambiguity-based covering, we found that this cover contains no pair that has alignment score lower than 0.5. On the other hand, probabilistic covering also consider various pairs with low alignment score that results in lower precision and recall.

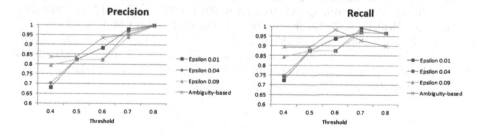

Fig. 3. A comparison with ambiguity-based covering

5   Conclusions

This paper describes a novel approach to schema covering in order to mitigate uncertainty and improve covering results: probabilistic schema covering. In order to propose this approach, we have solved the problem of finding a mechanism to integrate probabilistic model into schema covering. In order to generate a probabilistic schema cover, we first construct its possible set of covers and then we assign probability to each cover. The assigned probabilities must satisfy a consistency constraint and their entropy must also be maximized. Throughout the experiments, we have shown that probabilistic schema covering is a robust approach and competitive to traditional schema covering approach.

References

1. Hung, N.Q.V., Luong, X.H., Miklós, Z., Quan, T.T., Aberer, K.: Collaborative schema matching reconciliation. In: CoopIS, pp. 222–240 (2013)
2. Hung, N.Q.V., Tam, N.T., Chau, V.T., Wijaya, T.K., Miklós, Z., Aberer, K., Gal, A., Weidlich, M.: SMART: a tool for analyzing and reconciling schema matching networks. In: ICDE, pp. 1488–1491 (2015)
3. Hung, N.Q.V., Tam, N.T., Miklós, Z., Aberer, K.: On leveraging crowdsourcing techniques for schema matching networks. In: Meng, W., Feng, L., Bressan, S., Winiwarter, W., Song, W. (eds.) DASFAA 2013. LNCS, vol. 7826, pp. 139–154. Springer, Heidelberg (2013). https://doi.org/10.1007/978-3-642-37450-0_10
4. Hung, N.Q.V., Luong, X.H., Miklós, Z., Quan, T.T., Aberer, K.: An MAS negotiation support tool for schema matching. In: AAMAS, pp. 1391–1392 (2013)
5. Hung, N.Q.V., Tam, N.T., Miklós, Z., Aberer, K.: Reconciling schema matching networks through crowdsourcing. EAI, e2 (2014)
6. Hung, N.Q.V.: Reconciling schema matching networks. Ph.D. thesis, Ecole Polytechnique Federale de Lausanne (2014)
7. Gal, A., Sagi, T., Weidlich, M., Levy, E., Shafran, V., Miklós, Z., Hung, N.Q.V.: Making sense of top-k matchings: a unified match graph for schema matching. In: IIWeb, p. 6 (2012)
8. Saha, B., Stanoi, I., Clarkson, K.L.: Schema covering: a step towards enabling reuse in information integration. In: ICDE, pp. 285–296 (2010)
9. Gal, A., Katz, M., Sagi, T., Weidlich, M., Aberer, K., Hung, N.Q.V., Miklós, Z., Levy, E., Shafran, V.: Completeness and ambiguity of schema cover. In: CoopIS, pp. 241–258 (2013)
10. Hung, N.Q.V., Wijaya, T.K., Miklós, Z., Aberer, K., Levy, E., Shafran, V., Gal, A., Weidlich, M.: Minimizing human effort in reconciling match networks. In: Ng, W., Storey, V.C., Trujillo, J.C. (eds.) ER 2013. LNCS, vol. 8217, pp. 212–226. Springer, Heidelberg (2013). https://doi.org/10.1007/978-3-642-41924-9_19
11. Hung, N.Q.V., Tam, N.T., Miklós, Z., Aberer, K., Gal, A., Weidlich, M.: Pay-as-you-go reconciliation in schema matching networks. In: ICDE, pp. 220–231 (2014)
12. Arnold, P., Rahm, E.: Enriching ontology mappings with semantic relations. Data Knowl. Eng. **93**, 1–18 (2014)

Demo Papers

TEXUS: Table Extraction System for PDF Documents

Roya Rastan[1], Hye-Young Paik[1], John Shepherd[1], Seung Hwan Ryu[1(✉)],
and Amin Beheshti[2]

[1] School of Computer Science and Engineering,
University of New South Wales, Sydney, Australia
{rastan,hpaik,jas,seungr}@cse.unsw.edu.au
[2] Department of Computing, Macquarie University, Sydney, Australia
amin.beheshti@mq.edu.au

Abstract. Tables in documents are a rich and under-exploited source of structured data in otherwise unstructured documents. The extraction and understanding of tabular data is a challenging task which has attracted the attention of researchers from a range of disciplines such as information retrieval, machine learning and natural language processing. In this demonstration, we present an end-to-end table extraction and understanding system which takes a PDF file and automatically generates a set of XML and CSV files containing the extracted cells, rows and columns of tables, as well as a complete reading order analysis of the tables. Unlike many systems that work as a black-boxed, ad-hoc solution, our system design incorporates the open, reusable and extensible architecture to support research into, and development of, table-processing systems. During the demo, users will see how our system gradually transforms a PDF document into a set of structured files through a series of processing modules, namely: locating, segmenting and function/structure analysis.

Keywords: Table extraction · TEXUS · Table processing
Information extraction · Document processing

1 Introduction

Tables, a widely-used structure for data presentation in documents, utilise layout to arrange information and convey meaning to human readers. Because tables are a rich source of inter-related data, it would also be useful if their contents could be automatically extracted and used by computers. However, the diversity of layouts and variety of encoding (e.g. HTML, PDF, plain text) of tabular data makes its extraction and understanding a challenging problem.

Even though the core concepts and tasks involved in implementing table extraction systems have been identified by researchers [1], how such system is designed and which aspects of the tasks are emphasised in a system differ significantly from solution to solution.

© Springer International Publishing AG, part of Springer Nature 2018
J. Wang et al. (Eds.): ADC 2018, LNCS 10837, pp. 345–349, 2018.
https://doi.org/10.1007/978-3-319-92013-9_30

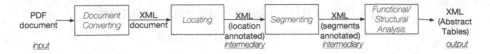

Fig. 1. TEXUS table extraction flow

Given the wide variety of tables, existing table processing methods adopt one of two general strategies: deal with the variety by requiring manual intervention from users or develop a domain-dependent solutions that cannot be applied to other application contexts [2].

Considering the drawbacks of existing systems and approaches, we present a system that employs a component and service-based design paradigm that promotes extensibility, re-usability and does not require human intervention.

TEXUS (Table EXtraction and Understanding System) is implemented based on the general architecture for table extraction and understanding proposed in our previous work [3]. We define a set of generic table extraction components and precisely describe the interfaces between them. One useful aspect of such a design is the flexibility it provides to develop components for specific kinds of extraction and to make the choice of an appropriate set of components *during* the table processing task. Each component produces a structured output (an XML file) which is kept throughout the processing steps. This means users can stop the extraction process at any point if desired (e.g., obtaining table "locating" results only), and the intermediate results themselves can be used for detailed analysis and debugging purposes.

2 System Overview

As shown in Fig. 1, we consider the process of extracting and understanding[1] tables from a document as a multi-step document transformation process as an automated pipeline [3,5]. Each step in the process is associated with a module dedicated to carrying out a well-focused task (e.g., locating tables). The results of each step adds 'annotation tags' or adds new sections to the XML documents. In this section, we give brief descriptions of the each module in the processing pipeline.

Document Converting. The first step is to create an XML file that represents our view of PDF documents. Our *Document Converting* module [4] uses the open source PDF wrapper XPDF[2] to transform the input document to an XML representation, following TEXUS document model [3]. We take *Text Chunks* as the basic elements of a PDF document. A Text Chunk is an atomic object (i.e. textual element such as a character, a word or a sentence), which is totally

---

[1] It is generally accepted that tables can be understood if one can detect the hierarchical structure of table headers properly and determine how each table data cell can be uniquely accessed through them.

[2] http://www.foolabs.com/xpdf.

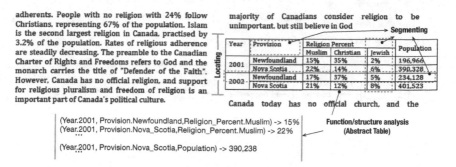

adherents. People with no religion with 24% follow Christians, representing 67% of the population. Islam is the second largest religion in Canada, practised by 3.2% of the population. Rates of religious adherence are steadily decreasing. The preamble to the Canadian Charter of Rights and Freedoms refers to God and the monarch carries the title of "Defender of the Faith". However, Canada has no official religion, and support for religious pluralism and freedom of religion is an important part of Canada's political culture.

majority of Canadians consider religion to be unimportant, but still believe in God

Canada today has no official church, and the

Fig. 2. Two-column PDF document with embedded table

contained within a document page. *Text Chunks* are based on the *Text String* Object[3]. Any document element, such as an image, that is not composed of text is treated as part of a *Non-Text Object*.

Locating. As illustrated in Fig. 2, the aim of locating is to find the starting line and ending line (i.e., boundaries) of each table in the document, which we refer to as 'potential table region'. A table region containing possible table is identified by analysing how the text chunks appear in lines. The locating step ultimately results in identification of the boundaries that separate the table from the rest of the document. Our implementation can detect multiple tables in a document. The algorithm of this module can be described as follows. A table region is considered to be a sequence of adjacent lines in the document, where each of the lines is identified as a 'table line'. A table line is a line in a page containing two or more text chunks, which has been identified as (a) being suitably separated from the surrounding text, (b) falling on the same line (determined by top and bottom values covering roughly the same range), and (c) having a consistent pattern with surrounding table lines. The boundaries of a table region is determined by considering the coordinates of the first and last table lines.

Segmenting. The segmenting module detects the inner boundaries of the table as cells, rows and columns. That is, after this step, a table is viewed as a collection of cells, where cells are aligned horizontally in rows and aligned vertically in columns. First, the algorithm of the module looks for a "dominant" table line pattern to determine table rows, and then recognise lines that deviate from the pattern. These lines could be considered as potential header lines or uncertain table lines (e.g., summary lines like 'Total'). Next, the algorithm forms columns. Using the coordinates in text chunks, starting from the table's dominant pattern, we build a list of text chunks horizontal boundaries, then scans the table and checks cell boundaries against these to determine the vertical extent of each column. Finally, we determine table cells. Most table cells are clearly delimited from its surrounding cells.

---

[3] From the PDF specification (http://www.adobe.com/devnet/pdf/pdf_reference. html.

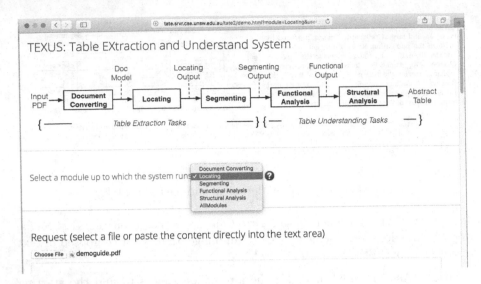

Fig. 3. TEXUS web application

Functional and Structural Analysis. After segmenting, we move further into analysing the relationships between the header cells and data cells. Some table extraction systems consider the segmentation task as the final output. However, to understand a table, one needs to detect the *reading order* of the table. This is to decide, ultimately, how to correctly line up table header and column cells to each data cells. In Fig. 2, for example, the first data cell containing value '15%' can be reached via `Year`, then `2001`, combined with `Provision`, then `newfoundland`, followed by `Religion Percent`, then `Muslim`. In TEXUS, this is done through *Functional and Structural Analysis* [5] and our module can automatically detect complicated arrangement of headers and columns.

This allows a computer-extracted table to contain pure data, separated from its presentation layout or styling features. This final output represents the "Wang's abstract table model" [6] which is a well known and highly cited table model in the table processing community.

3   Demonstration

In the demonstration, we will show the complete implementation of the system as well as the features that have not been published before. The audience of our demonstration will be taken through a custom Web application built to show the detailed functionality of each table processing module in the pipeline. We will use the ICDAR 2013 competition dataset which consists of 67 PDF files containing 150 tables with diverse layouts and complexity[4].

---

[4] http://www.tamirhassan.com/competition.html.

As in Fig. 3, TEXUS Web application offers a *graphical user interface* (GUI) allowing users to execute the table processing pipeline. Prior to executing the pipeline, the user has to upload a PDF file and select a module she wants to run, say "segmenting". If segmenting is chosen, all modules up to and including segmenting will run, namely document converting, locating and segmenting. Once processing is done, the system will display the results from each module in separate viewing panels as XML documents (raw output). In more detail, the results will show the progress of the processing, the intermediate outputs produced along the pipeline, as well as all the processing histories up to the point of executing the selected module. Note that the system will display different results, depending on which module has been selected. Also, we demonstrate that it is possible to map the results to another standard format CSV for further processing (e.g., importing and manipulating them in MS Excel). We also show that these outputs can be switched to HTML pages with custom visualisations.

References

1. e Silva, A.C., Jorge, A., Torgo, L.: Design of an end-to-end method to extract information from tables. Int. J. Doc. Anal. Recogn. 8(2–3), 144–171 (2006)
2. Embley, D.W., Hurst, M., Lopresti, D., Nagy, G.: Table-processing paradigms: a research survey. IJDAR 8(2–3), 66–86 (2006)
3. Rastan, R., Paik, H.-Y., Shepherd, J.: TEXUS: a task-based approach for table extraction and understanding. In: DocEng, pp. 25–34 (2015)
4. Rastan, R., Paik, H.-Y., Shepherd, J.: A PDF wrapper for table processing. In: DocEng, pp. 115–118 (2016)
5. Rastan, R., Paik, H.-Y., Shepherd, J., Haller, A.: Automated table understanding using stub patterns. In: Navathe, S.B., Wu, W., Shekhar, S., Du, X., Wang, X.S., Xiong, H. (eds.) DASFAA 2016. LNCS, vol. 9642, pp. 533–548. Springer, Cham (2016). https://doi.org/10.1007/978-3-319-32025-0_33
6. Wang, X.: Tabular abstraction, editing, and formatting. Ph.D. thesis, University of Waterloo (1996)

Visual Evaluation of SQL Plan Cache Algorithms

Jan Kossmann[✉], Markus Dreseler, Timo Gasda, Matthias Uflacker,
and Hasso Plattner

Hasso Plattner Institute, Potsdam, Germany
jan.kossmann@hpi.de

Abstract. Caching optimized query plans reduces the time spent optimizing SQL queries at the cost of increased memory consumption. Different cache eviction strategies, such as LRU(-K) or GD(F)S exist that aim at increasing the cache hit ratio or reducing the overall cost of cache misses. A comprehensive study on how different workloads and tuning parameters influence these strategies does not yet publicly exist. We propose a tool that enables both such research as well as performance tuning for DBAs by visualizing the effects of changed parameters in real time.

Keywords: Query plan caching · Cache eviction · Query execution

1 Introduction

The importance of choosing a query plan that uses the available compute and memory resources efficiently can hardly be overstated. But while a good query plan can mean the difference between milliseconds and minutes of execution, finding it in the vast space of logically equivalent plans comes with its own costs. For workloads like the Join Order Benchmark [3], parsing and optimizing can take hundreds of milliseconds and in single cases even surpasses the execution time[1]. Luckily, this cost can be amortized if query plans are cached and reused [2].

Most commercial databases such as SAP HANA [1], Oracle 11g [5], and Microsoft SQL Server [4] use such a query cache. For SAP HANA, the cache consumes "a few GB out of a few TB of main memory to guarantee cache hit ratios above 99%" [1]. Others, such as Oracle BI 11g, use much smaller caches with only 1024 entries and warn users not to "raise this value without consulting Oracle Support Services" [5]. This serves to demonstrate why a careful selection of cache algorithms and their parameters is of relevance for the overall database performance. Surprisingly, only little academic research has been published that evaluates different cache implementations and eviction strategies.

We work on getting a better picture on how different cache implementations and eviction strategies influence the cache effectiveness and how this differs from workload to workload. To do so, we capture KPIs like the cache hit ratio and

---

[1] Query 28c takes roughly 600x longer to plan than to execute in PostgreSQL.

© Springer International Publishing AG, part of Springer Nature 2018
J. Wang et al. (Eds.): ADC 2018, LNCS 10837, pp. 350–353, 2018.
https://doi.org/10.1007/978-3-319-92013-9_31

Fig. 1. Screenshot of the Cache Visualizer. The left side shows the different caches, the main graph shows the performance of different compared cache algorithms. Parameters can be chosen on the right.

the overall time saved by the caches. When interpreting the results, we found it very helpful to have a visualization[2] that shows how changed parameters affect the KPIs. The traditional approach is to run a benchmark, modify the cache algorithm in the DBMS, and rerun the benchmark. This is not time-efficient and makes a live exploration of different influence factors impossible. Our presented system lets different cache algorithms compete against each other in real time. This allows the user, e.g., the DBA, to compare different algorithms, explore tuning factors and, thereby, tune the overall system performance.

A workload mix, chosen by the user, is assembled from a list of pre- or user-defined queries. It is then sent to our research DBMS Hyrise[3]. Currently, these queries include the TPC-C and -H as well as the Join Order[4] Benchmarks. Internally, we also work with a workload of a live ERP system. The system can be extended with further query sets. After assembling a workload mix, users can configure parameters that affect the caches. Most important is the cache size, which determines the number of queries that caches can hold. Algorithm-specific settings, such as K for LRU-K can also be chosen. Based on these, the KPIs of different caches are gathered and visualized in real-time as seen in Fig. 1.

While a high *cache hit ratio* usually indicates a well-working cache, it ignores the different costs associated with generating the query plans. Algorithms can take this cost into account to make sure that an expensive query is not evicted by

---

[2] https://vimeo.com/epicchair/sqlplancache.
[3] https://github.com/hyrise/hyrise.
[4] https://github.com/gregrahn/join-order-benchmark.

a query that is only slightly more frequent but significantly cheaper to optimize. Because of this, we found the *saved optimizer cost* to be a more accurate measure of a cache algorithm's performance and use it as the main KPI.

These costs depend on the implementation of the SQL parser, planner, and optimizer. What is a good configuration for one DBMS can be subpar for others. To account for this, our Cache Visualizer works with the optimizers in other DBMSs, currently MySQL and PostgreSQL. Queries are sent to these backends, the cost of optimizing is tracked and is then fed back into Hyrise's caches.

Since we are focusing on comparing cache algorithms and reducing the overall time spent in the optimizer, the plan execution time is out of scope. To increase the tool's throughput, plans are not executed. This is not a limitation of the architecture and could be enabled for tracking other components.

2   System Overview

Figure 2 shows the system's architecture. The selected queries and cache tuning parameters are sent to the Cache Visualizer's backend in Hyrise. Here, different caches are probed for an existing query plan. If a cache miss occurs, the query is planned using the selected DBMS's backend. Queries are only planned once, not repeatedly for each cache algorithm, because the time taken for planning is independent of the simultaneously evaluated cache algorithms. The result is then offered to the different caches. In the final step on the server side, the information on which cache had a miss and how long the required generation of the plan took is given back to the frontend. Here, it is aggregated and the metrics for the main graph are calculated.

Currently, our system provides five cache eviction strategies: LRU, LRU-K, GDS, GDFS, and a randomized strategy. Other strategies can be easily integrated by implementing an abstract cache interface.

In addition to the default metric *saved optimizer cost*, other metrics can be selected in the visualization options located above the graph. On the right, different DBMS backends and parameters for the caches can be selected.

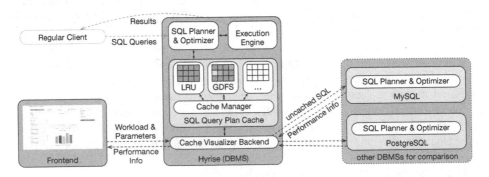

Fig. 2. Architecture of the Cache Visualizer. (Color figure online)

The frontend interacts with Hyrise to provide additional information and options to the user. This includes the cache visualization seen on the left, where both the fill level (red blocks) and ongoing evictions (white blocks) are shown. In the future, more information such as the most recent use or the cost will be presented for each entry. Hovering over an entry in the cache gives the stored query. Clicking on an entry will evict the entry manually.

3   Practical Use of the Tool and Demonstration

This tool makes it possible to compare the behavior of different plan cache algorithms depending on a number of parameters chosen by the user. Being able to see how they directly react to changes in the workload and the parameters allows researchers, database administrators, and developers to get a better understanding of how to tune a query plan cache. We are using this tool in ongoing research that looks at the cacheability of enterprise workloads. These differ from synthetic benchmarks in the number and complexity of tables and queries. In addition, the distribution of query executions rapidly changes over the workday which especially challenges cache algorithms.

The screenshot in Fig. 1 allows a glance into the findings made possible. We can see how a change in the workload affects the different cache hit ratios. While GDS adapts quickly and takes only little time to reach the previous cache hit ratio, LRU-K takes longer because the wrong entries are chosen for eviction. Interestingly, the random eviction strategy performs quite well. This is a finding that can also be seen in the enterprise workload that we analyzed with this tool.

During the live demonstration, we will introduce the different configuration options available in the visualizer. After this, the audience will be able to interact with the tool, test different workload and parameter configurations, and see how the cache algorithms outperform each other. We expect that this leads to fruitful discussions on how to optimize databases' query plan caches and provoke additional questions that can be answered with the support of the tool.

References

1. May, N., et al.: SAP HANA - the evolution of an in-memory DBMS from pure OLAP processing towards mixedworkloads. In: Datenbanksysteme für Business, Technologie und Web (BTW) (2017)
2. Attaluri, G.K., Wisneski, D.J.: Method and system for transparently caching and reusing query execution plans efficiently. US Patent 6,466,931, October 2002
3. Leis, V., et al.: How good are query optimizers, really? In: Proceedings of the VLDB Endowment, November 2015
4. Microsoft: Execution Plan Caching and Reuse. https://technet.microsoft.com/en-us/library/ms181055(v=sql.105).aspx. Accessed 01 Mar 2018
5. Oracle: Oracle Fusion Middleware System Administrator's Guide for Oracle Business Intelligence Enterprise Edition 11g. https://docs.oracle.com/cd/E25178_01/bi.1111/e10541/configfileref.htm. Accessed 01 Mar 2018

Visualising Top-k Alternative Routes

Lingxiao Li$^{(\boxtimes)}$, Muhammad Aamir Cheema, David Taniar,
and Maria Indrawan-Santiago

Monash University, Melbourne, Australia
{lingxiao.li,aamir.cheema,david.taniar,maria.indrawan}@monash.edu

Abstract. Alternatives to the shortest path are a standard feature of modern navigation services where more than one *suitable* paths between source and destination are presented to the users so that they can use a path of their choice for navigation. Although there exist several approaches to compute top-k alternative paths, these techniques define *suitable* paths differently, hence, the top-k alternative routes generated by these techniques may be different. Unfortunately, there is no work that quantifies or experimentally compares the quality of the alternative routes generated by these techniques. This demonstration visualises the top-k alternative routes generated by two state-of-the-art techniques as well as the routes provided by Google Maps. The visualisation makes it easy for the users of the demonstration to compare the quality of the routes generated by each technique. The source code of the demonstration is also made publicly available which makes it easy to incorporate results by other techniques and mapping services and thus compare routes provided by these.

Keywords: Shortest paths · Route planning · Alternative paths

1 Introduction

Computing the shortest path between two given locations in a road network is a fundamental problem and has been well studied for several decades. A lot of efficient techniques and algorithms have been proposed (e.g., see [1]), which can achieve nearly real-time shortest path computation based on the extensive preprocessing. These efficient algorithms are applied in many navigation systems and services to provide general driving directions.

In many applications such as navigation systems, providing only the shortest path may not meet the user's personal preferences. For example, a user may be interested in looking at multiple *suitable* routes and manually choose a route of their choice. Therefore, most commercial mapping services (such as Google Maps) provide more than one *suitable* routes (called top-k alternative routes hereafter) so that the users can choose a route of their choice from these routes. Unfortunately, the algorithms used by the commercial service providers are proprietary and the underlying techniques are not made public. Furthermore,

© Springer International Publishing AG, part of Springer Nature 2018
J. Wang et al. (Eds.): ADC 2018, LNCS 10837, pp. 354–358, 2018.
https://doi.org/10.1007/978-3-319-92013-9_32

computing the top-k routes has not received much attention from the research community. Although there exists a few works [2,5] that compute top-k alternative routes, the definition of top-k alternative routes used by each technique is different and it is not clear which of the previous approaches (including the commercial services) produces the top-k alternative routes of better quality. Thus, it is important to analyze the routes generated by these algorithms to understand their quality. In this demonstration, we provide a first step to address this gap by providing a visualisation for the routes so that the users can compare the quality of routes generated by different approaches.

Contributions. Our main contributions are summarised as follows:

- To the best of our knowledge, we are the first to provide a web-based application that enables users to visualize top-k alternative routes generated by Google Maps and two state-of-the-art algorithms: *Plateau* [5] and *Single Via-path* [2]. The demonstration allows the users to select source and destination, a value of k and visualizes the top-k routes generated by the selected approach. Thus, the users can compare the routes generated by these approaches and analyse the route quality.
- The source code[1] of the demonstration is made publicly available which makes it easier for the users to embed other/new techniques in the demonstration and compare the quality of their results.

2   Related Work

A related problem is to compute top-k shortest paths [4] which produces k paths between source and destination having the smallest lengths. However, these *top-k shortest paths* usually have a high degree of pair-wise similarity. To overcome this limitation, [3] proposed an approximate algorithm for finding k-Shortest Paths with limited overlap. The author set up the overlap ratio θ to check the overlap amount between any two different paths. Unfortunately, such techniques suffer from at least one of the two main limitations: (1) without using a threshold for the maximum length of the paths, the computed alternative path may be too long to be interesting for the user because the main criteria is to minimize pair-wise overlap among paths (and some suitable paths may be omitted due to having a very small overlap with the shortest path); and (2) the exact algorithm proposed in the paper cannot handle large road networks. The two state-of-the-art algorithms for generating top-k alternative routes are *Plateau* [5] and *Single Via-path* [2]. Due to the space limitations, the details are not presented and the readers are instead referred to [2,5].

---

[1] https://github.com/lingxiao29/VisualisingTop-kAlternativeRoutes.

3   System Architecture

Our system is built upon the Java Spring[2], which is a high-level Java Web framework. There are two main components of our system: the back-end and the front-end.

Front-End. The front-end is a web interface which has two main functionalities: (1) post user's query request to back-end (see Fig. 1(a)), and (2) plot the paths data on Google Maps[3]. The users can click on the map to add two markers as source and destination, respectively. Then, the user can select an algorithm which will be used to compute alternative paths. The user can also select a value of k for top-k paths. After clicking the submit button, the top-k alternative paths are displayed on the Google Maps.

Back-End. The back-end is mainly responsible for request mapping and paths finding. After the server is started, the road network dataset will be loaded automatically. The datasets are from the 9th DIMACS Implementation Challenge[4]. Each dataset contains an undirected graph that represents a part of the road network in the United States. In this paper, we only use the Colorado road dataset to do the demonstration. When the back-end gets the query request, the first step is geo-coordinate matching. We match the nearest nodes from the road network as the source and destination points. Then, according to the user's selection, relevant algorithms is invoked to compute top-k alternative paths. For the *Plateau* and *Single Via-Path* approaches, we have optimized their implementations to improve the running time. However, the details are not presented due to space limitations. As for the third method, Google Maps, we directly call the Google Map API direction service[5] to get the results.

4   Demonstration

Figure 1 depicts the web GUI of our system. Figure 1(a) shows the initial web page, where the user can specify the query parameters and submit the query request to the local server to get the alternative routes. For example, a user issues a query with two red markers as query points and the number of retrieving results *3* for each algorithm. After submitting this query to the server, routes are displayed in the result page. Specifically, the user can use a tick-box to toggle on/off the algorithms. Figures 1(b) and (c) present the routes of *Single Via-Path* method and *Plateau* method respectively. Figure 1(d) displays the comparison of *Plateau* and *Google Map* query result. The user also can zoom in the map to experience the local (within the city) path finding.

---

[2] https://spring.io/.

[3] https://developers.google.com/maps/documentation/.

[4] http://www.dis.uniroma1.it/challenge9/download.shtml.

[5] https://developers.google.com/maps/documentation/javascript/directions.

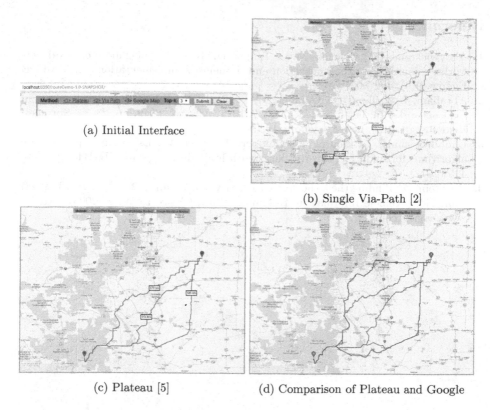

(a) Initial Interface

(b) Single Via-Path [2]

(c) Plateau [5]

(d) Comparison of Plateau and Google

Fig. 1. System interface and query results

5   Conclusion

In this paper, we present an alternative routes query system on the road network. Our system integrates three different approaches to compute the admissible alternative routes. Namely, *Plateau*, *Single Via-Path* and *Google Maps*. Moreover, a web interface is also developed to enable user interactively explore the different queries and visualise the query result. Based on our demonstration and compensation, we aware that *Plateau* approach can generate more reasonable alternative routes. Although, it is not fully documented and published.

Acknowledgements. Muhammad Aamir Cheema is supported by DP180103411.

References

1. Abeywickrama, T., Cheema, M.A., Taniar, D.: K-nearest neighbors on road networks: a journey in experimentation and in-memory implementation. Proc. VLDB Endow. **9**(6), 492–503 (2016)
2. Abraham, I., Delling, D., Goldberg, A.V., Werneck, R.F.: Alternative routes in road networks. In: Festa, P. (ed.) SEA 2010. LNCS, vol. 6049, pp. 23–34. Springer, Heidelberg (2010). https://doi.org/10.1007/978-3-642-13193-6_3
3. Chondrogiannis, T., Bouros, P., Gamper, J., Leser, U.: Exact and approximate algorithms for finding k-shortest paths with limited overlap. In: EDxBT, pp. 414–425 (2017)
4. Eppstein, D.: Finding the k shortest paths. SIAM J. Comput. **28**(2), 652–673 (1998)
5. Cambridge Vehicle Information Technology Ltd., Choice Routing (2005). http://www.camvit.com

Author Index

Printed in the United States
By Bookmasters